D0900266

"DUMAS *An Autobiography-Anthology Including the Best of Dumas"*

Edited by GUY ENDORE

Author of "King of Paris"

1962

DOUBLEDAY & COMPANY, INC., *Garden City, N.Y.*

Library of Congress Catalog Card Number 61–12517
Copyright © 1962 by Guy Endore
All Rights Reserved
Printed in the United States of America
First Edition

To my daughter
MARCIA
*for valuable assistance in the selection
of excerpts from the multitudinous works of
Alexandre Dumas*

TABLE OF CONTENTS

Chapter I

SENSE OF THE FUTURE

EVERYTHING about Alexandre Dumas is bigger than life-size. The very first quote from his works, for this Dumas anthology, will demonstrate that. Here, for example, is a sentence taken from the opening lines of his *Memoirs*:

I was born at Villers-Cotterêts on July 24, 1802, in a house on rue de Lormet, at present in the possession of my good friend Cartier, who however has agreed to sell it to me some day, so that I may go to die in the same room where I was born, and thus return to the night of the future at the same spot where I emerged from the night of the past.

How admirably he dramatizes himself! Picturing himself as a phenomenon, as some sort of special apparition, bursting mysteriously and generously into our visible world, and committed to disappear just as mysteriously at the very same spot where he first manifested himself.

He had that faculty of making himself interesting. When, for example, during the republican demonstrations and riots in Paris in the year 1832, he found himself in trouble and felt that he must leave town quickly, he ran to his publisher Gosselin, to ask for an advance for a book he would write until matters calmed down.

But when Gosselin heard that Dumas wanted to write a book about Switzerland, he refused to advance him a penny. Switzerland had been overdone. There were far too many books about that country. What Gosselin failed to understand was that the book Dumas would do would be not so much a book about Switzerland as a book about Dumas in Switzerland. Thus one of the most popular books about Switzerland, a book that is still being reprinted more than a century after publication, went to the publisher Dumont, instead of to Gosselin.

Dumas had a real gift for drama. Nevertheless, when facts failed him, he could always improve on them. Those vast *Memoirs* of his, to give only one illustration, were not written as he liked to say, during his "exile," when he was a "refugee" from the police of Napoleon III. The reason Alexandre Dumas ran away to Brussels had nothing to do with the coming to power in 1851 of Napoleon III.

It just happened that when Victor Hugo was fleeing to Brussels for fear of his life, that Dumas happened to be bankrupt. His Théâtre Historique had failed, and his beautiful house (which still exists), a house on which he had spent over a quarter of a million francs, had to be knocked down for a mere 32,000.

So off he ran, as if he too had been playing an important political role. But he didn't remain in exile long. His creditors soon agreed upon a settlement, and Dumas began to shuttle back and forth between Brussels and Paris, while writing and publishing both in serial and in book form those *Memoirs* which he proudly described as written by a "republican son of a republican general," and which would eventually run to twenty-nine volumes, though now generally issued in six hefty ones.

Yes, he did things in a big way. He was born for size. Not only was he big physically, six feet three tall, and after his fortieth year tending to excessive portliness, but he could boast of an exciting heritage. His father had been one of Napoleon Bonaparte's best generals. And as if that were still not enough drama, that general had had a Negro slave-woman for a mother. And a French marquis for a father!

The French marquis was Antoine-Alexandre Davy de la Pailleterie. He had left France to become a sugar planter on the then partially French-owned island of San Domingo. He had had a son from one of his slaves, Louise-Cessette Dumas. This son, a mulatto, had left the sugar island after the death of his mother, had first lived with his father, then quarreled with him, had dropped his rank of marquis (perhaps after being disavowed by his father), and had joined the French army as a dragoon under the name of Thomas Dumas.

Came the French revolution. When every soldier carried a marshal's baton in his knapsack. Thomas rose rapidly. He was a man of enormous strength, able, so it was said, to grip a horse between his knees so tightly that he could then clasp his arms around a beam overhead and pull himself and his mount off the floor.

In battle he would get into such a rage that his face turned a dark purple and Austrians fled before him screaming: "The Black Devil!" Such was his nickname. But he was also called Monsieur Humanité, because of his kindness and his gentle concern for his soldiers and inferiors. He loved the people. And he so hated unnecessary warfare that he was bound to fall out with Napoleon, who wreaked a terrible revenge on him that cost General Dumas his health and abbreviated his life.

The stories that his son Alexandre Dumas would later tell about this general are not exaggerated. That is proved by so eminent an historian as Colonel W. R. Phipps, who, in his five-volume work on *The Armies of the French Republic*, says that even Alexandre Dumas, the novelist, could not do justice to the heroic exploits of his incredible father, exploits that are part of the records of French military archives.

Napoleon's vindictiveness went so far that, after the father's death, it struck at his wife and children, depriving them of any sort of pension and forcing them to existence in virtual poverty. Young Dumas, as a result, grew up rather wild, more interested in poaching than in going to school, but all the healthier and all the cleverer for this early training in the woods near Villers-Cotterêts.

The school he eventually entered was that of Abbé Grégoire, called by courtesy a "college" though really nothing more than a village grade school. And his first day in school will furnish us now with our second quote for this anthology. Young Dumas was then ten years old, rather good to look at, still pink-skinned and curly-haired.

In his *Memoirs* he would claim that his fair-skinned and blue-eyed complexion was due to his father's having forced his mother to drink plenty of brandy while she was pregnant, so that it was not until he was fifteen that his complexion turned dark and his hair became frizzy. His eyes, however, naturally remaining bright blue all his life.

Little is said nowadays about Dumas's Negro ancestry. But his contemporaries did not spare him. Balzac, a rival serial writer, referred to Dumas as "that Negro." Tricks were played on him—circus Negroes from the United States being bribed once to swarm about him with cries of: "Cousin! Dear Cousin!" And his literary enemies parodying him under the name of Dumasnoir, which sounds like a perfectly good French name, but can be resolved into Dumas *noir*, Dumas *black*. And this word *black* being the same as Negro, which in French is also the word for ghost writer—Dumas being often under attack for his supposed (and actual) use of ghost writers, exaggerated by some, denied by others.

Dumas was in general a good sport about these aspersions. So that even his son permitted himself this remark: "My father is so vain that he is capable of hitching behind his own carriage in order to make people believe that he is rich enough to afford a Negro footman." And his good friend Charles Hugo, brother of the poet, observed: "Everybody has read Dumas. But no one has read all of Dumas—not even Dumas himself."

Now for the quote from the *Memoirs* depicting Dumas at the age of ten, just entering school:

My entrance into Abbé Grégoire's school had been planned ahead, with an old coat from the days of my grandfather, the Marquis, cut down into a suit for me. Dark café-au-lait in color, with the black warp glistening through in a pattern of black dots.

And thus, on an autumnal Monday morning, at eight o'clock, I wended my way to that well from which I intended to drink deep of all knowledge. I walked slowly, with grave steps, befitting the importance of the occasion, and with my nose up in the air, proud of the volumes I had under my arm, a whole library of grammars and sacred histories, dictionaries and the like, first principles of education. And already rejoicing in the startling effect I must produce when I burst in on the generality of mankind.

A kind of tunnel-like passage led from the rue de Soissons to the courtyard of Abbé Grégoire's school. In addition there was a great door. This door stood wide open.

I looked through the passage, deep into the courtyard: there was not a soul to be seen.

Was I late? Was everyone already in class? Quickly I crossed the threshold. At once the door behind me closed, and I heard wild cries of joy, and at the same time a dew fell upon me. A dew? Say rather a downpour. Coming at me from all sides of a double row of barrels.

I wasn't in the least amused and took to my heels to get out of the range of this showerbath, but not before a momentary hesitation due to the surprise, had exposed me to a certain amount of moisture, so that before I had made the half-dozen paces necessary to escape to the other end of the vaulted passage, I was dripping wet.

I had been something of a crybaby. There were times when I would just sit down in some corner and cry all by myself. In those days I also had the habit of speaking of myself in the third person. And people in a rather teasing way had taken to speaking to me in the same way. So that when my mother would find me crying she would ask:

"Why is Dumas crying?"

And I would answer: "Dumas is crying because he has tears."

An answer that would somehow satisfy my mother who would leave me alone to cry myself out at my ease.

One can thus understand that if I cried so readily for no reason at all, I could certainly shed tears when I had some genuine cause.

And what better cause could one ask for than this dampening humiliation that I had had to suffer, plus the injury to my new suit? And it was a very watery little lad that Abbé Grégoire found when he returned from saying Mass and found me sitting on the steps of the school.

When the Abbé first saw me I was surrounded by some twenty young rascals who pretended to have a real sympathy for my tears. The Abbé pushed his way through these hypocrites and walked up the two or three steps to my side. Then, being as myopic as a mole, he put his quizzing glass to his eye and stared at me, while asking me what was the matter.

I was about to tell him when I saw twenty fists reaching out towards me, twenty threatening visages giving me such menacing looks, that I broke out instead into a loud bawl. Abbé Grégoire wheeled about, but he saw nothing but twenty faces breaking into smiles and twenty hands sticking themselves into pockets.

"What's going on here?" Abbé Grégoire asked.

"We know nothing at all," said the hypocrites. "That's how he's been since he got here."

"What? He's been crying all that time?"

"Yes, he has. He certainly has. Yes that's so, isn't it?" the twenty replied. And those who knew me of old added: "Dumas is crying."

"But why is Dumas crying?" the Abbé insisted.

"Why it's because Dumas has tears," said those who knew the tradition.

"Come here, my friend," said the Abbé.

I whimpered and went up to him. "Here I am," I said, between sobs.

He felt my clothing.

"But he's drenched to the bone!" cried the Abbé.

This caused me to redouble my lamentations.

"Naturally," said one of the older boys, "he's been bawling for hours."

"Look here," said the Abbé sternly. "You mean to assert that it is his tears that have soaked him like this?"

"What else?" the older boy replied stoutly.

I cried out at that. "Monsieur l'abbé," I argued, "I'm as wet in the back as I am in front. My tears couldn't have done that!"

Abbé Grégoire verified my condition.

"He's right," he said. "That means no recreation period this noon. And my ruler on everyone's knuckles immediately. Plus three hundred extra verses to learn for tomorrow morning!"

What a weeping! What a gnashing of teeth! Dante in hell never heard the like. But that was directed at the Abbé. Whilst beneath this noise I heard an almost inaudible rumble of threats that made shivers run down my skin. Nevertheless, the pupils had to submit. They got their knuckles bruised vigorously, for the Abbé was not one to spare the rod, and he followed the old traditions of schooling without pity. But that only increased the silent menaces that I could read on every face.

I saw that the drenching I had got would soon be as nothing to the hail of fists that was bound to descend upon me. I could see the storm gathering.

The first result, however, was that no one wrote a line that morning. Every student insisted that the Abbé had struck him so hard with his férule, that their hands were too numb to hold a pen.

The Abbé had to grant them this concession.

And at midday what a clamor arose because no one could stay in! Incredible were the number of engagements that could not be broken, the errands that had to be made, the parental orders that brooked no postponement.

I can't begin to remember all these excuses. Only three have somehow stuck in my mind: Saunier couldn't skip his clarinet lesson. Ronet had to go home because he was constipated and had to take a purgative. Leloir was obligated to go and draw his conscription number.

The result? Abbé Grégoire put the whole punishment off for the next day, and Saunier had his clarinet lesson, Ronet took his castor oil, while Leloir went off to draw his lot.

And as for myself I soon found myself alone in the school, and went off home.

My head filled with profound reflections. As little as there may have been to laugh at in my experience, would I not have done better to have taken it in a spirit of merriment? Instead of crying. To have followed Democritus the laughing philosopher, instead of dark Heraclitus, the weeping philosopher?

Naturally my mother observed my sadness and questioned me, but I said nothing, for I felt that I had talked enough for one day.

At one o'clock I was back in school. For each of us had gone back to our homes for the midday meal—which in most cases, be it said, had been no more than a piece of dry bread.

My nose was fixed on my paper, where I was writing out the declensions of *rosa*. But even the briefest glance was enough to reveal to me the gathering storm, lit by flashes of lightning. The climate grew ever darker and more threatening, and there was nothing so absorbing in my work on the word *rosa*, that I was not aware of how I was to be pulverized just as soon as school was over for that day.

Indeed I was able to gather, from all the glances and gestures that passed around me, that by general agreement it had been decided that Bligny, a tall gangling youth, son of the local draper, was to be my executioner.

To me this Bligny seemed much bigger than he actually was, because, being two years older than me, I could not help but look up to him, although actually we were of about the same size.

A duel with him was something that I could hardly look forward to with pleasure. All the same I was prepared to go through with it, for I always had vividly in mind the duels that my father had fought, and the necessity of living up to them.

Filled with such forebodings I can't say that I did my best in school. Poor *rosa* suffered many an error. And then suddenly it was four o'clock, Abbé Grégoire offered up his prayer, and the class suffered through it.

It was time to go. I fussed over tying up my bundle of books. I hoped that by the time I was ready to go the way would be clear. But I couldn't deceive myself. I had accumulated too many threats of vengeance upon my head, to get off so cheaply.

What to do? Whisper my fears to Abbé Grégoire? So that either he, or his sister Alexandrine, would accompany me home? No. This bit of cowardice would only put off the day of reckoning. There would have to come a day, sooner or later, when I would have to face it out with one or another of my schoolmates.

Just think: in my ten-year-old head, all these thoughts kept bumping into each other. And I finally resolved to go through with it, whatever it might be. Against an angry bull, I had heard somewhere, the best defense is to grab the horns.

But it was with a heavy heart and a deep sigh that I said goodnight to Abbé Grégoire and went down the steps.

And there they were. Waiting for me. The whole school, sitting in a semicircle on the steps, like Romans about to watch a gladiatorial combat. And at the bottom, with his coat off and his sleeves rolled up, was Bligny.

My resolve to meet my fate did not flinch. No. But for just a fraction of a second there was a hesitation in my advance. My heart dropped when I saw all these preparations, and I did have a slight recoil, which didn't escape my comrades who jeered me with one great howl and snicker, along with the most outrageous epithets.

I knew that I was turning pale. I could feel the shivers going up and down my cold skin. An icy sweat broke out on my forehead. But at the same time I was very clear about what all this might mean in my life. That I had to choose between being the permanent butt of all my schoolmates, exposed every day to their merciless contempt, against a few punches that would blacken my eyes or split my lips, but which would be over and done with.

I strained all my will power. Clutched at whatever courage I could find in myself, and biting down hard I reached my decision. Not without a battle, of course. But from which I emerged with my morale victorious over my flesh, my reasoning over my instincts.

But obscurely there was something else. I needed words. I felt that I could not keep up my stand unless I had the spur of words. Unless I whipped myself with speech.

"So that's how it is," I found myself saying. "It's to be you, Bligny?"

"Yes," he said. "That's how it's going to be."

"You want to fight? Really?"

"Yes. I do."

"You're sure? Are you?"

"Yes, I'm sure."

"Very well. You've got it coming!"

And I put down my books, threw off my jacket, and I launched myself head on against my antagonist, crying:

"So you want a fight, eh? You want a fight? Well—you just wait, you! You just wait!"

It was then I learned another thing: that I later discovered the Marshal de Saxe, that great military philosopher had already said: that the whole art of war consists in pretending not to be afraid and thus making one's enemy afraid.

By thus pretending not to be scared, I whipped Bligny.

Not that I whipped him without some resistance on his part. No. But my onrush, my flailing fists that struck him at once on his mouth and on his eyes, caused him to retreat so that the best he could do was give me one feeble punch on the nose.

The whole thing didn't last a minute. And I had the field of battle to myself.

Nor must I forget to honor my fellow-students. It was me they applauded!

So that as I went to pick up my books, and slip into my jacket, I kept repeating the words that summed up my whole military philosophy: "Well you just!—well you just!—well you just!"

Which, translated, may be interpreted to mean: "Look out you! That's how I am! I may be a coward and full of tears—but watch out! If you push me too far I'm capable of turning into an Alexander, a Hannibal, a Caesar. So you just!—"

And the whole semicircle of spectators understood me very clearly, for they let me through their ranks without a murmur.

I walked proudly through the passage to the big door, where only a few hours before I had been so crudely affronted, but was now as if it were my arch of triumph.

Thus it was that Dumas first discovered his deep-seated need for words. How speech could build up his morale. Turn him from a coward into a brave man. From a retiring child who would sit alone and weep, into an active youngster.

And what a word user he became! Several times he ran for political office but without ever winning, and during his candidacy he would put out such a notice as this one printed up for him sometime during the year 1848, when he was over forty-five.

WORKINGMEN OF SEINE-ET-OISE

Friends! Do you wish me to represent you? Here are my qualifications.

I will say nothing of my 10 years of education, nothing of my 4 years as legal clerk, and 7 years of experience in an official capacity.

But I call your attention to 20 years spent as a writer, working not less than 10 hours a day, adding up to 73,000 hours.

During that time I composed the following:

400 VOLUMES

Leaving aside the sums paid to the author in royalties, these 400 works published in editions of 4000, and sold for 5 francs a copy, brought in 11,753,000 francs. Divided as follows:

To the compositors	264,000
Printers	528,000
Papermakers	633,000
Binding women	120,000
Covers alone	28,000
Bookstores	2,400,000
Advertising, brokerage, traveling and other expenses	1,600,000
Wholesalers	1,600,000

Freight   100,000
Lending libraries charging
   40 centimes a day per
   volume   4,480,000
                                        _____
                          total 11,753,000

Taking 3 francs a day as an average rate of pay, and 300 days of work in a year, my books have paid the wages of 692 persons for 20 years.

35 PLAYS

My 35 plays have averaged 100 performances each, and excluding my own share, have brought in the following sums:

Stage directors	1,400,000
Actors	1,225,000
Decorators	210,000
Costumers	140,000
Theatre owners	700,000
Supernumeraries	350,000
Watchmen and firemen	70,000
For coal and kindling	70,000
Illuminating oil and gas	525,000
Ticket-vendors	60,000
Musicians	257,000
Charity	630,000
Billboard men	80,000
Sweepers	20,000
Stagehands	180,000
Insurance	60,000
Bookkeeping, etc.	190,000
Hairdressers	93,000

                                        _____
                          total 6,260,000

Thus my plays have given a livelihood to some 347 persons during the 10 years I have been writing plays for Paris productions.

But these plays have also traveled throughout the provinces. This would account for at least 3 times the Parisian figure, or 1,041.

Adding rough work, coachmen, and the claque, we get an additional 70.

Which would work out to a GRAND TOTAL of 2,150 persons, who during an average of 15 years, earned their living directly through my writing activity.

ALEXANDRE DUMAS

There is something monstrous and at the same time something beautiful in this industrial approach to writing: a human activity that makes work for millions all over the earth. Why not? Man's brain, man's emotions, man's need for amusement and instruction, these too must be fed. And the underprivileged of this world are just as starved emotionally and intellectually as they are physically. Writing is thus as important as farming. Unless we are all content to remain nothing more than well-fed brutes.

As a young boy Dumas's mind was vigorously stimulated by the Napoleonic era. As much as Napoleon was hated by every mother of Europe, France included, he was admired by every lad. Dumas relates:

As a result of the mass conscriptions of the years 1811 and 1814, and as a result of the million men scattered throughout the valleys and the mountains of Spain, the snows and the rivers of Russia, the mud of Saxony and the sands of Poland, a whole generation of Frenchmen aged twenty to twenty-two, had disappeared.

The rich had bought substitutes, paying them ten, twelve, and even 15,000 francs, and had bought them again and again, in order to stay out of service, but against this Napoleon had invented his Guard of Honor, open only to the wealthiest, a fatal and pitiless lure that brooked no substitutes, and thus even the most privileged had left to fight along with the others.

One became a conscript at the age of sixteen, and remained available for call to the colors, until forty.

All over France mothers counted the age of their sons with terror, and seemed ready to go to battle against time in order to halt the flow of days that ran by with such pitiless rapidity.

How often my mother would squeeze me to her bosom all of a sudden, and give vent to a deep sigh and tears that could not be restrained.

"Oh!" she would cry, "When I think that soon you will be a soldier. That that terrible man will take you. That man who always takes and never gives. And will send you to die on some battlefield near Leipzig or Moscow! . . . Oh my dear child, my dear child . . . !"

But the historical greed exists in all of us: the desire to take some part, however small, in the history of man. And despite the danger of himself becoming a soldier, and dying in battle, Alexandre, and many others in his little town, for all that they had already had enough of Napoleon's glories, nevertheless watched with excitement the French armies going off to fight the combined armies of the English, the Germans, and other allies.

Dumas says:

It must be admitted it gave us great pleasure to see the old uniforms once again, and the old cockades moving along the road from the isle of Elba to Paris, and the grand standards, riddled with the bullets of Austerlitz, Wagram, and Moskova, carefully transported in their cylindrical-shaped cases.

It was a wonderful spectacle to watch the Old Guard, a military type that has completely disappeared in our day, the very embodiment of the ten years of imperial rule we had recently passed through, the active and glorious spirit of France.

In three days' time, 30,000 men—30,000 giants—resolute, composed, almost gloomy in their attitude, passed by, every one of whom realized that a share of the responsibility of the great Napoleonic dynasty weighed upon him, to be cemented by his blood, and all of whom, like those beautiful caryatides of Pujet, which so frightened the chevalier de Bernin when he landed at Toulon, seemed proud of this responsibility, although they felt that they might break down under the weight that was one day to crush them.

Those men who marched thus with such a firm tread to Waterloo, to their graves, must never be forgotten! They typified the devotion, the courage, the honor of the noblest, the warmest, the purest blood of France! They embodied twenty years of struggle against all Europe. They were of the Revolution, our mother; they were of the Empire, our nurse; they were not the French nobility, but the nobility of the French people.

I saw them all pass by. All. Down to the last remnants of the Egyptian army, 200 Mamelukes with their baggy red pantaloons, their turbans, and their curved sabres.

There was something more than sublime in the spectacle: it was a religious, sacred, and holy sight to see these men. For they were as surely and as irrevocably condemned to death as were the gladiators of old, and, with them, they could have said: *Caesar, morituri te salutant!*

Only, these were going to die, not in order to serve the pleasures of a people, but to insure its liberty. And they went to their death not by compulsion, but of their own free will, by their own unfettered choice.

The gladiator of old was but a victim; in the case of our men it was self-sacrifice.

They passed through one morning; and the sound of their steps faded, and the last strains of their music died away in the distance. I remember that the music they played was the air of *Veillons au salut de l'empire.* . . .

The next announcement that appeared in the papers was that Napoleon had left Paris on June 12 to join the army.

Napoleon always followed the road his Guard had taken; so he must pass through Villers-Cotterêts.

I confess I had an intense desire to see this man, who, in making his heavy hand felt throughout France, had, in a peculiarly hard fashion, ground down a poor atom like myself, lost among thirty-two million of human beings whom he continued to crush, while forgetting my very existence.

On the eleventh we received official news of his passing; horses were commanded to be in readiness at the posting stables.

He was to set off from Paris at three o'clock in the morning; so he should pass through Villers-Cotterêts about seven or eight o'clock.

At six o'clock I was waiting at the end of the rue de Largny with the most able-bodied portion of the population, namely, those who could run as fast as the imperial carriages.

But really the best way to see Napoleon would be where the relays were to be changed, and not as he drove by.

I realized this, and, as soon as I caught sight of the dust of the first horses, a quarter of a league away, I set off for the posting house.

As I approached, I heard the rumble of wheels behind me coming nearer.

I reached the posting house, and on turning round I saw the three carriages flying over the pavement like a turbulent stream, the horses dripping with sweat, their postilions got up in fine style, powdered and beribboned.

Everybody rushed for the emperor's carriage, and naturally I was one of the foremost.

He was seated at the back, on the right, dressed in a green uniform with white facings, and he wore the star of the Legion of Honour.

His face was pale and sickly-looking, as though his head had been clumsily carved out of a block of ivory, and it was bent slightly forward on his chest; his brother Jerome was seated on his left; and the aide-de-camp, Letort, was opposite Jerome, on the front seat.

He lifted his head, looked round him, and asked: "Where are we?"

"At Villers-Cotterêts, sire," someone replied.

"Six leagues from Soissons, then," he answered.

"Yes, sire, six leagues from Soissons."

"Hurry up."

And he relapsed into the semistupor out of which he had roused himself while the carriage was being got ready to proceed.

When the relays were in and fresh postilions were in their saddles, the stable lads who had taken out the horses waved their caps and cried: "*Vive l'empereur!*"

The whips cracked; the emperor made a slight inclination with his head in return for the greeting. The carriages set off at full gallop, and disappeared round the corner of the rue de Soissons.

The splendid vision had vanished.

Ten days passed by, and we heard of the crossing of the Sambre, the taking of Charleroi, the battle of Ligny, and the engagement at Quatre-Bras.

Thus the first echoes were those of victory.

We only learnt the results of the events of the fifteenth and the sixteenth on the eighteenth—the day of the battle of Waterloo.

We awaited further news eagerly. The 19th passed by without

bringing any; the papers reported that the emperor had visited the battlefield of Ligny, and had ordered assistance to be given to the wounded.

General Letort, who faced the emperor in his carriage, was killed at the taking of Charleroi, and Jerome, who had sat with them, had had his sword hilt broken by a bullet.

The twentieth rolled by slowly and sadly; the sky looked black and threatening; it poured with rain for three whole days, and it was said that doubtless no fighting could take place in such weather.

All at once the rumor spread that some men who had brought bad news had been arrested and taken before the mayor. They declared, we were assured, that a decisive battle had been fought and lost, that the French army had been annihilated, and that the English, Prussians, and Dutch were marching on Paris.

Everybody rushed to the town hall, I, of course one of the first.

And there we found ten or a dozen men, some still in their saddles, others standing by their horses, surrounded by the crowd, which was watching them; they were covered with blood, covered with mud, and were in rags.

They said they were Poles.

We could scarcely make out what they said; they spoke a few words of French, but with difficulty.

Some made out that they were spies; others that they were German prisoners who had escaped and wanted to rejoin Blucher's army, pretending to be Polish.

An old officer who spoke German came up and interrogated them in German.

They were more at home in that language, and replied more coherently. According to them, Napoleon had engaged the English on the eighteenth. The battle began at noon; at five o'clock the English were defeated; but at six o'clock Blucher had marched *au canon*, arriving with 40,000 men, and this decided the day in the enemy's favour: a decisive battle, they said. The retirement of the French army was a rout. And of that rout they were the advance guard of fugitives.

No one believed such disastrous news. They only replied: "You will soon see."

We threatened to arrest them, to fling them into prison, and to shoot them, if they lied. They gave up their arms, and declared they were at the mercy of the authorities of the town.

Two of them who were badly wounded were taken to the hospital. The rest were put in the prison adjoining the town hall.

It was nearly three or four o'clock in the afternoon. These men had come from Planchenoit in forty-eight hours; they had ridden more than a league and a half per hour, for the bearers of ill tidings travel on wings.

When some of the men had been sent off to the hospital and others to prison, everybody dispersed to spread the bad news over the town.

As the posting house is always the most reliable place at which to obtain news, my mother and I installed ourselves there.

At seven o'clock a courier arrived, covered with mud. His horse shook from head to foot, and was ready to drop with fatigue. He ordered four horses to be ready for a carriage which was following him, then he leapt on his horse and set off on his journey again.

It was in vain we questioned him: he either knew nothing, or would not say anything.

The four horses were taken out of the stables and harnessed in readiness for the carriage: a rapidly approaching heavy rumble announced it was coming, soon we saw it appear round the corner of the street and draw up at the door.

The master of the post came forward and stood stupefied. I took hold of his coat tails and asked: "Is it he? The emperor?"

"Yes."

It was indeed the emperor, just in the same place and carriage, with one aide-de-camp near him and one opposite him, as I had seen him before.

But his companions were neither Jerome nor Letort.

Letort was killed, and Jerome was commissioned to rally the army by Laon.

It was just the same man, it was just the same pale, sickly, impassive face, but his head was bent a little more forward on his chest.

Was it merely from fatigue, or from grief at having staked the world and lost it?

As on the first occasion, he raised his head when he felt the carriage pull up, and threw exactly the same vague look around him which became so penetrating when he fixed it upon a person or scanned the horizon, those two unknown elements behind which danger might always lurk.

"Where are we?" he asked.

"At Villers-Cotterêts, sire."

"Good! Eighteen leagues from Paris?"

"Yes, sire."

"Go on."

Thus, as on the former occasion, when he put a similar question in almost the same words, he gave the same order and set off as rapidly.

That same night Napoleon slept at the Elysée.

It was exactly three months to the day since his return from the isle of Elba and his re-entrance into the Tuileries.

Only, between March 20 and the June 20, an abyss had opened which had swallowed up his fortune.

That abyss had been the battle of Waterloo!

When, at the age of sixty-one, Dumas arranged with the firm of Michel Lévy Frères the publication in fifteen (later in twenty-five) volumes of his collected plays, he prepared an introduction to *Volume I* which is entitled: *How I Became a Playwright*. It starts thus:

I had just reached the age of twenty . . .

A brave Abbé, respected and beloved by all his parishioners, not so much on account of his knowledge as on account of his charity and his indulgence, had tried in vain to instill in me some knowledge of Latin, and some bits of French poetics.

As for arithmetic, three schoolmasters in succession had given up all hope of making my poor brain absorb the most elementary notions of adding, subtracting, multiplying and dividing.

On the other hand there wasn't a horse that I couldn't ride, there wasn't a dance that I didn't go to, and where I couldn't dance all night after having gone twelve miles on foot to reach it. I could play tennis with the best. I knew every trick of fencing. And at thirty paces there wasn't a rabbit or a partridge that could escape my gun.

So, at this age of twenty, Dumas's mother, who had a tiny salt and tobacco license from which to make a living, came to her son one morning, as he was just waking up:

She cried and embraced me, and weeping she informed me: "My dear boy, I have just sold everything we own in order to be able to pay our debts."

"That's fine," I said.

"But my poor boy, don't you see that once our debts are paid, we have nothing left but two hundred and fifty-three francs?"

"That's our annual income from now on?"

My mother smiled sadly.

"You mean that's our total fortune?"

"That's it," she said.

"Very well," I said, "then you keep the two hundred and give me the fifty-three and I'm leaving for Paris."

"But what will you do there?"

"I will go to see the friends of my father. I will go see the Duke de Bellune. I will go see Sebastiani . . ."

He did see all these men, and eventually became a copyist in the office of the Duc d'Orléans. But meanwhile he had become fascinated by the theater. Concerning his first visit to a theater in Paris, he gave this lively account in his *Memoirs*.

I was completely green about Paris. I hadn't the vaguest notion of theatrical customs. I saw an enormous queue squeezed between wooden barriers, and did not dare even ask where the entrance money was taken. One of the habitués of this line no doubt perceived my confusion, for he called out to me:

"Monsieur! Monsieur!"

I turned around, wondering if he were addressing me.

"Yes . . . you, monsieur," continued the habitué, "you with the frizzy locks . . . do you want a place?"

"Do I want a place?" I repeated.

"Yes. If you put yourself at the bottom of this queue, you will never get in tonight. Five hundred people will be turned away."

This was Hebrew to me. Of his language I only gathered that

five hundred folk would be turned away and that I should be one of the number.

"Come, would you really like my place?" continued the habitué.

"Have you got a place, then?"

"Can't you see for yourself?"

I could see nothing at all.

"Taken in advance, then?" I asked.

"Taken since noon."

"And a good one . . . ?"

"What do you mean by good?"

Now it was the habitué who did not understand.

"Well," I went on, "shall I have a good place?"

"You can sit where you like."

"What! I can sit where I like?"

"Of course."

"How much did your place cost?"

"Twenty sous."

I reflected within myself that twenty sous to sit where I liked was not dear. I drew twenty sous from my pocket and gave them to the habitué, who immediately, with an agility that proved he was well accustomed to this exercise, climbed up the rails of the barrier, got over it and alighted by my side.

"Well," I said, "now where is your place?"

"Take it . . . but look sharp; for, if they push up, you will lose it."

At the same moment light broke in on my mind: "Those people, inside that barrier, have no doubt taken and paid for their places in advance, and it is in order to keep them they are penned in like that."

"Ah! good, I see!" I replied; and I strode over the barrier in my turn, the reverse way; so that, contrary to the action of my place seller, who had come without from within, I went from the outside within. I did not understand matters at all. After a second, there was a movement forward. They were just opening the offices. I was carried forward with the crowd, and ten minutes later, I found myself in front of the grating.

"Well, monsieur, aren't you going to take your ticket?" asked my neighbor.

"My ticket? What do you mean?"

"Of course, your ticket!" answered someone just behind me. "If you aren't going to take your ticket, at least allow us to take ours."

And a light thrust showed the desire of those behind me to have their turn.

"But," I said, "surely I have bought my place . . . ?"

"Your place . . . ?"

"Yes, I gave twenty sous for it, as you saw. . . . Why, I gave twenty sous to that man who sold me his place!"

"Oh, his place in the queue!" exclaimed my neighbors; "but his place in the queue is not his place inside the theater."

"He told me that, with his place, I could go where I liked."

"Of course you can go where you like; take a stage box. You can do what you like, and you can go where you like. But tickets for stage boxes are at the other office."

"Forward! forward! hurry up!" exclaimed those near me.

"Gentleman, clear the gangway, if you please," cried a voice.

"It is this gentleman, who will not take his ticket, and who prevents us from getting ours!" cried a chorus of my neighbors.

"Come, come, make up your mind."

The murmurs grew, and with them ringing in my ears, by degrees it dawned upon me what had been pretty clearly dinned into me—namely, that I had bought my place in the queue, and not my place in the theater.

So, as people were beginning to hustle me in a threatening fashion, I drew a six-franc piece from my pocket and asked for a pit ticket. They gave me four francs six sous, and a ticket which had been white. It was time! I was immediately carried away by a wave of the crowd. I presented my once white ticket to the check taker: they gave me in exchange a ticket that had been red. I went down a corridor to the left; I found a door on my left with the word *Parterre* written over it, and I entered. And now I understood the truth of what the habitué who had sold me his place for twenty sous had said. Although I had scarcely fifteen or twenty people in front of me in the queue, the pit was nearly full. A most compact nucleus had formed beneath the lights, and I realized then that those must be the best places.

I immediately resolved to mix with this group, which did not look to me to be too closely packed, and find myself a good place among them. I climbed over the benches, as I had seen several other people do, and balancing myself on the tops of their curved backs, I hastened to reach the center.

I was becoming, or rather, it must be admitted, I was, a very ridiculous object. I wore my hair very long, and, as it was frizzy, it formed a grotesque aureole round my head. Moreover, at a period when people wore short frock coats, hardly reaching to the knee, I wore a coat which came down to my ankles. A revolution had taken place in Paris, which had not yet had time to reach as far as Villers-Cotterêts. I was in the latest fashion of Villers-Cotterêts but I was in the last but one Parisian mode. Now, as nothing generally is more opposed to the latest fashion than the last mode but one, I looked excessively absurd, as I have already had the modesty to admit. Of course, I appeared so in the eyes of those toward whom I advanced; for they greeted me with shouts of laughter, which I thought in very bad taste.

I have always been exceedingly polite; but at this period, coupled with the politeness I had acquired from my maternal education, there woke in me a restless, suspicious hastiness of temper which I probably inherited from my father. This hastiness made my nerves an easy prey to irritation. I took my hat in my hand—an action which revealed the utter oddity of my way of wearing my hair—and the general hilarity among the group in the rows to which I desired to gain access redoubled.

"Pardon me, gentlemen," I said in the politest of tones, "but I should like to know the cause of your laughter, so that I may be able to laugh with you. They say the piece we have come to see is extremely sad, and I should not be sorry to make merry before I have to weep."

My speech was listened to in the most religious silence; then, from the depths of this silence, a voice suddenly exclaimed:

"Oh! that head of his!"

The apostrophe seemed to be exceedingly funny, for it had hardly been uttered before the bursts of laughter were redoubled; but the hilarity had scarcely begun afresh before it was accompanied by the sound of a stinging smack in the face which I gave to the wag. "Monsieur," I said, as I slapped him, "my name is Alexandre Dumas. Until after tomorrow, you will find me at the *Hôtel des Vieux-*

Augustins, in the road of the same name, and after tomorrow at No. 1 place des Italiens."

It would seem that I spoke a language quite unknown to these gentlemen; for, instead of replying to me, twenty fists were flourished threateningly, and everybody shouted:

"Put him out! put him out!"

"What!" I cried, "put me to the door? That would be a nice thing, upon my word, seeing that I have already paid for my place twice over—once in the queue, and then again at the box office."

"Put him out! put him out!" cried the voices afresh, with redoubled fury.

"Gentlemen, I have had the honor to give you my address."

"Put him out! put him out!" cried the people, in strident, raucous tones.

All the people present had risen from their seats, were leaning over the gallery, and were almost half out of the boxes. I seemed to be at the end of an immense funnel with everybody gazing at me from all sides.

"Put him out! put him out!" cried those who did not even know what the commotion was about, but who calculated that one person less would mean room for one more.

I was debating what course to take, from the depths of my funnel, when a well-dressed man broke through the crowd, which deferentially opened a way for him, and he asked me to go out.

"Why am I to go out?" I asked in great surprise.

"Because you are disturbing the performance."

"What! I am disturbing the play? . . . The play has not begun yet."

"Well, you are disturbing the audience."

"Really, monsieur!"

"Follow me."

My guide led me into the corridor, from the corridor to the office, and from the office into the street. When in the street he said: "There! don't do it again." And he returned to the theater.

I saw that I had got off very cheaply, since I thought I was to be put under arrest, and here I found myself released after a custody of only five minutes. I stood for a moment on the pavement, whilst

I made this judicious reflection, and seeing that my guide had re-entered, I too decided to do the same.

"Your ticket?" said the ticket collector.

"My ticket? You took it from me just now, and, as a proof, it was a white one, for which you gave me in exchange a red ticket."

"Then what have you done with your red ticket?"

"I gave it to a woman who asked me for it."

"So that you have neither ticket nor check?"

"Why, no, I have neither ticket nor check."

"Then you cannot go in."

"Do you mean to say I cannot enter, after having paid for my ticket twice over?"

"Twice?"

"Yes, twice."

"How did you do that?"

"Once in the queue, and again at the box office."

"You humbug!" said the ticket collector.

"What did you say?"

"I said you cannot go in, that is what I said."

"But I mean to get in, nevertheless."

"Then take a ticket at the office."

"That will be the second."

"Well, what does that matter to me?"

"What does it matter to you?"

"If you have sold your ticket at the door, it is no affair of mine."

"Ah! so you take me for a dealer in checks?"

"I take you for a brawler who has just been turned out for disturbing the peace, and if you go on doing it, you'll not be led out into the road the next time, but into the police station."

There could be no mistaking the threat. I began to understand that, without intending it, I had infringed the law—or rather custom, which is far more jealous of contravention than the law.

"Ah, is this so?" I said.

"That is about it," said the collector.

"Well, well, you are the stronger of the two," I said.

And I went out.

When outside the door, I considered how stupid it was to have come to see a play, to have paid for two places to see it—a place in the queue and a place at the office—to have seen only a curtain representing hangings of green velvet, and to come away without seeing anything else. I went on to reflect that, since I had already paid for two tickets, I might as well incur the expense of a third, and as people were still going in and a double queue circled the theater so that the door formed as it were the clasp to the girdle, I placed myself at the end of the queue which looked to me to be the shortest. It was the opposite queue to the one I had gone in by before; it was not so dense, as it led to the orchestra, the front galleries, the stage boxes and the first and second rows of stalls. This was what I was informed by the clerk at the box office when I asked for a ticket for the pit. I looked up, and, as he had indicated, I saw upon the white plan the designation of the places to be obtained at that particular office. The cheapest places were those in the orchestra and second row of stalls. Seats in the orchestra and in the second row of stalls cost two francs fifty centimes. I took two francs fifty centimes from my pocket, and asked for an orchestra seat. The orchestra ticket was handed to me, and my play-going cost me five francs all told.

No matter: it was no good crying over spilt milk! My dinner had not cost me anything, and tomorrow I was to enter the Duc d'Orléans' secretarial offices; I could well afford to allow myself this trivial orgy. I reappeared triumphant before the check barrier, holding my orchestra ticket in my hand. The collector smiled graciously upon me, and said: "On the right, monsieur." I noticed this was quite a different direction from the first time. The first time I had tacked myself on to the right-hand queue and gone in at the left; the second time, I followed the left queue and they told me to enter on the right. I augured from this that since I had this time reversed the order of my proceedings, the manner of my reception would also be reversed, and, consequently, that I should be welcomed instead of rejected.

I was not mistaken. I found quite a different stamp of people in the orchestra from those I had found in the pit, and, as the girl who showed me to my seat pointed out to me a vacant place towards the center of a row, I set to work to reach it. Everyone rose politely to allow me to pass. I gained my seat, and sat down by the side of a gentleman, wearing gray trousers, a buff waistcoat and black tie. He

was a man of about forty or forty-two. His hat was placed on the
seat I came to fill. He was interrupted in the perusal of a charming
little book—which I learnt later was an Elzevir—apologized as he
took up his hat, bowed to me and went on reading. "Upon my word!"
I said to myself, "here is a gentleman who seems to me better
brought up than those I have just encountered." And, promising to
enter into friendly relations with my neighbor I sat down in the
empty stall.

It was not surprising that, interested as I was in literature, I should
endeavor to find out what the book was which could inspire such a
powerful influence over my neighbor, who was so deeply absorbed
in his reading, that metaphorically speaking, he gave himself up,
bound hand and foot, into my power. I had more than a quarter of
an hour in which to make this investigation before the curtain rose,
therefore I conducted it at my leisure. First of all, I tried to see the
title of the book; but the binding was carefully hidden by a paper
cover, so it was impossible to read the title on the back of the book.
I rose; in that position I could look down on the reader. Then,
thanks to the excellent sight I have the good fortune to possess, I
was able to read the following curious title on the opposite side to
the engraved frontispiece:

LE PASTISSIER FRANÇOIS

*Où est enseignée la manière de faire toute sorte
de pastisserie
Très-utile à toutes sortes de personnes;
Ensemble le moyen d'apprester toutes sortes
d'oeufs pour les jours maigres et autres
En plus de soixante façons.*

AMSTERDAM

CHEZ LOUIS ET DANIEL ELZEVIER

1655

"Ah! ah!" I said to myself, "now I have it! This well-mannered
gentleman is surely a gourmand of the first order, M. Grimod de
la Reynière perhaps, whom I have so often heard described as a

rival of Cambacérès and of d'Aigrefeuille. But stay, this gentleman has hands and M. Grimod de la Reynière has only stumps." At that moment, the polite gentleman let his hand and the book he held fall on his knees; then, casting his eyes upward, he appeared to be lost in profound reflection. He was, as I have said, a man of forty or forty-two years of age, with an essentially gentle face, kindly and sympathetic; he had black hair, blue-gray eyes, a nose slightly bent to the left through an excrescence, a finely cut, clever-looking, witty mouth—the mouth of a born storyteller.

I was yearning to get up a conversation with him—a hobbledehoy of a country bumpkin, ignorant of everything, but *anxious to learn*, as they put it in M. Lhomond's elementary lessons. His benevolent countenance encouraged me. I took advantage of the moment when he stopped reading to address a word or two to him.

"Monsieur," said I, "pray forgive me if my question seems impertinent, but are you extremely fond of eggs?"

My neighbor shook his head, came gradually out of his reverie, and, looking at me with a distraught expression, he said, in a very pronounced Eastern French accent:

"Pardon me, monsieur, but I believe you did me the honor of addressing me . . . ?"

I repeated my sentence.

"Why do you suppose that?" he said.

"The little book you are reading so attentively, monsieur—excuse my rudeness, but my eyes fell involuntarily on the title—contains recipes, does it not? for cooking eggs in more than sixty different ways?"

"Oh yes, true . . ." he said.

"Monsieur, that book would have been of great use to an uncle of mine, a curé, who was, or rather still is, a great eater, and a fine sportsman: one day he made a bet with one of his *confrères* that he would eat a hundred eggs at his dinner; he was only able to discover eighteen or twenty ways of serving them . . . yes, twenty ways, for he ate them by fives at a time. You see, if he had known sixty ways of cooking them, instead of a hundred, he could have eaten two hundred."

My neighbor looked at me with a certain attention which seemed to imply that he was asking himself: "Am I by any chance seated next to a young lunatic?"

"Well?" he said.

"Well, if I could procure such a book for my dear uncle, I am sure he would be most grateful to me."

"Monsieur," said my neighbor, "I doubt if, in spite of the sentiments which do a nephew's heart the greatest credit, you could procure this book."

"Why not?"

"Because it is exceedingly rare."

"That little old book exceedingly rare?"

The bibliomaniac smiled disdainfully.

"Do you know, monsieur," he said to me, "what a copy of the *Pastissier françois* is worth?"

"Why, I should judge it to be worth a couple of francs. At most five."

"A copy of the *Pastissier françois*, monsieur, is worth from two hundred to four hundred francs."

"From two to four hundred francs . . . ?"

"Yes, indeed . . . Only a week ago, old Brunet, the author of *Manuel des libraires*, an enthusiastic Elzeviriomaniac, inserted a notice in the papers that he was willing to pay three hundred francs for a copy such as this. Luckily, Frank did not see the notice."

At that moment the call bell sounded, the curtain rose, and while I prepared myself to listen, my neighbor plunged more deeply than ever into his precious Elzevir.

The overture was a crash of instruments, undoubtedly intended to represent a storm. The scene opened in the cave of Staffa. Malvina could be seen sleeping on a tomb. Oscar sat on another. A third enclosed Lord Ruthven, who was to come out of it at a given moment. The part of Malvina was taken by Madame Dorval; Oscar, or the angel of marriage, by Moessard; Lord Ruthven, or the Vampire, by Philippe.

Alas! who could have known at that moment, when I was looking so eagerly at the stage, taking in the whole scene, decorations and characters combined, that the day would come when I would attend Philippe's funeral, his real one, and watch by Madame Dorval's deathbed?

In the prologue, there was another angel, called Ithuriel, the angel of the moon, talking with the angel of marriage. This was Mademoiselle Denotte. At this moment I cannot say whether she is living or dead.

Malvina had lost herself in hunting; the storm terrifying her, she had taken shelter in the cave of Staffa. There, unable to keep awake, she had fallen asleep on a tomb. An angel of marriage (male) came to watch over her. Then an angel of the moon (female), who had slid down on a ray of the pale goddess, and entered through the cracks of the basaltic roof, asked why the angel of marriage sat there, and, above all, how it came about that there was a young girl lying here in the grotto of Staffa.

Oscar, the angel of marriage, replied that, inasmuch as Malvina, sister of Lord Aubrey, was to espouse Lord Marsden next day, he had been summoned by the importance of the occasion, and that his worried air, when Ithuriel interrupted him in the act of silently gazing upon this beautiful betrothed girl, was due to his foreknowledge of the misfortunes in store for the young maiden, who was about to fall from the arms of Love into those of Death. Then Ithuriel began to understand.

"Explain thyself," said Ithuriel, "is it true that horrible phantoms *come* sometimes . . . ?" He used the word *viennent*, in the present indicative.

My neighbor trembled, as though an asp had bitten him in his sleep.

"*Vinssent!*" he cried—"*vinssent!*" Using the same verb, *venir*, but in the subjunctive, meaning *may come*.

Cries of "Silence!" burst forth all over the theater, and I too clamored loudly for silence, for I was enthralled by this opening.

The angel of the moon, interrupted in the middle of her sentence, threw an angry look across the orchestra, and went on:

"Is it true that horrible phantoms come (*viennent*) under the cloak of the rights of marriage, to suck blood from the throat of a timid maiden?"

"*Vinssent! vinssent! vinssent!*" murmured my neighbor.

Fresh cries of "*Hush!*" drowned his exclamation, which it must be confessed was less bold and less startling this time than the first.

"My God! think of writing a play on such a subject!" murmured my neighbor.

It seemed to me that he was too critical; for I thought this dialogue was couched in the finest style imaginable. Several persons who had heard my neighbor gave vent to various whispered comments on the presumption of this indefatigable interrupter; but, as he buried himself in his *Pastissier françois*, the murmurs ceased.

It is unnecessary to point out that the young betrothed asleep on the tomb was also the innocent heroine who was destined to be the bride of the Vampire, and had the public been in any doubt, all their doubts would have been dispersed after the last scene of the prologue.

I sat entranced.

During all this I watched my neighbor almost as much as the play, and, to my great satisfaction, I had seen him close his Elzevir and listen intently to the final scenes. But when the curtain fell, he uttered an exclamation of disdain accompanied by a deep-drawn sigh.

"Pooh!" he said.

The whole house applauded enthusiastically, save my neighbor, who still growled under his breath. Such inveterate animosity against a play which appeared to me to be full of interest astonished me, coming from a person who seemed so well disposed as he. He had not merely contented himself with noisy exclamations, as I have indicated, but, still worse, during the whole of the last scene he had played in a disturbing fashion with a key which he several times put to his lips in order to produce a shrill whistle.

"Really, monsieur," I said, "I think you are very hard on this piece."

My neighbor shrugged his shoulders.

"Yes, monsieur, I know it, and the more so because the author considers himself a man of genius, a man of talent, the possessor of a good style; but he deceives himself. I saw the piece when it was played three years ago, and now I have seen it again. Well, what I said then, I repeat: the piece is dull, unimaginative, improbable. Yes, see how he makes vampires act! Three years ago I thought the next act pretty bad; it will seem worse to me today. So, with your permission I shall leave."

"If you really must, monsieur . . ."

"Yes, really you must let me go."

"But first may I ask your advice?"

"With the greatest pleasure . . . Speak."

"Before I came into the orchestra, I entered the pit, and there I had a slight breeze."

"Ah! So that was you, was it?"

"Yes."

"You were boxed on the ear!"

"Yes."

"What occasioned you to allow yourself that diversion?"

I told him my adventure, and asked him if I ought to forewarn my witnesses overnight, or if it would be time enough next morning. He shook his head.

"Oh, neither tonight nor tomorrow morning," he said.

"What! neither tonight nor tomorrow?"

"No; it would be useless trouble."

"Why so?"

"Because you fell into a nest of hired applauders."

"A nest of hired applauders! . . . What are they?" I asked.

"Oh! young man," exclaimed my neighbor in paternal accents, "do your utmost to preserve your holy innocence!"

"But suppose I beg you to put an end to it . . . ?"

"Have you ever heard that in former times there were emperors of Rome?"

"Certainly."

"Do you remember the name of the fifth of those emperors?"

"I think it was Nero."

"Right . . . Well, Nero, who poisoned his cousin Britannicus, disemboweled his mother Agrippina, strangled his wife Octavia, killed his wife Poppaea with a kick in the stomach, had a bad tenor voice, and occasionally sang false! That did not matter whilst Nero sang before his roystering companions or before his courtesans at the Palatine; neither was it of much consequence when Nero sang as he watched Rome burn: the Romans were too much occupied with the fire to pay any attention to a semitone too high or a flat too low. But when he took it into his head to sing in a public theater, it was a different matter: every time the illustrious tenor deviated in the slightest degree from musical correctness, some spectator allowed himself—as I shall permit myself to do, if you insist on my remaining to the end of this silly melodrama—to whistle in derision.

"Of course the spectator was arrested and promptly flung to the lions; but as he passed before Nero, instead of saying simply, according to custom, 'Augustus, he who is about to die salutes thee!' he said, 'Augustus, I am to die because you sang false; but when I am dead, you will not sing the more correctly.' This final salutation, taken up and added to by other culprits, annoyed Nero: he had the whistlers strangled in the corridors, and no one whistled any more.

"But it was not enough for Nero—that *hankerer after the impossible*, as Tacitus called him—it was not enough that no one whistled any more, he wanted everybody to applaud him. Now, he could indeed strangle those who whistled, but he could not exactly strangle those who did not applaud; he would have had to strangle the whole audience, and that would have been no light job: Roman theaters held twenty, thirty, forty thousand spectators! . . . As they were so strong in numbers, they could easily have prevented themselves from being strangled.

"So Nero went one better: he instituted a body composed of Roman nobles—a kind of confraternity consisting of some three thousand members. These three thousand chevaliers were not the emperor's pretorians, they were the artist's bodyguard; wherever he went, they followed him; whenever he sang, they applauded him. Did a surly spectator raise a murmur, a sensitive ear allow its owner to utter a slight whistle, that murmur or whistle was immediately drowned by applause. Nero ruled triumphant in the theater.

"Well, my dear sir, that race of chevaliers has been perpetuated under the name of *claqueurs*. The Opera has them, the Théâtre-Français has them, the Odéon has them—and is fortunate in having them!—finally, the Porte-Saint-Martin has them. Nowadays their mission is not only to support poor actors—it consists even more, as you have just seen, in preventing bad plays from collapsing. They are called Romans, from their origin; but our *romains* are not recruited from among the nobility. No, managers are not so hard to please in their choice, and it is not necessary to show a gold ring on the first finger; provided they can show a couple of big hands, and bring these large hands rapidly and noisily together, that is the only quartering of nobility required of them. So, you see, I am quite right to warn you not to upset two of your friends for one of those rapscallions. . . . Now that I have enlightened you, will you allow me to leave?"

I knew it would be impertinent to retain my neighbor any longer. Though his conversation, which had covered a wide range of subjects in a short time, was agreeable and highly edifying to myself, it was evident he could not say the same of mine. I could not teach him anything, save that I was ignorant of everything he knew. So I effaced myself with a sigh, not daring to ask him who he was, and allowing him to pass by with his *Pastissier françois* hugged with both hands to his breast, fearing, no doubt, lest one of the chevaliers of whom he had just spoken, curious in the matter of rare books, should relieve him of it.

I watched him withdraw with regret: a vague presentiment told me that this man would become one of my closest friends.

Chapter II

COMÉDIE-FRANÇAISE

Such was Alexandre Dumas's introduction to the theater of Paris, where he was to play eventually (and his son after him) such a tumultuous role, not only as playwright, but also as producer and owner of a fine theater, and also as the lover of a number of actresses.

But we have overshot ourselves. Coming back to Dumas's first appearance in Paris, we have said nothing about how he managed to earn a living while still unknown. The plan he had in mind when he left his native village was to look up the generals who had been companions in arms with his father, and no sooner had he reached Paris than he bought himself the *Almanac of Twenty-five Thousand Addresses,* and paid visits to both Marshal Jourdain and Marshal Sebastiani, both wealthy and important men still. But he was badly received and neither man would believe that this ill-dressed and unkempt youth was the son of their old friend.

Equally inhospitable was the Duc de Bellune. And the only one of his father's former friends who showed him any kindness was General Foy. But he didn't know if there was anything that he could do for Alexandre. Quoting again from the *Memoirs:*

"What's to be done with you?" the general asked in the kindest of voices.

"I'm ready for anything," I said.

"Well, what can you do?"

"I'm afraid there isn't much," I confessed.

"But you've had some training—in mathematics, for example."

"Nothing, I'm afraid."

"Some notions, at any rate, of algebra, geometry, physics."

I felt the crimson rising to my cheeks as he paused after each subject, expecting me to admit some knowledge. Sweat broke out on my forehead as I realized for the first time just how ignorant I really was.

"No, General," I stammered. "I know none of them."

"You were a clerk in Villers-Cotterêts, so you no doubt absorbed some smattering of law."

"No, General."

"Well, then, Latin? Or Greek?"

"Latin, a little. But Greek, no, not at all."

"Can you speak any foreign language?"

"Italian."

"Hm. What about accounts. Can you keep them?"

"No, not in the least," I admitted, even though I was going through the tortures of the damned.

General Foy sympathized with me. "You've given me nothing with which to work," he said, "But still—who knows? I certainly don't want to abandon you. Here, write down your address, and we'll see . . ."

Scarcely had I written my name than he clapped his hands. "Saved!" he cried.

"What do you mean?"

"You write a beautiful hand! You shall be a copyist in the offices of the Duc d'Orléans, at the Palais Royal, with a salary of 1200 francs a year."

It wasn't much money, but he could manage to live on it, and eventually bring his mother to Paris. But he was always ashamed of this scene, for he had been told, years before, that only people with a miserable hand ever got anywhere in life.

He would describe his duties thus, in his *Memoirs:*

Lassagne (who was to become Dumas's close friend and teach him many things about the life and arts of Paris) arranged my daily work. It was entirely mechanical, and consisted in copying out, in the finest handwriting possible, the largest possible number of letters: these, according to their importance, had to be signed by M. Oudard, M. de Broval, or even by the Duc d'Orléans. In the midst of this correspondence, which concerned the whole range of administration and which often, when addressed to princes or foreign kings, passed from matters of administration to politics, there occurred reports connected with the contentious affairs of M. le Duc d'Orléans; for the Duc d'Orléans himself prepared his litigious business for his counsel, doing himself the work that solicitors do for barristers—that is to say, preparing the briefs. These were nearly always entirely in the handwriting of the Duc d'Orléans, or at all events corrected and annotated in his large thick writing, in which every letter was fastened to its neighboring letter by a solid stroke, after the fashion of the arguments of a logical dialectician, bound together, entwined, succeeding each other.

I was attacking my first letter, and, by the advice of Lassagne, who had laid great stress on this point, I was dispatching it in my very best handwriting, when I heard the door of communication between Oudard's office and ours open. I pretended, with the hypocrisy of an old hand, to be so deeply absorbed in my work that no noise could distract my attention, when I heard the creak of steps advancing towards my desk and then they stopped by me.

"Dumas!" called out Lassagne to me.

I raised my head and I saw, standing close to me on my left, a person who was totally unknown to me.

"Monsieur le Chevalier de Broval!" said Lassagne, stressing his exclamation.

I rose from my seat.

"Do not disturb yourself," he said. And he took the letter I was copying, which was nearly finished, and read it.

I took advantage of this respite to examine him.

M. le Chevalier de Broval, as everyone knows, had been one of the faithful followers of M. le Duc d'Orléans. He had never left him during the last portion of his exile, serving him sometimes as secretary, at other times as diplomatist. In this latter capacity he had been mixed up in all the lengthy discussions over the marriage of the Duc d'Orléans with Princess Marie-Amélie, daughter of Ferdinand and Caroline, King and Queen of Naples; and in connection with this marriage he had gained the Order of Saint-Janvier, which he wore on a braided coat on high festivals, next to the cross of the Legion of Honor.

He was a little old man of about sixty years of age, with short stubbly hair; he was slightly lame, walked crookedly in his left side, had a big nose, which told its own tale, and small gray eyes, that expressed nothing; he looked a typical courtier, polite, obsequious, fawning to his master, kind by fits and starts, but generally capricious with his subordinates; he thought a great deal of trifles, attaching supreme importance to the manner in which a letter was folded or a seal was fastened; he really imbibed these notions from the Duc d'Orleans himself, who was even more particular over little details than perhaps was M. de Broval.

M. de Broval read the letter, took my pen, added an apostrophe or a comma here and there; then, replacing it in front of me: "Finish it," he said.

I finished it.

He waited behind me, literally pressing on my shoulders.

Every fresh face I saw in turn had its intimidating effect on me. I finished with a very shaky hand.

"There it is, Monsieur le chevalier," I said.

"Good!" he exclaimed.

He took a pen, signed, threw sand over my writing and over his; then, giving me back the epistle, which was for a simple inspector —as, at first, they did not risk confiding more than that to my inexperienced hand—he said:

"Do you know how to fold a letter?"

I looked at him with astonishment.

"I ask you if you know how to fold a letter. Answer me!"

"Yes, yes . . . at least, I believe so," I replied, astonished at the fixed stare his little gray eyes had assumed.

"You believe? Is that all? You are not sure?"

"Monsieur, I am not yet sure about anything, as you see, not even about the folding of a letter."

"And there you are right, for there are ten ways of folding a letter, according to the rank of the person to whom it is addressed. Fold this one."

I began to fold the letter in four.

"Oh! what are you about?" he said.

I stopped short. "Pardon, monsieur," I said, "but you *ordered* me to fold the letter, and I am folding it."

M. de Broval bit his lip. I had laid emphasis on the word "ordered" in the spoken phrase as I have just underlined it in the written phrase.

"Yes," he said; "but you are folding it square—that is all right for high functionaries. If you give square-folded letters to inspectors and subinspectors, what will you do for ministers, princes and kings?"

"Quite so, Monsieur le chevalier," I replied; "will you tell me what is the correct way for inspectors and subinspectors?"

"Oblong, monsieur, oblong."

"You will pardon my ignorance, monsieur; I know what an oblong is in theory, but I do not yet know what it is in practice."

"See . . ."

And M. de Broval condescended willingly to give me the lesson in things oblong I had asked of him.

"There!" he said, when the letter was folded.

"Thank you, monsieur," I replied.

"Now, monsieur, the envelope?" he said.

I had never made envelopes, except for the rare petitions I had written for my mother, and once on my own account in General Foy's office, so I was still more ignorant about the making of envelopes than about the folding. I took a half sheet of paper in my left hand, a pair of scissors in my right hand, and I began to cut the sheet.

M. le Chevalier de Broval uttered a mingled cry of surprise and terror.

"Oh! good Lord!" he said, "what are you going to do?"

"Why, Monsieur le chevalier, I am going to make the envelope you asked me to make."

"With scissors?"

"Yes."

"First learn this, monsieur: paper should not be cut, it should be torn."

"Oh!" I exclaimed.

"It should be torn," repeated M. de Broval; "and then in this case there is no need even to tear the paper, which perhaps you do not realize either?"

"No, monsieur, I do not."

"You will learn . . . It only wants an English envelope."

"Ah! an English envelope?"

"You do not know how to make an English envelope?"

"I do not even know what it is, Monsieur le chevalier."

"I will show you. As a general rule, monsieur, square letters and square envelopes are for ministers, for princes and for kings."

"Right, Monsieur le chevalier; I will remember."

"You are sure?"

"Yes."

"Good . . . And for heads of departments, chief assistants, inspectors and subinspectors, oblong letters and English envelopes."

I repeated: "Oblong letters and English envelopes."

"Yes, yes, of course . . . There, that is what we call an English envelope."

"Thank you, monsieur."

"Now the seal . . . Ernest, will you light me a taper?"

Ernest hastened to bring us the lighted taper; and now, I confess to my shame, my confusion increased: I had never hitherto sealed my letters except with wafers—that is to say, when I had sealed them.

I took the wax in so awkward a fashion, I heated it in such a queer way, I blew it out so quickly, for fear of burning the paper, that this time I excited pity rather than impatience in the breast of M. de Broval.

"Oh! my friend," he said, "have you really never even sealed a letter?"

"Never, monsieur," I replied. "Who was there for me to write to, buried away as I have been in a little country town?"

This humble confession touched M. de Broval.

"See," he said, heating the wax, "this is how one seals a letter."

And, believe me, he sealed the letter at arm's length, with as steady a hand as though he had been twenty-five years of age. Then, taking a large silver seal, he pressed it on the lake of burning wax, and did not withdraw it until the impress was clearly defined and I could see the escutcheon with the three heraldic fleurs-de-lis of Orléans, surmounted by the ducal coronet.

I was disheartened, I must confess.

"Write the address," M. le Chevalier de Broval said imperiously.

I wrote the address with a trembling hand.

"Good, good!" said M. le Chevalier de Broval; "don't be discouraged, my boy . . . It is all right; now countersign it."

I stopped, completely ignorant of what a countersign was.

M. de Broval began to realize, as General Foy had done, how ignorant I was. He pointed with a finger to the corner of the letter. "There," he said, "write there *Duc d'Orléans*. That is to frank the letter. You hear?"

I heard well enough; but I was so profoundly upset that I hardly understood what was said.

"There!" said M. de Broval, taking up the letter and looking at it with a satisfied air, "that is all right; but you must learn all these things. . . . Ernest,"—Ernest was M. de Broval's favorite, and in his genial moments the old courtier called him by his Christian name—"Ernest, teach M. Dumas to fold letters, to make envelopes and to seal packets." And at these words took himself off.

The door had scarcely shut before I was begging my comrade Ernest to begin his lessons, and he gave himself up to the task at once with hearty good will. Ernest was a first-rate hand at folding, making envelopes and sealing; but I put my whole will into it, and it was not long before I equaled and surpassed my master's skill.

When I gave in my resignation, in 1831, to the Duc d'Orléans, who had become King Louis-Philippe, I had attained to such perfection in the third accomplishment, especially, that the only regret he expressed was this:

"The devil! that is a pity! You are the best sealer of letters I have ever seen."

While I was taking my lesson in folding and sealing under Ernest, Lassagne was reading the papers.

"Oh!" he suddenly exclaimed, "I well recollect that!"

"What is it?" I asked.

Instead of answering me, Lassagne read aloud: "A scene which recalls that of la Fontaine at the first representation of *Florentin* took place, yesterday evening, at the third performance of the revival of the *Vampire*. Our learned bibliophile, Charles Nodier, was expelled from Porte-Saint-Martin theater for disturbing the play by whistling. Charles Nodier was one of the anonymous authors of the *Vampire*."

"So!" I cried, "my neighbor of the orchestra was Charles Nodier!"

"Did you have any talk with him?" asked Lassagne.

"I did nothing else during the intervals."

"You were fortunate," continued Lassagne. "Had I been in your place, I should have greatly preferred the intervals to the play."

Thus he discovered who his mysterious neighbor had been: Charles Nodier, a very minor writer, but important as a precursor of the Romantic movement in French literature.

Nodier was also the librarian of the Arsenal library, so-called because it was housed in that gloomy old structure facing the Seine, a massive building first erected under François *le premier*, and then, after being wrecked in several gunpowder explosions and rebuilt several times, finally turned over to be a repository of books.

Nodier and his family had a fine huge apartment in the building, and every Sunday opened it to all that was stimulating in French artistic circles. Dumas was eventually to be one of that group, when Nodier came to admire Dumas's first important play, *Christine*, so enthusiastically. Thus he met Victor Hugo and his brother Charles, and the sculptor Barye, and the painter Boulanger, and the poets Vigny and Musset and Lamartine, who all came there to recite and to argue and to eat and dance. Here the Romantic movement really began, and eventually swept the world—and is with us still to this day, though often scorned as a lesser form of art.

Of course there were years of clerking for the Duc d'Orléans before Dumas reached the point of being an accepted artist. Indeed he began very humbly by trying to write some theatrical pieces that were little more than skits before he tried his hand at a full-scale play.

He joined himself in this endeavor with his fellow employee, Lassagne. And he tells, in Volume III of his *Memoirs*, Chapter 4 (of the Waller translation), what a furore was stirred up in the office when it was discovered that a mere copyist was so daring and ambitious as to want to be an author.

The reader will notice that in this extract Dumas refers to his having to support his mother, himself, and his son, on his small pay of 125 francs a month. And the reader will imagine that the editor of this anthology has skipped the chapters in the *Memoirs* referring to Dumas's love affair, his marriage, and the birth of his son. But nothing has been skipped.

Except one sentence, or rather a part of a sentence, referring to the day of July 24, 1824, when Dumas says: "On the day when the duc de Montpensier made his appearance in the world at the Palais Royal, a son was born to me on the fourth floor of the Place des Italiens." That is all.

But we know that the mother's name was Catherine Lebay. That she had occupied, when Dumas first took a room in Paris, a neighboring room on the same garret floor, and that she earned her living from some sort of needlework. The child, of course, was the one that was to grow up and become Alexandre Dumas *fils*, the author of a number of moralistic plays that influenced Ibsen and then George Bernard Shaw, and in particular of the play which we know of in English as *Camille* (though actually the heroine's name was Marguerite) because she had a passion for camellia flowers, wearing white ones most of the month, red ones only on a certain few days.

Dumas never married the mother, and in fact soon abandoned her, but he legitimized his son, and made himself responsible for his care and upbringing. But since his own fortunes were now up, now down, the degree of this care fluctuated considerably, and the son's feelings toward his father varied from admiration and passionate affection, to hatred. And there was even a moment, when the son walked in his sleep with a knife in his hand, wanting to kill his father. Just a momentary aberration, but indicative of a powerful mixture of love and hostility churning deep in his young soul.

Here, then, is the quote concerning Dumas's earliest efforts to become a writer:

Lassagne had told me to think of a subject for a vaudeville. I had done so, and I believed I had found one. It was in the *Arabian Nights*, one of the episodes in the travels of Sinbad the sailor, I believe. I say "I believe," for I am not quite sure, and the matter is not really worth the trouble of ransacking my desk to find out. Sinbad, the indefatigable traveler, reaches a country where they bury wives with their husbands, and husbands with their wives. He imprudently marries; his wife dies, and he has a narrow escape of being buried with her. A mere trifle. But the episode suggested a vague plan, which I took to Lassagne.

Lassagne read it, and, if that were possible he was more kindly disposed toward me even than at the first, when he saw how determined I was to succeed. With the exception of a few corrections, which he undertook to make, he decided that the scheme would serve. He therefore communicated with a clever young fellow named Vulpian, a friend of his, who was also later to become one of mine. Vulpian is one more name to be marked with a cross in these recollections; for he is dead. We met together two or three times and shared the task.

At the first meeting, each of us had his part ready. We joined the three pieces together and made them into something like a harmonious whole. Lassagne undertook to put the polishing touches to the work, which took him three or four days. When this was done, the three authors, pronouncing it to be perfect, decided it should be read under the title of *La Noce et l'Enterrement* [The Wedding and the Burial] at the Vaudeville, where Lassagne and Vulpian knew Desaugiers.

Unluckily, Desaugiers, who was already affected with the disease that eventually killed him, was at home undergoing a second or third operation, and could not be present at the reading. The upshot of his absence was that *La Noce et l'Enterrement* received almost as abrupt a refusal at the Vaudeville as my previous effort, written with my friend Rousseau, *La Chasse et l'Amour* had received at the Gymnase. It seemed I was not to be favored with good luck while I shared my work with others. I felt terribly discouraged. But I felt worse still the day after the reading, when Lassagne put in an appearance at the office with an expression of gloom on his face. It was so rarely he was depressed that I rose from my seat feeling sure something was wrong.

"What is the matter now?" I asked.

"Oudard," he said.

"Our boss?" I exclaimed.

Lassagne explained that somehow or other it had leaked out, although my name had not been breathed at the reading, that I had written a play with him; and, in consequence, Oudard has just sent for him.

"Well?"

"Well, he made out I had given you a taste for literature; he says this taste will ruin your future career and he has made me pass my word of honor not only to cease helping you in any other play, but also to cast aside the one already finished."

"And did you promise?" I asked.

"I felt obliged to do so for your sake, Dumas. Your General Foy has passed away and is no longer able to uphold your interests here. I don't know who has done you a bad turn by speaking to Monsieur de Broval, but they do not at all look upon your literary propensities with friendly eyes."

I do not think my heart ever felt heavier. The two or three hundred francs which *La Chasse et l'Amour* had brought in had so sensibly lightened our circumstances, that I had been looking forward to the time when I should be drawing not merely twenty to twenty-five francs more per month, but earning four times that amount by literary work. Moreover, a portion of what *la Noce et l'Enterrement* was to bring me in was already hypothecated to my moneylender and ticket speculator, Porcher, who had advanced me 300 francs.

What Lassagne now told me pretty well overthrew all my castles in Spain. It seemed to me most cruel to forbid me working for the drama out of office hours, and to insist that my mother, my son and I should be compelled to live on a meager 125 francs per month. This feeling was so strong that it fired me with courage to go straight to Oudard. I entered his office with tears in my eyes, but my voice under control.

"Is it true, monsieur," I asked, "that you have forbidden Lassagne to work with me?"

"Yes," was his reply. "Why do you ask me that?"

"Because I should not have thought you would have had the courage to do so."

"What do you mean by that?"

"Well, it seems to me a man needs courage to condemn three persons to live on a hundred and twenty-five francs a month."

"And it seems to me you ought to think yourself very fortunate to have the hundred and twenty-five francs per month, instead of despising them."

"I do not despise them, monsieur; on the contrary, I am very grateful to those who give them to me; only, I repeat that the sum is not sufficient and that I think I ought to be allowed the right to add to it so long as it does not interfere with attention to my office work."

"It may not interfere with your office work now, but it very soon will."

"That will be the time, then, for you to be anxious."

"It is really no affair of mine," said M. Oudard. "I simply and solely convey the views of the chief director."

"Of Monsieur de Broval?"

"Yes, of Monsieur de Broval."

"I thought Monsieur de Broval pretended to foster literature."

"Literature? Perhaps he does . . . but do you call *la Chasse et l'Amour* and *la Noce et l'Enterrement* literature?"

"Most surely not, monsieur. But my name was not put on the bills at the Ambigu, where *la Chasse et l'Amour* was played, and it will not be put on the bills of the theater, whatever it may be, which may accept *la Noce et l'Enterrement*."

"Still, if you are ashamed to own those productions, why make them?"

"First, monsieur, because at present I do not feel myself able to do better, and because, such as they are, they bring comfort to our poverty . . . yes, monsieur, to our poverty—I do not shrink from the truth. One day, you somehow learnt that I had sat up several nights to copy some stage plays which brought in four francs an act, and that under the same conditions, I copied out Monsieur Théaulon's comedy, the *Indiscret*—well, you complimented me then on my pluck."

"Quite true."

"How then, may I ask, am I more guilty in making my own plays than in copying out those of others? You must, of course, be aware that Adolphe also writes plays?"

"Which Adolphe?"

"Adolphe de Leuven."

"What then?"

"Why, I heard you speak to Monsieur de Broval the other day in support of Adolphe's request for a post in the offices of the Duc d'Orléans."

"Monsieur Adolphe de Leuven was highly recommended to me."

"And I, monsieur, was not I also highly recommended to you? True, de Leuven was highly recommended to you by Benjamin Constant, General Gérard and Madame de Valence, whilst I was only recommended to you by General Foy."

"And what does that mean?"

"It means that Adolphe de Leuven's patrons are alive while my supporter is dead."

"Monsieur Dumas! . . ."

"Oh! do not be put out. I see I have hit the right nail on the head."

"Then you absolutely insist on continuing your writing?"

"Yes, monsieur; I desire to do so both from inclination, and from necessity."

"Very well, produce literature like Casimir Delavigne's and instead of blaming you, we will give you encouragement."

"Monsieur," I replied, "I am not Monsieur Casimir Delavigne's age, who has been poet laureate since 1811; neither have I received the education Monsieur Casimir Delavigne had at one of the best colleges in Paris. No, I am only twenty-two; I am busy educating myself every day, probably at the cost of my health, for all I learn—and I assure you I am studying many subjects—I learn when other people are fast asleep or amusing themselves. So I cannot, just at this moment, produce work like Monsieur Casimir Delavigne's. But, Monsieur Oudard, I would ask you, in conclusion, to listen carefully to what I am about to say, strange though it may sound to your ears: if I did not believe I could do different work in days to come than Monsieur Casimir Delavigne's, well, monsieur, I should meet you and Monsieur de Broval more than halfway in your wishes, and at this very instant I would give you my sacred promise, I would take a solemn oath, never to touch literature again."

Oudard looked at me with expressionless eyes; for my pride took his breath away. I bowed to him and went out. Five minutes later, he went to M. Deviolaine to tell him of my insane carryings on. M. Deviolaine inquired if it were really in his presence, if it were really to him, that I had said such monstrous things.

"Yes, it was in my presence and to me," said Oudard.

"I will tell his mother about it," said M. Deviolaine; "and if he continues possessed with this madness, send him to me. I will take him into my office and see that he doesn't go altogether stark staring mad."

And, indeed, my mother was told that very same night. When I returned from making up the portfolio, I found her in tears. M. Deviolaine had sent for her, and told her of all that had passed between M. Oudard and me that morning. Next day, the crime of which I had been guilty was public property throughout the offices. The sixty-three clerks of His Royal Highness never lost an opportunity of saying to each other as they met: "Have you heard what Dumas said to Monsieur Oudard yesterday?"

And the clerk to whom the question was addressed would reply with either a Yes or a No. If he replied in the negative, the story was related with corrections, embellishments and exaggerations, that did the greatest credit to the imagination of my colleagues. During the whole day and for several days to follow, homeric laughter could be heard throughout the corridors of the Maison de la rue Saint-Honoré No. 216. There was one solitary bookkeeping clerk who had only been engaged the previous day, and whom no one as yet knew, who did not laugh.

"Why," said the others to him, "you aren't laughing."

"No."

"Why don't you laugh?"

"Because it doesn't seem to me a laughing matter."

"What! Don't you think it a huge joke that Dumas said he would do better things than Casimir Delavigne?"

"In the first place, he did not say he would do better, he said he would do something different."

"It is all the same."

"No, it is quite different."

"But do you know Dumas?"

"Yes, and because I know him I tell you he will do something; I don't know what it will be, but I tell you that that something will astonish everybody, save myself."

This employee, who had just joined the office, in the bookkeeping department, was my old German and Italian master, Amédée de la Ponce.

So there were two people out of the seventy-two persons, heads and employees, who composed His Royal Highness's official staff, who did not despair of me! Lassagne and he.

From this time began the warfare of which Lassagne had warned me when I first entered the office. But, no matter what it was going to be like, or how long it was going to last, I made up my mind to fight to the end.

A week later, a ray of comfort came to me. Vulpian came to tell Lassagne and me that our play had been accepted by the theater of the Porte-Saint-Martin for Serres's debut.

So it will be seen I was gently drawing nearer to the Théâtre-Français, but I had learned Italian enough to understand the proverb *"Che va piano va sano."*

The author's rights were also higher. The theater of the Porte-Saint-Martin paid eighteen francs for a vaudeville, and allowed twelve francs' worth of tickets.

So this meant for me eight francs per night instead of six—exactly double, this time, what my office work brought me in.

La Noce et l'Enterrement was played on November 21, 1826. My mother and I saw my play from the orchestra. As my name did not transpire, and as I was totally unknown, I experienced no inconvenience from allowing myself the satisfaction of being present. The play succeeded admirably; but, even as the Roman emperors, in their days of triumph, were reminded by a slave that they were mortal, so, lest my success should intoxicate me, Providence placed a neighbor on my left who remarked, as he rose at the fall of the curtain:

"Come, come, it isn't such stuff as this that will uphold the theater."

My neighbor was right, and he knew what he was talking about all the more in that he was a fellow writer.

The play was acted some forty times, and, as Porcher generously left me half my rights, claiming only the remaining half to liquidate previous advances, the four francs per night that I received from the tickets helped us to get over the winter of 1826–1827.

Dumas's method of turning himself into a dramatic author is explained in the following extract from his *Memoirs*, Volume III, Chapter 10. The reader will note Dumas's intense interest in the money side of writing. He not only wanted to become a writer, but he wanted to make money out of it. And he did.

This commercialization of writing is a phenomenon largely of the nineteenth century, though it had appeared many times before in history, for example, with Daniel Defoe, more than a hundred years before. Shakespeare himself was obviously a commercial writer. But it is with the nineteenth century that one finds the writer appealing directly to the people for their suffrage, both in applause and money.

In the previous quote, Dumas had referred to Casimir Delavigne as a writer who did not need the approval of the public, did not have to lure the people's money out of their pockets, in order to make his living. And he had pointed out that his writing would be "different." Casimir Delavigne was born in wealth, early became fa-

mous, and held the post of librarian to the Duke of Orléans, where
Dumas was nothing but a copyist. He had also become a member of
the Academy just about that time. His popularity was largely due
to his political stand, rather than to his works, though they seemed
to have had tremendous appeal during his lifetime. So that while at
the time when Dumas was making his first efforts, Delavigne seemed
to loom far above him, yet soon afterward Gautier would speak of
Delavigne as a second-rate, or even fourth-rate writer.

Such is fame. But now for the quote:

I have referred to the immense services the English actors had
done me; Macready, Kean, Young had in turn completed the work
begun by Kemble and Miss Smithson. I had seen *Hamlet, Romeo,
Shylock, Othello, Richard III*, and *Macbeth*. I had read and devoured
not only the whole of Shakespeare, but even the whole of the
foreign dramatic output. I had recognized that, in the theatrical
world, everything emanated from Shakespeare, just as in the external
world everything owes its existence to the sun; that nothing could
be compared with him; for, coming before everyone else, he was yet
as supreme in tragedy as Corneille, in comedy as Molière, as original
as Calderon, as full of thought as Goethe, as passionate as Schiller.
I realized that his works contained as many types as the works of all
the others put together. I recognized, in short, that, after the Creator
Himself, Shakespeare had created more than any other being.

As I have stated, when I saw these English artists—actors who
forgot that they were on a stage—the life of the imagination became
actual life through the power of Art; their convincing words and
gestures seeming to transform them from actors into creatures of
God, with their virtues and their vices, their passions and their
failings—from that moment my career was decided. I felt I had
received that special call which comes to every man. I felt a confidence in my own powers that I had lacked until then, and I boldly
hurled myself upon the unknown future that had hitherto held such
terrors for me. But, at the same time, I did not disguise from myself
the difficulties in the way of the career to which I had devoted my
life; I knew that it would require deeper and more special study
than any other profession; that before I could experiment successfully on living nature I must first perseveringly study the works of
others.

So I did not rest satisfied with a superficial study. One after the other, I took the works of men of genius, like Shakespeare, Molière, Corneille, Calderon, Goethe and Schiller, laid them out as bodies on a dissecting table, and, scalpel in hand, I spent whole nights in probing them to the heart in order to find the sources of life and the secret of the circulation of their blood.

And after a while I discovered with what admirable science they galvanized nerve and muscle into life, and by what skill they modeled the differing types of flesh that were destined to cover the one unchangeable human framework of bone.

For man does not invent. God has only given the created world into man's hands, but left it to him to apply it to his needs. Progress simply means the daily, monthly and everlasting conquest of man over matter. Each individual as he appears on the scene takes possession of the knowledge of his fathers, works it up in different ways, and then dies after he has added one ray more to the sum of human knowledge which he bequeaths to his sons—one star in the Milky Way! I was thus not only trying to complete my dramatic work but also my dramatic education. But that is an error: one's work may be finished someday, but one's education never!

I had just concluded my play, after two months' peace and encouragement in my humble post in the archives office, when I received notice from the secretariat that, as my position was almost a sinecure, it had been done away with, and that I must hold myself ready to enter the forestry department—under M. Deviolaine. So the storm that had been hanging over my head for long had burst at last. I said good-by to old father Bichet with tears in my eyes, and to his two friends MM. Pieyre and Parseval de Grandmaison, who promised to follow my career with sympathetic interest wherever I might be. The reader knows M. Deviolaine. During the five years I had been in the government offices I had been looked upon as a *bête-noir*, so I entered upon my new official work under no very favorable auspices.

The struggle began immediately I took up my new duties. They wanted to herd me together with five or six of my fellow clerks in one large room, and I revolted against the proceeding. My companions were good enough to explain to me in all innocence that they found it an advantageous way of killing time—that deadly enemy to employees—to sit together, for then they could talk. Now, talk was just what I most dreaded; to them it was a pleasure, to me a torture, for chattering distracted my own ever-increasing imaginative ideas.

No, instead of wanting to be in this big office, strewn thick with supernumeraries, clerks and assistants, I had my eye on a sort of recess separated by a simple partition from the office boy's cubicle, and in which he kept the ink bottles that were returned to him empty. I asked if I might take possession of this place. I might as well have asked for the archbishopric of Cambrai, which was just vacant.

A fearful clamor went up at this demand, from the office boy to the head of the department (*directeur général*). The office boy asked the clerks in the big room where he could put his empty bottles henceforth; the clerks in the big room asked the assistant head clerk (a man who when I broke into tears upon hearing that Byron had died, asked me: who is Byron?); these clerks asked me whether I thought myself too good to work with them; the assistant head clerk asked the chief clerk whether I had come to the forestry department to give or to receive orders; the chief clerk asked the head of the department if it were usual for a clerk paid fifteen hundred francs to have an office to himself, as though he were a head clerk at four thousand. The head of the department replied that it was not only absolutely contrary to administrative customs, but that no such precedent would be allowed me, and that my claim was most presumptuous!

I was trying to fit myself into the unlucky recess which, for the moment, formed the sum of my ambition, when the head clerk walked haughtily from the office of the head of the department, bearing the verbal command that the rebellious employee, who had dared for one moment to entertain the ambitious hope of leaving the ordinary ranks, should at once return to his place there. He transmitted the order immediately to the assistant head clerk, who passed it on to the ordinary clerks of the large office, who transmitted it to the office boy!

There was joy throughout the department: a fellow-clerk was to be humiliated and, if he did not take his humiliation in a humble spirit, he would lose his situation! The office boy opened the door between his cubicle and mine; he had just come from making a general clearance throughout the office and had brought back all the empty bottles he could manage to unearth.

"But, my dear Feresse," I said, watching him uneasily, "how do you think I can manage here with all those bottles, or, rather, how are all those bottles going to fit in with me—unless I live in one of them, after the style of *le Diable boiteux?*"

"That's just it!" leered Feresse, as he deposited fresh bottles by the old ones. "*Monsieur le Directeur général* does not look upon it in that light: he wishes me to keep this room for myself, and does not intend a newcomer to lay down the law."

I walked up to him, the blood mantling my face.

"The newcomer, however insignificant he may be, is still your superior," I said, "so you should speak to him with your head uncovered. Take your cap off, you young cub!"

And, at the same moment, I gave the lad a backhander that sent his hat flying against the wall, and took my departure. All this happened in the absence of M. Deviolaine; therefore I had not the last word in the matter. M. Deviolaine would not return for two or three days; so I decided to go home to my poor mother, and there await his return. But, before I left the office, I went and told Oudard all that had happened, who said he could not do anything in the matter, and I told M. Pieyre, who said that he could not do much.

My mother was in a state of despair: it reminded her too much of my return home from Maître Lefèvre's in 1823. She rushed off to see Madame Deviolaine.

Madame Deviolaine was an excellent woman but narrow-minded, and she could not understand why a clerk should have any other ambition beyond that of ultimately becoming a first-class clerk; why a first-class clerk should desire to become anything beyond as assistant chief clerk; why an assistant chief clerk should have any other ambition than that of becoming chief clerk, and so forth. So she did not hold out any promises to my mother; for that matter, the poor woman had not much influence over her husband, as she well knew, and she but rarely tried to exercise what little she did possess.

Meanwhile, I had begged Porcher to come to our house. I showed him my almost completed tragedy, and I asked him whether, in case of adverse circumstances, he would advance me a certain sum.

"Confound it!" Porcher replied. "A tragedy! If it had been a vaudeville I do not say but that I would! However, *get it received* and we will see."

"Get it received!" Therein, of course, lay the whole question.

My mother returned at that moment, and Porcher's answer was not of the kind to reassure her. I wrote to M. Deviolaine, and begged that my letter might be given him on his return; then I waited.

We spent three days of suspense; but during those three days I stayed in bed and worked incessantly. Why did I stop in bed? That requires an explanation. Whilst I was at the secretariat, and had to be at the office from ten in the morning until five in the evening, returning there from eight until ten o'clock, I had to traverse the distance between faubourg Saint-Denis No. 53 to the rue Saint-Honoré No. 216, eight times a day, and I was so tired out that I could rarely work if I sat up. So it was my habit to go to bed and sleep, first putting my work on the table near my bed. I would sleep for two hours, and then at midnight my mother woke me and went to sleep in her turn.

That was the reason I worked in bed. This habit of working in bed attained such hold of me that I kept it up long after I had gained freedom of action, doing all my theatrical work thus. Perhaps this revelation may satisfy those physiologists who dilated upon the kind of rude passion which has been noted in my earliest works, and with which, perhaps not unreasonably, I have been reproached. I contracted another habit, too, at that time, and that was to write my dramas in a backward style of handwriting: this habit I never lost, unlike the other, and to this day I have one style of handwriting for my dramas and another for my romances.

During those three days I made immense progress with *Christine*. On the fourth day, I received a letter from M. Deviolaine, summoning me to his office. I hurried there, and this time my heart did not beat any the faster; I had faced the worst that could happen and I was prepared for anything.

"Ah! there you are, you cursed blockhead!" cried M. Deviolaine, when he saw me.

"Yes, monsieur, here I am."

"So! so, monsieur!"

I made no reply. What was there to say?

"So we are too grand a lord to work with ordinary mortals?" M. Deviolaine continued.

"You are mistaken, sir. Quite the contrary. I am not a sufficiently grand lord to work with the others, that is why I want to work alone."

"So you ask for an office to yourself, on purpose to do nothing in it but to write your dirty plays?"

"I ask for an office to myself so that I can have the right to think while I am working."

"And if I do not let you have an office to yourself?"

"I shall try to earn my living as an author. You know I have no other resource."

"And if I do not immediately send you packing, you may be very sure it is for your mother's sake and not for your own."

"I am fully aware of that, and I am grateful to you on my mother's account."

"Very well, take your office to yourself, then; but I give you warning that . . ."

"You will give me double the work of any other clerk?"

"Exactly so."

"It will be unjust, that is all; but, since I am not the stronger, I shall submit."

"Unjust! Unjust!" shrieked M. Deviolaine. "I would have you know that I have never done an unjust thing in my life."

"It would seem there is a beginning for everything."

"Did you ever see—oh, did you ever see such a young rip!" continued M. Deviolaine, as he paced up and down his office. "Did you ever see! did you ever see . . . !"

Then, turning to me again, he said:

"Very well, I will not treat you unjustly; no, indeed no, you shall not have more work to do than the others; but you shall have as much, and you shall be watched to see that you get through it! Monsieur Fossier shall receive orders from me to carry out this inspection."

I moved my lips.

"What next! Have you something now to say against M. Fossier?"

"No, only that I think him ugly."

"Well, what then?"

"Why, I would much rather he were good-looking, on his own account first and also for my sake."

"But what does it matter to you whether Monsieur Fossier be ugly or beautiful?"

"If I have to meet a face three or four times in a day I should much prefer it to be agreeable rather than disagreeable."

"Well, I never met such a cursed young puppy in all my days! You will soon want me to choose my head clerks to suit your taste . . . ! Get out! Go back to your office, and try to make up for lost time."

"I will do so; but, first, I want to ask a promise from you, monsieur."

"Well, upon my word, if he isn't actually going to impose his own conditions on me!"

"You will accept this one, I am sure."

"Now, what do you wish, *Monsieur le poète?*"

"I should like you yourself each day to overlook the work I have done and see how I have done it."

"Well, I promise that. . . . And when is the first performance to take place?"

"I can hardly tell you; but I am very sure you will be present at it!"

"Yes, I will be there, in more senses than one; you may be quite easy on that score. . . . Now, go and behave yourself!"

And he made a threatening gesture, upon which I went out.

M. Deviolaine kept his word to me. He gave me plenty of work to do without overdoing me. But, as he had promised, M. Fossier always came and brought the work to me himself, and if, by ill luck, I was not at my desk, M. Deviolaine was instantly informed of my absence.

But none of these hindrances prevented me from finishing *Christine.* I had, however, scarcely written the famous last line—

"*Eh bien, j'en ai pitié, mon père . . . Qu'on l'achève!*" (The lines spoken by Queen Christine as she is having her lover assassinated. A monk begs her to have pity of the poor bleeding wretch. Whereupon the Queen says: "Yes, I will have pity. Finish him off!")—when I found myself in as embarrassing a situation as any poor girl who has just given birth to a child outside the pale of legitimate matrimony. What was I to do with this bastard child of my creation, born outside the gates of the Institute and the Academy? Was I to stifle her as I had smothered her elders? That would have been hard lines indeed! Besides, this little girl was strong and quite capable of living; it seemed good, therefore, to acknowledge her; but first it was necessary to find a theater to receive her, actors to clothe her, and a public to adopt her!

Oh! if only Talma were living! But Talma was dead and I did not know anyone at the Théâtre-Français. Perhaps it might be possible for me to manage it through M. Arnault. But he would ask to see the work on behalf of which his services were requested, and he would not have read ten lines before he would fling it as far from him as poor M. Drake had the rattlesnake that bit him at Rouen. I went to look for Oudard. I told him that my play was completed and I boldly asked him for a letter of introduction to the Théâtre-Français. Oudard refused under pretense that he did not know anyone there. I had the courage to tell him that his introduction as head of the secretariat of the Duc d'Orléans would be all-powerful.

He replied, after the manner of Madame Mechin, when she did not incline to promote any particular end:

"I will never lend my *influence* in that direction."

I had several times noticed a man with thick eyebrows and a long nose, in the secretarial department, who took his tobacco Swiss-fashion. This man periodically brought the ninety theater tickets to all parts of the house that M. Oudard had the prerogative of giving away every month, at the rate of three per day. I did not know who this man was, but I asked. I was told that he was the prompter.

I lay in wait for this prompter, took him by surprise in the corridor, and begged him to tell me what steps were necessary to obtain the honor of a reading before the Committee of the Théâtre-Français. He told me I must first deposit my play with the examiner; but he warned me that so many other works were already deposited there that I must expect to wait at least a year. As though it were possible for me to wait a year!

"But," I asked, "is there no short cut through all these formalities?"

"Oh dear me, yes!" he replied, "if you know Baron Taylor."

I thanked him.

"There is nothing to thank me for," he said.

And he was right; there wasn't anything to thank him for, for I did not know Baron Taylor in the slightest.

"Do you know Baron Taylor?" I asked Lassagne.

"No," he answered, "but Charles Nodier is his intimate friend."

"What of that?"

"Well, did you not tell me that you once talked with Charles Nodier a whole evening at a representation of the *Vampire?*"

"Certainly."

"Write to Charles Nodier."

"Bah! he will have forgotten all about me."

"He never forgets anything; write to him."

I wrote to Charles Nodier, recalling to his memory the Elzevirs and the vampires, and in the name of his well-known kindliness toward young people I entreated him to introduce me to Baron Taylor.

It can be imagined with what impatience I awaited the reply.

Baron Taylor himself replied, granting my request and fixing an appointment with me five or six days later. He apologized at the same time for the hour he had fixed; but his numerous engagements left him so little time that seven o'clock in the morning was the only hour at which he could see me.

Although I am probably the latest riser in Paris, I was ready at the appointed hour. True, I had kept awake all the night. Taylor then lived at No. 42 rue de Bondy, fourth floor. His suite of rooms consisted of an anteroom filled with books and busts; a dining room full of pictures and books; a drawing room full of weapons and books; and a bedroom full of manuscripts and books.

I rang at the door of the antechamber, my heart beating at a terrible rate.

The good- or ill-natured mood of a man who knew nothing about me, who had no inducement to be kindly disposed toward me, who had received me out of pure good nature, was to decide my future life. If my play displeased him, it would stand in the way of anything I could bring him later, and I was nearly at the end of my courage and strength.

I had rung the bell, gently enough, I admit, and no one had answered it; I rang a second time, as gently as at first; again no one took any notice of me. And yet, putting my ear close, I seemed to hear a noise indicative of something unusual taking place inside: confused sounds and snarls which now sounded like bursts of anger, and now, decreasing in pitch, seemed like a continuous monotonous bass accompaniment. I could not imagine what it could be; I was afraid to disturb Taylor at such a moment and yet it was the very hour he had himself fixed for my coming. I rang louder. I heard a door open, and simultaneously the mysterious noise from inside that had greatly roused my curiosity for the last ten minutes sounded louder than ever. At last the door was opened by an old serving-woman.

"Ah! monsieur," she said, with a flustered manner, "your coming will do M. le Baron an excellent turn. He is waiting anxiously for you; go in."

"What do you mean?"

"Go in, go in . . . do not lose a minute."

I went quickly into the sitting room, where I found Taylor caught in his bathtub like a tiger in his den, a gentleman near him reading a tragedy called *Hécube*. This gentleman had forced his entrance, no matter what was said to him. He had surprised Taylor as Charlotte Corday had surprised Marat when she stabbed him in his bath; but the agony that the King's Commissary endured was more prolonged than that of the Tribune of the People. The tragedy was two thousand four hundred lines long! When the gentleman caught sight of me, he realized that his victim was to be snatched away from him; he clutched hold of the bath, exclaiming:

"There are only two more acts, monsieur—there are only two more acts!"

"Two sword cuts, two stabs with a knife, two thrusts with a dagger! Select from among the arms round about—there are all kinds here—choose the one that will slice the best and kill me straight off!"

"Monsieur," replied the author of *Hécube*, "the government appointed you *commissaire du roi* on purpose to listen to my play; it is your duty to listen to my play—you shall hear my play!"

"Ah! that is just where the misfortune comes in!" cried Taylor, wringing his hands. "Yes, monsieur, to my sorrow I am *commissaire du roi!* . . . But you and such people as you will make me hand in my resignation; you and your like will force me to give it up and leave France. I have had an offer to go to Egypt, I will accept it; I will explore the sources of the Nile as far as Nubia, right to the Mountains of the Moon—and I will go at once and get my passport."

"You can go to China, if you like," replied the gentleman, "but you shall not go until you have heard my play."

Taylor gave one long moan, like a vanquished athlete, made a sign to me to go into his bedroom, and, falling back into his bathtub, he bowed his head in resignation upon his breast.

The gentleman went on.

Taylor's precaution of putting a door between him and his reader and me was quite useless; I heard every word of the last two acts of *Hécube*. The Almighty is great and full of compassion—may He bestow peace on that author!

At last, when the play was finished, the gentleman got up, and, at Taylor's earnest entreaty, consented to depart. I heard the old woman double-lock the door after him. The bath water had made good use of the time spent on the reading to grow cold, and Taylor came back into his bedroom shivering.

I would have sacrificed a month's pay to have found him a warmed bed to creep into. And the reason is not far to seek; for, naturally, a man who is half frozen, after just listening to five acts, is not in a favorable mood to hear five more acts.

"Alas! monsieur," I said to him, "I have happened upon a most unsuitable time, and I fear you will not be in the least disposed to listen to me, at least with the patience I could desire."

"Oh, monsieur, I will not admit that, since I do not yet know your work," Taylor replied, "but you can guess what a trial it is to have to listen to such stuff as I have just heard, every blessed day of my life."

"Every day?"

"Yes, indeed, and oftener! See, here is my agenda for today's Committee. We are to hear an *Epaminondas*."

I heaved a sigh. My poor *Christine* was caught between two cross fires of classicism.

"Monsieur le Baron," I ventured to say, "would you rather I came another day?"

"Oh! certainly not," said Taylor, "now we are here . . ."

"Very well," I said, "I will just read you one act, and if that tires you or bores you, you must stop me."

"All right," Taylor murmured. "You are more merciful than your confrères. And that is a good sign. . . . Go on, go on; I am listening."

Tremblingly I drew my play from my pocket; it looked a terribly big volume. Taylor cast a glance on the immense bulk with such an alarmed expression that I cried out to him:

"Oh, monsieur, do not be afraid! The manuscript is only written on one side of the paper."

He breathed again. I began. I was so nervous I could not see to read; my voice shook so that I could not hear my own voice. Taylor reassured me; he was unaccustomed to such modesty! I resumed my reading, and I managed somehow to get through my first act.

"Well, monsieur, shall I go on?" I asked in a faint voice, without daring to raise my eyes.

"Certainly, certainly," Taylor replied, "go on. Upon my word, it is excellent!"

Fresh life came to me, and I read my second act with more confidence than the first. When I had finished, Taylor himself told me to go on with the third, then the fourth, then the fifth. I felt an inexpressible desire to embrace him; but I refrained, for fear of the consequences.

When the reading was finished, Taylor leaped from his bed.

"You must come to the Théâtre-Français with me," he said.

"But what must I do there?"

"Why, get your turn to read your play as soon as possible."

"Do you really mean it? Shall I read it to the committee?"

"Not a day later than next Saturday." And Taylor called out, "Pierre!"

An old manservant came in.

"Give me all my clothes, Pierre."

Then turning to me, he said: "You will excuse me?"

"Oh, there is nothing to excuse . . . !" I replied.

On the following Thursday (for Taylor would not wait until the

Saturday, but had called a special committee) the committee,
whether from chance or because Taylor had praised my play ex-
travagantly, was a very large one; there were as many well-dressed
men and women present as though a dance were on the way. The
ladies decked out in gay hats and flowers, the gentlemen in fashionable dress, the large green carpet, the inquisitive looks which were
fixed upon me, every detail down to the glass of water which
Granville solemnly placed by my side—which struck me as very
ludicrous—all this combined to inspire me with profound emotion.

Christine was then quite different from what it is today: it was a
simple play, romantic in style, but founded on classical traditions. It
was confined to five acts; the action took place entirely at Fontainebleau, and it conformed with the unity of time, place, and action
laid down by Aristotle. Stranger still! it did not contain the character
of Paula, which is now the best creation in the play, and the real
dramatic mainspring of the whole work. Monaldeschi betrayed
Christine's ambition, but not her love. And yet I have rarely known
any work to have such a successful first reading. They made me
read the monologue of Sentinelli and the scene with Monaldeschi
three times over. I was intoxicated with delight. My play was received with acclamation. Only—three or four of the agenda papers
contained the following cautious phrase:

"A *second reading, or the manuscript to be submitted to an
author in whom the Committee has confidence.*"

The result of the deliberations of the Comédie-Française was that
the tragedy of *Christine* was accepted; but, on account of the great
innovations which it contained, they would not undertake to perform
it until after another reading, or until the manuscript had been
submitted to another author, to be named by them.

The whole thing had passed before my eyes like a mist. I had
seen face to face for the first time the kings and queens of the
tragic and comic stage: Mademoiselle Mars, Mademoiselle Leverd,
Mademoiselle Bourgoin, Madame Valmonzey, Madame Paradol, and
Mademoiselle Demerson, an engagingly clever *soubrette*, who played
Molière with great freshness, and played Marivaux with such finished
style as I never saw in anyone else. I knew I was accepted and that
was all I wished to know: the conditions I would fulfill, the difficulties I would overcome. Therefore I did not wait until the con-

clusion of the conference. I thanked Taylor, and I left the theater as proud and as lighthearted as though my first mistress had said to me: "I love you."

I made off for the faubourg Saint-Denis, ogling everybody I met, as much as to say: "You haven't written *Christine*; you haven't just come away from the Théâtre-Français; you haven't been received with acclamation, you, you, you!" And, in the joyful preoccupation of my thoughts, I did not take care to measure my steps across a gutter but stumbled into the middle of it; I took no notice of carriages, I jostled in and out among the horses. When I reached the faubourg Saint-Denis I had lost my manuscript; but that did not matter! I knew my play by heart. With one leap, I bounded into our rooms, and my mother cried out, for she never saw me back before five o'clock.

"Received with acclamation, mother! received with acclamation!" I shouted. And I began to dance round our rooms, which allowed but little space for such exercise. My mother thought I must have gone mad; I had not told her I was going to the reading for fear of disappointment.

"And what will Monsieur Fossier say?" my poor mother exclaimed.

"Oh!" I replied, suiting my words to the tune of *Malbrouck*, "Monsieur Fossier can say whatever he likes, and if he is not satisfied, I will send him about his business!"

"Take care, my dear lad," my mother replied, shaking her head, "it will be you who will be sent packing and in good earnest, too."

"All right, mother; so much the better! It will give me time to attend my rehearsals."

"And suppose your play is a failure, and you have lost your situation, what will become of us?"

"I will write another play that will succeed."

"But in the meantime we must live."

"Ah yes! it's very unfortunate that one has to live; happily, in seven or eight days we shall receive something on account."

"Yes, but while we are waiting for that, which you have not yet got, my lad, take my advice and return to your desk, so that no one may suspect anything, and do not boast of what has happened to a single person."

"I fancy you are in the right, mother; and although I asked the whole day off from Monsieur Deviolaine, I will return to my desk. It is half past two. Why, I shall yet have time to dispatch my day's work."

And I set forth at a run to the rue Saint-Honoré. The exercise did me good, for I needed fresh air and action; I felt stifled in our tiny rooms.

I found a pile of reports ready for me; I set to my task, and by six o'clock everything was finished. But by this time Feresse's anger against me amounted to hatred: I had compelled him to stay till the stroke of six before I had finished the last lines. I had never written so fast or so well. I reread everything twice for fear I might have interpolated some lines from *Christine* in the reports. But, as usual, they were innocent of poetic effusions. I gave them back to Feresse, who went with them to M. Fossier's office, growling like a bear.

I then went home to my dear mother, quite spent and utterly exhausted with the great events of that day. It was April 30, 1828.

I spent the evening, the night, and morning of the next day in rewriting my manuscript afresh. By ten o'clock, when I reached the administration, I found Feresse at the door of his office. He had been looking out for me since eight o'clock that morning, although he knew well enough that I never came in before ten.

"Ah! there you are," he said. "So you have been writing a tragedy, I hear."

"Who told you that?"

"Why, good gracious, it is in the newspaper."

"In the paper?"

"Yes, read it for yourself."

And he handed me a paper which did, indeed, contain the following lines:

"The Théâtre-Français today accepted with acclamation and unanimity a five-act tragedy in verse, by a young man who has not yet produced anything. This young man is in the administrative offices of M. le Duc d'Orléans, who made his path easy for him and who strongly recommended him to the reading committee."

You see how accurately the daily press gauged the situation! it has not lost the tradition even today. Nevertheless, although inaccurate enough in detail, the news was fundamentally true; and it circulated from corridor to corridor and from story to story. It flew from office to office, by means of people coming in and going out, just as though Madame la Duchesse d'Orléans had given birth to twins.

I was congratulated by all my colleagues, some with sincerity, others mockingly; only the chief of my office hid himself from view. But, since he kept me going with four times my usual amount of work, it was quite evident he had seen the paper. M. Deviolaine came in at two o'clock and at five minutes past two he sent for me. I walked into his office with my head in the air and my hands perched jauntily on my hips.

"Ah! there you are, you young blade!" he said.

"Yes, here I am."

"So you asked me for a holiday yesterday in order to play pranks!"

"Have I neglected my work?"

"That is not the question."

"Excuse me, Monsieur Deviolaine, on the contrary it is the only question."

"But don't you see that they have been making game of you?"

"Who has?"

"The actors of the Comédie-Française."

"Nevertheless, they have accepted my play."

"Yes, but they will not put it on the stage."

"Ah, we shall see!"

"And if they do produce your play . . ."

"Yes?"

"You will still need the approbation of the public."

"Why should you imagine it will not please the public since it has already pleased the Comedians?"

"Come now, do you want to make me believe that you, who only had an education that cost three francs a month, will be successful when such people as Monsieur Viennet and Monsieur Lemercier and Monsieur Lebrun fall flat? . . . Go along with you!"

"But instead of judging me beforehand, wouldn't it be fairer to wait?"

"Oh yes, wait ten years, twenty years! I sincerely hope I shall be buried before your play is acted, and then I shall never see it."

At this juncture, Feresse slyly opened the door.

"Excuse me, Monsieur Deviolaine," he said, "but there is a *Comedian* here (he carefully emphasized the word) asking for Monsieur Dumas."

"A Comedian! What Comedian?" M. Deviolaine asked.

"Monsieur Firmin, from the Comédie-Française."

"Yes," I replied quietly, "he takes the part of Monaldeschi."

"Firmin plays in your piece?"

"Yes, he takes Monaldeschi. . . . Oh, it is admirably cast: Firmin plays Monaldeschi, Mademoiselle Mars, Christine. . . ."

"Mademoiselle Mars plays in your piece?"

"Certainly."

"It is not true."

"Would you like her to tell it to you herself?"

"Do you imagine I am going to take the trouble to assure myself you are lying?"

"No; she will come here."

"Mademoiselle Mars will come here?"

"I am sure she will have the kindness to do that for me."

"Mademoiselle Mars?"

"Yes, you see that Firmin . . ."

"Stop! Go your own way! for upon my word you are enough to turn my brain! . . . Mademoiselle Mars . . . Mademoiselle Mars put herself out for you? Think of it! . . . Mademoiselle Mars!" and he raised his hands to heaven in despair that such a mad idea should ever enter the head of any member of his family.

A proper anthologist would at this point already begin quoting not from Dumas's *Memoirs*, but from his plays. But alas, our tastes have so changed in theatrical matters that I would almost be tantamount to ridiculing Dumas, to quote from them. Not that here and there bits could not be found that would stand up, but that the general impression would be such that if I quoted from his plays, it would militate against these charming extracts from his *Memoirs*.

One has to choose to quote from one or the other. Impossible, really, to quote from both.

I am skipping here many pages that deal with the humiliation that young Dumas had to suffer when despite the enthusiasm of Baron Taylor and the actors of the theater, his *Christine* was rejected. What considerations entered into that rejection need not be gone into here.

But what must be told is that the resulting pressures at his office led him to quit his job, to the consternation of his mother. He re-assured her by pointing out that he was entitled to a bonus that would support them for a good while. But he never got the bonus. What he got was the following communication from the Duc d'Orléans:

"The gratuities of Monsieur Alexandre Dumas are to be withheld, inasmuch as he is engaged in literary work."

"Nevertheless," says Dumas in his *Memoirs*, Volume III, Chapter 16, ". . . I took a bold step previously decided upon . . ." But before quoting this extract, I must inform the reader that he may be surprised to discover here that Dumas had a sister. If she was not previously mentioned, it is because, as a young child, rich relatives had taken charge of her, and she had never had to go through the troubles of Dumas and his mother. Here, then, is the quote:

Nevertheless, the night of the first performance, I took a bold step previously decided upon. I presented myself at the Palais Royal and asked to see M. le Duc d'Orléans. The request was so unusual and so audacious that, no doubt, the attendants expected I had an audience. They informed the Duc d'Orléans of my presence and of my request to speak to him. The Duc d'Orléans repeated my name over to himself twice and gave orders to admit me. "Ah! ah! is it you, Monsieur Dumas?" he said. "What good wind blows you hither or, rather, blows you back again?"

"Monseigneur," I said to him, "tomorrow they play *Henri III.*"

"Yes," he said, "I know that."

"Well, monseigneur, I have come to ask a favor of you, or rather an act of justice."

"What is it?"

"To give me your presence at my first representation. . . . A year ago, Your Highness was informed that I was an empty-headed, vain fool. For a year now I have been working as a humble poet. Without giving me a hearing, monseigneur, you have sided with those of your retinue who have been my accusers—perhaps Your Highness should have waited, but Your Highness thought otherwise and did not wait. Tomorrow things will be put to public trial, and all I come to beg of you, monseigneur, is that you will be present at the sentence."

The duke looked at me for a moment, and, seeing how calmly I met his scrutiny, he replied:

"I would have granted your request with great pleasure, Monsieur

Dumas, for various people have told me that if you were not a model of industry you were at least an example of perseverance; but, unfortunately, it is impossible."

"Your Highness probably means that a man who aspires to talk with people in high places should know better than to interrogate a prince; but, monseigneur, I have come to you in such exceptional circumstances that I will venture to ask whence arises that impossibility, for I must confess it disappoints me greatly."

"You shall judge for yourself; tomorrow I expect twenty to thirty princes and princesses to dinner."

"Would it not be a novel entertainment, monseigneur, to take these princes and princesses to see *Henri III*?"

"How could I take them to see it when dinner begins at six and *Henri III* begins at seven?"

"Let monseigneur advance his dinner one hour and I will delay *Henri III* for an hour; that would allow monseigneur three hours to assuage the hunger of his august guests."

"Well, that is not a bad idea. Not at all. Do you think the Théâtre-Français would consent to the delay?"

"They would be only too delighted to accommodate Your Highness."

"But where should I seat them? I only have three boxes."

"I asked the administration not to dispose of the first circle until I had seen Your Highness."

"You presumed, then, to think that I should consent to see your play?"

"I relied upon your sense of justice. . . . You see, monseigneur, I appeal to Philippe awakened."

"Very well. Go and tell Monsieur Taylor that, if the Comédie-Française consents to put back the representation an hour, I will be present at it, and in order to carry this out I will engage the whole circle."

"I will hasten there immediately, monseigneur."

"Are you satisfied?"

"Enchanted! I trust also that Your Highness will not have reason to repent of this kindness."

"I hope so too. . . . Away with you, and good luck!"

I bowed and left.

Ten minutes later, the theater had been told; twenty minutes later,
the Duc d'Orléans had received an answer in the affirmative. That
very evening letters were sent to the guests informing them of the
change of hour.

The long-expected day came at last! On that day there was neither
rehearsal nor any other meeting: I could remain by my mother's
side until the evening. They had given me a certain number of
theater tickets, especially tickets for the pit; the *claque, i.e.* hired
applause, was not such a recognized thing in those days as it is now,
and the post of *entrepreneur de succès* was almost a sinecure: it was
left to the care of one's friends and to the impartiality of the public.
The generosity of the theater allowed me to sign a pit ticket for
each of my old office companions. Porcher and his wife had each a
balcony ticket. I had a little box on the stage itself which held two
persons. My sister had one of the boxes in the first row, where she
entertained Boulanger, de Vigny, and Victor Hugo. I did not know
either Hugo or de Vigny, and they introduced themselves to me in
despair of getting a chance otherwise. I made the acquaintance of
both of them that night. M. Deviolaine had an orchestra ticket. The
whole of the remaining seats in the house had been taken for a week
past, and the exorbitant price of twenty louis was given for one box.

At a quarter to eight I kissed my mother, who, in the clouded
state of her brain, scarcely realized what a battle I was on the eve
of fighting. I met M. Deviolaine in the corridor.

"Well, you young rip!" he said, "so you have got your way at
last!"

"What did I tell you?"

"Yes, but we have yet to see what the public thinks of your
prose."

"You will see, since you are here."

"I shall see, I shall see," growled M. Deviolaine. "It is highly
probable that I shall see . . ."

I moved away from him, not knowing what he meant by his
words, and I reached my box, which, as I have said, was on the
stage. I could see the whole house from my box perfectly. Those
who were present at that performance will recollect what a splendid
sight it was: the first circle was filled with princes smothered under

the orders of five or six nations; the whole of the aristocracy crowded into the first and second rows of the boxes; ladies sparkled with diamonds.

The curtain rose. I have never experienced such a sensation as that which a breath of air from the theater caused me as it passed across my feverish brow. The first act was listened to with patience, although the narrative was long, cold, and tiresome. The curtain fell. The words of the Duc de Guise, "Saint-Paul! if I can only hunt out the men who assassinated Dugast!" were heartily applauded, and this warmed up both audience and actors.

I ran off to see how my mother was. On my return to the theater I met M. Deviolaine in the corridor; but, as soon as I appeared, he quickly retired into a small antechamber, on purpose, as I imagined, to avoid me. I did the poor dear man injustice! he had quite other intentions in his thoughts.

The second act began; it was an amusing one; the scene of the peashooter, concerning which I was much afraid, passed without any signs of objection, and the curtain fell amidst pretty general applause.

The third act was the one to decide the success of the play. In this act comes the scene between the page and the duchess, and the scene between the duchess and the duke—the scene where M. de Guise compels his wife to appoint a meeting with Saint-Mégrin. If the strong situations in that scene found favor with the public, the battle was won. The scene roused cries of horror, but, at the same time, peals of applause; it was the first time any dramatic scenes had been presented with great freedom—I might even call it with brutal frankness.

I went out; I was very anxious to see my poor mother and to embrace her, although she was then hardly in a condition to understand who it was that was embracing her.

How happy I should have been if she had been in the theater, instead of on her bed! She was sleeping quite peacefully; I kissed her without waking her, and returned to the theater. Under the porch I again met M. Deviolaine, who was going away.

"What!" I said, "are you not going to stay to the end?"

"How can I stay to the end, you brute?"

"Why can you not stay . . . ?"

"Because I am thoroughly upset! Because I am turned inside out . . . an attack of colic."

"Ah!" I exclaimed, laughing, "so that was why I saw you going to the lavatory?"

"Yes, that was the reason, monsieur. . . . You have already cost me fifty sous! at two sous each time it is . . . why, you will ruin me!"

"Bah! you exaggerate. Whatever could you do at the twenty-fifth time?"

"Nothing, you young puppy! And the last time, if I had not been stopped by the hair of my head, I should have disappeared entirely! Ah! what a business! . . . Oh dear! I am horribly ill!" and M. Deviolaine laid both hands on his stomach and began running towards the rue Saint-Honoré.

I went into the theater; as I had indeed foreseen, from the fourth act to the end it was more than a success, it was an increasing delirium: all hands applauded, even those of the ladies. Madame Malibran, who had only been able to find a seat on the third row, leaned right out of her box, holding on to a pillar to keep herself from falling. Then, when Firmin appeared to give the name of the author, the enthusiasm was so universal that even the Duc d'Orléans himself stood up and called out the name of his employé, the success of whose work—if not the most merited, at least the most striking of the epoch—had just caused him to be greeted as a poet.

That very night, when I returned home, I found a letter from M. le Baron de Broval, which I will give word for word:

"I cannot sleep without first telling you, my dear young friend, how very happy I am at your splendid triumph, without congratulating you and, above all, your estimable mother most heartily, for I know you felt more anxious on her behalf than on your own. My sister and I and all at the office sympathized deeply with you; and now we rejoice at a triumph justly deserved both on account of your very great and persevering talent and your filial devotion. I am very sure that the laurels and the success in wait for you in the future, will not stand in the way of your friendships, and I assure you that my feelings towards you are very warm.

BARON DE BROVAL

"10 *February* 1829"

This was the man who, five months before, had compelled me to renounce my salary!

To few men has it been given to see such a rapid change take place in their lives as took place in mine during those four hours of the representation of *Henri III*. I was totally unknown until that night, and, next day, whether for good or for evil, I was the talk of all Paris. From that night dated the hatreds of people whom I had never seen—hatreds roused by the unwelcome fame attached to my name. But friendships also dated from that epoch. What multitudes of people envied me that night, who had no idea that I spent it on a mattress on the floor by the side of my dying mother!

Next day, the room was filled with bouquets; I covered my mother's bed with them, and she touched them with the hand that was left unparalyzed, pulling them nearer to her or pushing them away, unconscious what all these flowers meant—and, possibly, even unconscious that they were flowers at all. By two o'clock in the afternoon, the day after the performance, my manuscript had sold for six thousand francs. These six thousand francs were paid me in six bank notes; and I went to show them to M. Deviolaine.

"What are those?" he asked.

"They are the price of my manuscript," I replied. "You see it amounts to Monsieur Laffitte's three thousand francs and three thousand francs besides."

"What!" cried M. Deviolaine, "are there idiots who have bought it of you?"

"You see for yourself."

"Well, they are brainless idiots!"

Then, handing me back the notes, and shrugging his shoulders, he said:

"You do not inquire how I am!"

"I did not dare. . . . How are you?"

"A little better, happily."

"Were you able to return to the theater?"

"Yes, I was there for the conclusion."

"Were you there when my name was given out?"

"The deuce I was!"

"And did it not give you a little gratification?"

"A little! Why, you rascal, I wept like a baby!"

"Come now! it cost you a lot to acknowledge that. . . . Let us shake hands."

"Ah!" said M. Deviolaine, "if only your poor father could have been there!"

"My mother could have been there if people had not made her so unhappy."

"Come, come! you are not going to tell me that it is my fault your mother is in bed, are you? Good gracious me! it tormented me sufficiently during your representation. I could not think of anything else; I believe it was that which gave me the beastly colic. . . . By the bye, what are they saying in the office?"

I showed him M. de Broval's letter. He read it through twice over.

"Well, I never . . . !" he said, as he handed it me back, shrugging his shoulders. "Shall you return to the office?"

"I? Dear me no!"

"Well, I think you are right. Shall you go and see Monsieur Fossier?"

"No, indeed."

"He likes you, nevertheless."

"Then why did he not write me a letter of congratulation, too?"

"Well, but he might have expected tickets for his daughter."

"That reminds me. Shall I save you a box for the second performance?" You hadn't a good place for the first . . . you were close to the door."

"You scoundrel! I was right where I was, near the door. . . . Do you believe this mad prank you have just played is going to bring you in any more than what you have just shown me?"

"Certainly I do."

"About how much?"

"Fifteen thousand francs."

"What!"

"About fifteen thousand francs."

"And how long will it have to run to gain that?"

"Perhaps two months."

"So in two months, you will have earned the whole year's salary of three chief clerks, including bonuses?"

"Call in your three chief clerks and tell them to do as much for themselves."

"Get out! I am afraid the very ceiling will fall on our heads while you are saying such monstrous things!"

"Tomorrow night, then?"

"Yes, tomorrow night, if I have nothing better to do."

I was quite easy. M. Deviolaine would not have anything better to do, nor would he have accepted a year of his salary to be kept away.

From M. Deviolaine's house I ran to M. Laffitte's. I was proud to be able to pay him what I owed him so promptly. I gave him his thousand crowns, and he returned me my promissory note and my manuscript. But I always remembered the service rendered me, which, coming when my mother was taken ill, was of priceless value.

Still, I had not reached the conclusion of my worries. When I returned to my temporary dwelling place, I found a letter from the Théâtre-Français asking me to go to the office there immediately. I rushed there, and found the Committee in a state of consternation from Taylor downward. They had received a letter from the Home Minister suspending *Henri III*. This was a far more serious matter than the suspension of my salary. Luckily, Taylor had made up his mind what should be done. He proposed I should urgently demand an audience of M. de Martignac. He himself undertook to take the letter and see that it was conveyed to him.

I sat down and wrote at once, asking for an audience for the next day. I received an answer two hours later. M. de Martignac would see me at seven next morning.

By seven next morning I was at his house. Oh! what a blessing it is to find a minister who is both polished and cultivated, like M. de Martignac! *rara avis*, as Juvenal would call it, and, worse still, a bird of passage! We remained together for an hour, not talking of the play, but of all sorts of subjects; in ten minutes, we came to an understanding over the play, and I carried my manuscript back, saved, this time not from annihilation, but from limbo. Oh! poor M. de Martignac! how well he understood art! How thoroughly well he knew that type of human being who obstructs all progress he meets with on the way, with a view rather of hindering others from advancing than of advancing himself!

It was not under M. de Martignac's administration that art, wherever it turned, encountered the notice, "This road is closed by order of the authorities." And to think that for twenty years the same men blocked the same avenues; that, from being old men, they grew into being decrepit ones, whilst we young men grew old; that, by dint of ill will and persecution, they managed to drive both Lamartine and Hugo into politics, Soulié and Balzac into their graves; that I stood almost alone, in my struggle against them; that they set their mark on things, like the seal of Solomon which enclosed the genii of the *Thousand and One Nights* in clay vases; and that all this political and literary compression will one day burst in their faces, killing and overturning all around it without injuring itself—wrinkled dwarfs who everlastingly stir up the glowing fires of revolutions!

Some things, at least, are very clear; that, for twenty years, these rulers were petty, paltry, contemptible; that they left behind them a sad and shameful memory amongst the Germans, Hungarians, Italians, along the banks of the Nile as well as on the shores of the Bosphorus, at Mogador even as at Montevideo, in the Old World as well as the New; that, during the whole of the time which transpired between the day on which M. Sébastiani made his announcement at the Tribune that "Order reigned at Warsaw," and that on which M. Barrot wrote in the *Moniteur* that "The French have entered Rome," they gave the lie not only with respect to every promise made by man—whether these promises came through M. de la Fayette or M. de Lamartine—but still, more, with respect to everything hoped of God, who destined France to be the polestar to other nations, who said to the people, "You wish to sail toward the unknown world, toward the Promised Land called Liberty; there is your compass. Spread your sails and follow boldly!"

Instead of keeping faith with men and fulfilling God's will, what did you do, you poor slaves of passion, and miserable servants of blindness? You made the sea rough and winds contrary for every noble vessel that set sail under divine inspiration. You know it is so, I am not telling you anything fresh; you know that whatever is young and noble and pure, that has not been dragged through the mud of the past, and reaches forth to ethereal regions in the future, is against you; you know that those whom you allowed to be murdered by Austrian rods, those whom you left shut up in pontifical dungeons, those whom you suffered to be shot down by Neapolitan cannon, were martyrs. You are aware that, whilst people may hail you, you tyrants, as you go to your places of entertainment, it is we who shall always have their devotion; you are aware, in short, that we, the torchbearers, are loved, whilst you, the workers of darkness, are detested. You know that should you ever be forgiven your deeds, it will be because of what we have said on your behalf; and hence come your persecutions—powerless, thank God, like all things that come from below and seek to harm what is above. . . .

Let us return to *Henri III*, which had nothing to do with all this, and which suddenly and unexpectedly found itself raised sky-high. My return was awaited with impatience, for they dared not advertise without the minister's permission. I brought them that permission, and they advertised. M. le Duc d'Orléans announced that he would be present at the second performance. When I reached the theater that night, I was told that he had already arrived and had asked me to go to his box. I did as I was bidden, between the first and second acts. The densely packed theater bore witness to the genuine strength of my success. The Duc d'Orléans received me most graciously.

"Now, Monsieur Dumas," he said, "are you not satisfied? You have gained your case against everybody—the public and myself included. Even Broval, Deviolaine and Oudard are enchanted."

I bowed.

"But for all that, do you know," he continued laughingly, "you have very nearly got me into serious trouble?"

"You, monseigneur?"

"Yes, I."

"How is that?"

"The king sent for me yesterday."

"The king?"

"Yes, indeed."

"And what about, monseigneur?"

"About your drama."

"About *Henri III*?"

" 'Are you aware of what I have been informed, *cousin?*' he said, laying emphasis upon the last word. 'I have been told that you have a youth in your offices who has written a play in which both you and I figure—I as Henri III, and you as the Duc de Guise?' "

"Monseigneur, you could of course have replied that the king was mistaken and that the young man was no longer in your employ."

"No; I much preferred to reply otherwise, and not to lie, since I mean to keep you on."

"Then what did Your Highness say? . . ."

"I said, 'Sire, people have misinformed you, and for three reasons: First, I do not beat my wife; secondly, Madame la Duchesse d'Orléans has not made me a cuckold; thirdly, Your Majesty has not a more faithful subject than myself.' Do you think my reply was equal to anything you would have advised me to make?"

"Indeed, monseigneur, it is infinitely more witty."

"And nearer the truth, monsieur. . . . Ah! the curtain is rising: go about your business; mine is to listen to you."

I bowed.

"By the bye," said the duke, "Madame la Duchesse d'Orléans desires to see you tomorrow morning, to inquire how your mother is."

I bowed and withdrew.

Oh! what a power is success, with its notoriety and fuss over a name; with its calm and serene supremacy of mind over matter! M. de Broval, M. Deviolaine, and M. Oudard were enchanted; the Duc d'Orléans had called me to his box to repeat a witty *mot* he had said to the king; and, finally, Madame la Duchesse d'Orléans would see me on the morrow to ask me news of my mother! Birth, it would seem, only bestows principalities; talent gives the dignity of princehood.

Next day, I paid my visit to the Duchesse d'Orléans, who was as gracious to me as could be; but, alas! why did all this kindness come so late? When I returned, I found in an envelope a newspaper, the name of which I have forgotten—some friend who was sensitive concerning my reputation had sent it me. It announced the success of *Henri III*, and added:

"That success, great though it be, is not surprising to those who know how these literary and political jobs are put up by the House of Orléans. The author is a wage earner in the household of His Royal Highness."

The article was painful as well as untruthful; a lie, because the House of Orléans, as was well-known, had not schemed to help me in any way; and painful, because the writer by the use of the word "wages" (*gages*) instead of salary, had evidently intended to imply that I was only a common servant.

I looked at my poor sick mother, who, unaware of what I was reading, was trying to express the first desires of returning consciousness by smiles of tender affection; and at such a moment as this I was compelled, by an individual whom I had never set eyes upon, whose very existence was unknown to me and who had no reason for hating me, to leave her in order to demand an apology for a gross and gratuitous insult!

I went to de la Ponce. I begged him to go to the office of the paper and arrange there and then, with the writer of the article, the conditions of a duel for the following morning. Such a long time has elapsed since then and I have so short a memory for injuries, that I have completely forgotten both the name of the paper and the name of the writer with whom I had the quarrel. I regret the latter, for he bore himself the responsibility for an article that was not his. As I cannot recollect his name, allow me to speak of him as M. X——.

De la Ponce returned in about an hour's time. The duel had been accepted for the next day but one, as M. X——, who acknowledged himself the author of the article, had a duel on the day between with Carrel. I went to call on Carrel, whom I had known for a long time, having met him at M. de Leuven's and also with Méry. Like myself, he, too, had been gratuitously insulted; like me, he had demanded satisfaction, and he was to meet my future adversary in a pistol duel at eight o'clock next morning.

Carrel complimented me on my success, and promised to do his utmost so that M. X—— would not be able to fight with me the day after. It was a sad fact that scarcely had I begun my dramatic career before, in less than a week, I was compelled to demand satisfaction from two men, not on account of criticisms passed upon my talent, but for injury done to my personal character.

A few words de la Ponce dropped led me to believe that pistols would be the weapons chosen, and Carrel confirmed me in this opinion; so, when I met Adolphe, I told him what had happened and begged him to come and practice shooting with me next day. Although I could not afford to squander money, I still had sufficient to permit myself a turn once a month at Gosset's. I had become a habitué there. We reached the place about ten o'clock.

"Philippe!" I shouted to the lad attendant as I passed in, "pistols number five and twenty-five balls."

Philippe came up.

"You can have twenty-five balls," he said, "but not pistols number five, unless you are going to practice alone."

"Why so?"

"Because they were lent this morning to a gentleman who had a duel, and you should see the state in which he brought them back."

And, indeed, the second number five pistol had the trigger guard broken and the butt end blown off.

"What did that?"

"Why! a bullet," said Philippe.

"Quite so, but what about the gentleman who held it?"

"He had two of his fingers cut."

"Cut?"

"Yes, cut!"

"So he had to pay the price of two of his fingers?"

"And also for the mending of the pistol."

"What was this gentleman's name?"

"I do not recollect his name; he was fighting with M. Carrel."

"Stuff and nonsense!"

"It's true."

"Are you certain?"

"Of course I am. Monsieur Carrel's seconds brought back the pistols."

"See," I said to Adolphe, "this will postpone my duel of tomorrow and no mistake."

And then I related to him that my adversary had arranged to fight a duel with Carrel that very day, and that it was probably he who had had his two fingers injured.

"It is very easy to find out," said Adolphe. "Let us go and inquire."

We went to M. X——'s house, and found that it was really he who had been fighting; he had had two fingers blown off—his third and little fingers. I sent up my visiting card by his manservant, and we took our departure. We had not gone more than two stories downstairs when we heard the man running after us. M. X—— begged me to go in. I found him smiling in spite of his wounds, and very courteous in spite of his attack.

"Pray excuse me, monsieur," he said, "for the liberty I took in asking you to come back and see me; I use the privilege of a wounded person."

"Is your injury a serious one, monsieur?" I asked.

"No—I escaped with the loss of two fingers from my right hand; and since I still have three left with which to write and tell you how sorry I am for having made myself unpleasant toward you, I have all I need."

"You still have the use of your left to shake hands with me, monsieur," I said, "and that would be better than tiring your right over anything imaginable."

We shook hands; conversed on indifferent topics; and then, ten minutes later, we took leave of one another. We have never seen each other since, and, as I have said, I have totally forgotten his name. I bear my memory a grudge, for I shall ever remember him with pleasure.

Singular freak of chance! If this man had not had a quarrel with Carrel, and if Carrel had not deprived him of his two fingers, he would have fought with me, and he might have killed me or been killed by me. And for what reason, I ask you?

Chapter III

THE TEMPER OF REVOLUTION

IF THERE is any single contribution to the art of writing that we can credit Dumas with, I believe it would come under the heading of pace. Rapid pace in literature is now so taken for granted, that we think little of it. But read Sir Walter Scott, read Fenimore Cooper, read any and all of those who may be considered predecessors of Dumas in the field of historical writing and the chief difference that strikes one is that of pace.

Pace was nothing new. Music had it. The *commedia del arte* had it. Sports had it. But the world prior to our modern times considered pace as something undignified.

The rush, that we so admire today, had to work its way into the world by fighting against the serried opposition of those who held rigidly to the ceremonial and fixed world that then existed. The world that was considered changeless. The world of the religious procession, the world of dynasties, where the ancestral was held in perpetual respect, where the classics were worshiped, and what was good enough for my father must be good enough for me.

The art of printing, the discovery of America, all the thousand developments that came about slowly over the centuries and finally accumulated into the storm of progress in which we are now living, brought pace into its own. It had to come into literature. And Dumas was one of the earliest to show what that pace meant in storytelling.

Take this selection from the fourth volume of the *Memoirs*, which is, curiously enough, an incident involving Dumas in an attempt to preserve old values from destruction.

I was awakened next morning by my servant Joseph. He was standing by my bedside calling me with ever-increasing loudness.

"Monsieur! . . . Monsieur!! . . . Monsieur!!! . . ."

At the third *monsieur*, I groaned, rubbed my eyes, and sat up.

"Well," I asked, "what is the matter?"

"Oh, don't you hear, monsieur?" Joseph exclaimed, holding his head with his hands.

"How should I hear, you idiot? I was asleep."

"But fighting is going on all around us, monsieur!"

"Really?"

He opened the window.

"Listen! it sounds as if it were in the courtyard."

And, indeed, the firing seemed to me to come from no very distant point.

"The deuce!" I said, "where does it come from?"

"From Saint-Thomas-d'Aquin, monsieur."

"What! from the church itself?"

"No, from the Artillery Museum. . . . Monsieur knows that a post is stationed there."

"Ah! true," I exclaimed, "the Artillery Museum! I must go there."

"What! Monsieur is going there?"

"Certainly."

"Oh, good heavens!"

"Quick, help me! . . . Just a glass of Madeira or Alicante wine! . . . Oh! the wretches! they will pillage everything!"

That, indeed, was the thought which preoccupied my mind, and that was what made me run to the place where I heard the firing going on. I remembered the archaeological treasures that I had seen and handled, one after another, for the studies I had written on Henri III, Henri IV, and Louis XIII, and saw them all being scattered among the hands of people who did not know their value: marvelous rich treasures of art being given to the first comer who would exchange them for a pound of tobacco or a packet of cartridges.

I was ready in five minutes and darted off in the direction of Saint-Thomas-d'Aquin. For the third time, the assailants had been repulsed. This was easily explained: they were madly attacking the museum by the two openings leading through rue de Bac and rue

Saint-Dominique. The firing of the soldiers raked the two streets and
swept them clean with deplorable facility. I looked at the houses
in the rue de Bac, which on both sides formed the corner of the
rue Gribauval, and I judged that their backs must look upon the
place Saint-Thomas-d'Aquin, and that from their upper stories one
could easily dominate the post of the Museum of Artillery.

I confided to some of the combatants the plan suggested to me by
the view of the position: it was instantly adopted by them. I pounded
at the door of one of the two houses, No. 35 rue du Bac, and it
was opened after a long wait; still, it did open finally, and eight to
ten armed men entered with me and we rushed upstairs to the
higher stories. I and three or four other fellows reached an attic,
which was rounded off at the top to fit the shape of the roof above
it, and here I established myself with as much safety as if I had been
behind the parapet of a bastion.

Then firing began again, but with quite different results now. In
ten minutes the military post had lost five or six of its men. Suddenly, all the soldiers disappeared and the firing died down. This
must, we thought, be some kind of ambuscade, so we hesitated before
quitting our entrenchments. But the porter of the museum soon appeared at the door making unmistakable signs of peace. So we went
down. The soldiers had scaled the walls and run away over the surrounding courts and gardens. A portion of the insurgents was already
crowding up the corridors when I reached the museum.

"For God's sake, friends," I cried, "respect the armor!"

"What! Why should we respect it?"

"I like that joke," replied one of the men to whom I addressed
myself. "Why, to take the weapons is the very reason we are here!"

It then occurred to me that, of course, this must have been the sole
object of the attack, and that there would be no means of saving the
magnificent collection from pillage. I considered: the only thing left
to do was to take my share of the most valuable of the armor.

One of two things would happen: either they would keep the
arms or bring them back to the museum. In either case, it was better
that I should take charge of some of the precious things, rather than
anyone else. If I kept them, they would be in the hands of a man
who knew how to appreciate them. If they were to be restored, they
would be in the hands of one who would give them up.

I ran to the best place, where there was an equestrian trophy of the Renaissance period. I seized a shield, a helmet, and a sword which were known to have belonged to François I, also a magnificent arquebuse which had belonged, according to the same tradition, to Charles IX, and had been used by him to fire upon the Huguenots. This tradition has become almost historic, on account of the quatrain which the arquebuse carries, inlaid in silver letters, on its barrel, forming one single line from the breech to the sighting-point:

> *"Pour mayntenir la foy,*
> *Je suis belle et fidele;*
> *Aux ennemis du Roy*
> *Je suis belle et cruelle!"*

I put the helmet on my head, the shield on my arm; I hung the sword by my side, put the arquebuse on my shoulder, and so made my way, bending under their weight, to the rue de l'Université. I nearly fell when I reached the height of my fourth floor. If these were, indeed, the very shield and buckler that François I had worn at Marignan, and if he remained fourteen hours in the saddle with these in addition to his other armor, I could well believe in the prowess of Ogier the Dane and Roland and the four sons of Aymon.

"Oh! monsieur," Joseph exclaimed, when he caught sight of me, "where have you been, and whatever is all that old iron?"

I did not attempt to correct Joseph's idea with respect to my booty; it would only have been waste of time. I simply told him to help me to take off the helmet, which nearly suffocated me. I laid them all down on my bed and rushed back for more of this splendid quarry. I brought back next the cuirass, ax, and the bulk of the arms.

Later I gave all my fine trophies back to the Artillery Museum, and I still possess the letter of the former director, thanking me for their restitution, and giving me free entry on days not open to the general public.

Too long for quotation in its entirety in this compilation, is Dumas's story of his participation in the 1830 revolution that swept the Bourbons out of power in France. A few pages, however, from here and there, will serve to show amidst what drama and excitement Dumas wrote—and wooed.

"General," I said to Lafayette, "did I not hear you tell Arago just now that you were short of powder?"

"Quite true," the general said, "but perhaps it would have been better if I had not mentioned it."

"Will you let me go and fetch some?"

"You?"

"Yes, me. Why not?"

"But from where?"

"Wherever there may happen to be some. Either at Soissons, or perhaps at La Fère."

"They will not give you any."

"Then I shall be compelled to seize it!"

"What? You? You will seize it?"

"Yes."

"By force?"

"How else? Wasn't the Louvre taken by force?"

"You must be mad, my friend," the general replied.

"I swear that I'm not. I'm as sane as ever."

"Come, come, you're tired out. You can scarcely talk. I know you spent the night here. So now, go home and rest."

"General, I must have an order from you in order to get the powder."

"Well, you shan't get it."

"Do you mean you don't wish to try?"

"I mean I don't wish you shot for trying."

But Dumas insisted and got his orders and went off to Soissons. Those who wish to follow his various adventures there, a lone republican among a lot of royalists, must read it in the unabridged version. But he forced powder out of them everywhere. And in addition hoisted the tricolor above the various places, pulling down the Bourbon flag.

The high point of these adventures was the moment when Dumas, alone, went to the house of the king's lieutenant, Monsieur de Linières, and there, in the presence of three other officers, all armed with their swords, demanded the surrender of some two hundred pounds of powder.

I entered and closed the door behind me. I had hardly come face to face with these four officers before I regretted the rifle which I had left outside, for I realized that grave matters were going to be discussed. I felt for the pockets of my waistcoat to see if my pistols were there. They were. Safe and sound.

"Monsieur," the commander said to me in a jeering tone, "I have sent for Monsieur le Marquis de Lenferna and Monsieur Bonvilliers, in your absence, who are my colleagues in the military command in this town, in order that you may lay before them the object of your mission here, as you did to me."

I saw I must assume the same tone of conversation as that used by M. de Linières, so I replied:

"Well, monsieur, the object of my mission is simple enough: it is merely a question of my taking the powder that I have found in the magazine and transporting it to Paris where they are short. . . . And, in respect of that same powder, allow me to inform you, Commander, that you were wrongly instructed: there are two hundred pounds of powder in the magazine—not two hundred cartridges."

"Whether two hundred pounds or two hundred cartridges is not the question, monsieur: the question is that you have come to seize powder from a military town containing a garrison of eight hundred men."

"Monsieur does, indeed," I replied, "put the question on its true footing: I have come to take powder from a garrison town containing eight hundred men, and here is my order for so doing."

"You are probably backed by an armed force to carry out the order, in case we refuse to comply with it?"

"No, monsieur; but I have a most determined intention of taking that powder, since I swore to General Lafayette I would either take it or be killed. That is why I asked your leave for the opening of the magazine doors, and I now renew my request."

"And you think that alone, Monsieur Dumas . . . I think you told me your name was Dumas?"

"Yes, monsieur, that is my name."

"You can force me to sign such an authorization? You have noticed probably that there are four of us?"

I had noticed still more—the commander's jeering tones and that, from the wording of his sentences, the situation was growing warm;

I therefore edged myself gradually back until I was master of the door and, while doing so, I placed my hands inside my coat pockets and silently prepared the double locks of my pistols. I then suddenly drew them from my pockets and pointed the muzzles toward the group in front of me.

"True, there are four of you, messieurs . . . but there are five of us!" And I took a step forward and said, "Messieurs, I give you my word of honor that if the order is not signed within the next five seconds I will blow out the brains of all four of you, and I will begin with you, Monsieur le Lieutenant de Roi—honor to whom honor is due!"

I had turned deadly pale, but in spite of my pallor my face expressed immovable determination. The double-barreled pistol which I held in my right hand was only a foot and a half off M. de Linières' face.

"Beware, monsieur!" I said to him. "I am going to count the seconds," and after a pause I began, "One, two, three . . . !"

At this moment a side door opened and a woman burst into the room in a paroxysm of terror.

"Oh! my love, yield! yield!" she cried. "It is a second revolt of the Negroes! . . ."

And, saying this, she gazed at me with terrified eyes.

"Monsieur," began the commander of the fort, "out of regard for my wife . . ."

"Monsieur," I replied, "I have the profoundest respect for Madame, but I too have a mother and a sister and hope, therefore, you will have the goodness to send Madame away, so that we can thrash this matter out between men alone."

"My love!" Madame de Linières continued to implore, "yield! yield! I implore you! Remember my father and mother, both massacred at Saint-Domingo!"

I had not until then understood what she meant by her words, "It is a second revolt of Negroes!"

She had taken me for a Negro, from my fuzzy hair and complexion, burnt deep brown by three days' exposure to the sun and by my faintly Creole accent—if, indeed, I had any accent at all, from the hoarseness that had seized me. She was beside herself with terror, and her fright was easily understood; for I learned, later, that she was a daughter of M. and Madame de Saint-Janvier, who had been mercilessly killed under her very eyes during a revolt. The situation was now too strained to be prolonged much further.

"But, monsieur," the commander exclaimed in despair, "how can I yield before one single man?"

"Would you like me, monsieur, to sign a paper attesting that you gave me the order with a pistol at your head?"

"Yes, yes! monsieur," shrieked Madame de Linières.

Then turning to her husband, whose knees she had been clasping, she reiterated: "My love! my love! give him the order! Give it to him, I entreat you!"

"Or would you prefer," I continued, "that I went and hunted up two or three friends so that our numbers may be equal on both sides?"

"Indeed yes, monsieur, I should much prefer that course."

"Be on your guard, Monsieur le Vicomte! I go, relying on your word of honor; I go, because I have you at my mercy and could blow out the brains of every one of you. . . . I can promise you it would soon be done. . . . Shall I find you on my return where you are and as you are?"

"Yes, yes! monsieur," exclaimed Madame de Linières.

I bowed courteously, but without ceding one jot.

"It is your husband's word of honor I require, madame."

"Well, then monsieur," the king's lieutenant said, "I will give you my word."

"I presume that it includes these gentlemen equally?"

The officers bowed in the affirmative. I uncocked my pistols and replaced them in my pockets. Then, addressing myself to Madame de Linières:

"Reassure yourself, madame," I said. "It is over. In five minutes, gentlemen, I shall be back here."

I went out, picking up my gun, which I found in its corner outside the door. I had gone beyond my resources, for I did not know where to look for Hutin; and Bard was guarding an important point. But chance served me; for, as I stepped into the street, I saw Hutin and one of his friends, who, faithful to their rendezvous, were waiting ten yards away from the house: the friend was a young man called Moreau, a warm patriot of Soissons. They both had double-barreled guns. I beckoned to them to come into the courtyard. They came in, not knowing quite what was expected of them. I went upstairs; parole had been strictly maintained and none of the gentlemen had left his place. I went to the window and opened it.

"Messieurs," I said to Hutin and Moreau, "have the goodness to inform Monsieur le Commander that you are ready to fire upon him and upon the other persons I shall point out to you, if he does not instantly sign an authorization for taking the powder."

For answer, Hutin and Moreau cocked their guns. Madame de Linières followed all my movements and those of her husband with haggard eyes.

"That will do, monsieur," the king's lieutenant said. "I am ready to sign." And, taking a piece of paper from his desk, he wrote:

"I authorize M. Alexandre Dumas to take away all the powder belonging to the artillery which is in the magazine Saint-Jean—King's Lieutenant and Commander of the Fort,

VICOMTE DE LINIERES"

"Soissons, 31 *July*, 1830"

I took the paper which the count handed me, bowed to Madame de Linières, made my apologies to her for the unavoidable fright I had caused her, and went out.

Not for a moment, however, did Dumas lose sight of his career, while these stirring events were involving him. Which brings up once more the question of how much personal participation is necessary in order to develop greatness in a writer. Could Dumas have been Dumas had he lived quietly in Capri or Hoboken?

Read this excerpt from Dumas's *La Reine Margot*:

In the course of the bloody battle at Calais where the French defeated the English, but not without tremendous losses of their own, the Duc de Guise received a terrible wound.

His servants and officers brought him to Château Neuf, where they placed him on a camp bed.

He lay unconscious. His face, swimming with gore, had been pierced through and through by a lance, which had broken off, and left the iron embedded. It had penetrated the cheek under the right eye, pushing its way clear through to the nape of the neck, just below the left ear, and projecting beyond for another seven inches.

A horrible sight.

Around the bed, some ten or twelve surgeons stood appalled at a task far beyond them. An air of desolation reigned.

No one did a thing. They just stood and argued.

That was when Ambroise Paré, who did not form part of the duke's court, entered. Just in time to hear one of the surgeons remarking in a loud voice:

"It is agreed then, that after general consultation, we have reached the painful conclusion that the duke's wound is fatal. There is no other course but to extract the fragment of the lance from the duke's face, and that operation would kill monseigneur at once."

"So you prefer to do nothing—and let him die?" Ambroise Paré cried out boldly. He stood behind the front rank of spectators, but with a single glance had already judged the condition of the injured man to be next to hopeless.

The surgeon who had been speaking raised his head to find out who was this impudent interrupter, and seeing no one of any importance, he went on:

"Foolhardy is the only word for anyone who would dare lay impious hands on that majestic countenance, and risk, with no chance of success whatsoever, that the death of our hero be hastened all the more?"

"I!" declared Ambroise Paré, stepping bravely, with head erect, amidst the gathering of surgeons. And while a patter of angry comments exploded about him, he went calmly to the body and leaned over it in order to examine the wound more closely.

"So it is you, Master Ambroise Paré!" said the surgeon-in-chief with something of contempt in his voice, for the one all considered a madman. How dared he differ with them? "Are you forgetting," he asked, "that you are not one of the surgeons belonging to the Duc de Guise?"

"Since his usual surgeons have abandoned him," Ambroise Paré said firmly, "I consider that he has only one surgeon: and that is myself."

And with that Ambroise Paré turned back to examining the wound on the apparently lifeless body of the duke.

"Well," said the surgeon-in-chief, with an ironical smile, "now that you've had your chance to examine the wound, do you still persist in your diagnosis, that the iron must be extracted?"

"I persist," said Paré, resolutely.

"And where are the marvelous surgical devices with which you will accomplish it?"

"These two hands," said Paré.

"I protest!" cried the surgeon furiously. "To add to the illustrious sufferer's last agony can only be called profanation!"

All the other surgeons joined in, shouting their various protests.

"Then you have some other method of saving the prince's life," Ambroise rejoined.

"How can we?" the surgeons asked, "when it is so obviously impossible."

"Then this doomed body is mine," said Ambroise, and he stretched out his arms over it, as if taking possession.

"Then we disassociate ourselves," said the surgeon-in-chief, and he and his colleagues made a symbolic movement of leaving the room. While from the officers and servants came the question, addressed to Paré:

"But what do you intend to do?"

"The Duc de Guise is apparently dead," said Paré, "therefore I shall treat him as if he were actually dead."

So saying, he took off his doublet and tucked up his sleeves.

"Imagine making experiments on monseigneur, as if he were no more than a dead animal!" cried an outraged practitioner, wringing his hands at such scandalous behavior.

"Worse than that!" Ambroise Paré replied, without turning his eyes from the patient. "I am going to treat him not as a man, and not even as an animal, but as a thing. Observe!"

And he bent over and boldly stemmed one foot on the breast of the duke.

A cry of doubt, of terror, of menace, ran through the assembly.

A nobleman tapped Paré on the shoulder saying: "Take care, master. You are here among the friends and servants of the duke, and if you should fail, I will not be able to answer for your safety."

Ambroise turned around, a sad smile on his face. "Indeed," he said simply.

"You're risking your neck!" an officer exclaimed.

Paré lifted his eyes to heaven with a look both serious and melancholy, then he said: "I accept. But at least—while I'm busy—I don't want any disturbance."

Everyone recognized the authority of genius, and as with a common motion, all stood back and kept quiet.

In the solemn silence that ensued nothing was heard but the labored breathing of the tense onlookers.

Ambroise Paré put his left knee upon the duke's chest, and, leaning over, took the shattered wood of the lance projecting from the wound, and with the tips of his fingers began to move it gently this way and that, gradually increasing his pressure on it.

The unconscious duke started up as if in horrible pain.

And an answering movement came from the spectators, who in their fright turned pale.

Ambroise Paré himself paused for a second, struck with terror. Fine beads of sweat burst upon his brow. But a moment later he was back at work.

At the end of a minute—a minute that endured longer than an hour—the iron was extracted.

Ambroise Paré quickly flung it from him, and bent over the gaping wound.

When he looked up again his face was suffused with the flush of joy. But then he was all seriousness again, as he dropped to his knees and let his thanks pour out to God, while tears of joy and relief flowed over his cheeks.

It was a sublime moment. The master said nothing, but everyone understood, without a word being spoken, that now there was hope. The servants wept unashamedly. Some bent to kiss the hem of the surgeon's coat.

Not a word was said by anyone. All waited for the master to speak.

At last, in a grave, but not unemotional voice, Paré said: "I am prepared to answer now, for the life of Monseigneur de Guise."

And in fact, an hour later the Duc de Guise was already sufficiently restored to show signs of consciousness, and soon was even speaking.

"Not a word, I beg you," warned the surgeon, while bandaging the wound.

"I'll be silent," said de Guise. "But first, answer me one question. Just one."

"What is it, monseigneur?"

"Do you think, Master Paré, that the effects of this horrible wound may cripple me either in mind or body?"

"Not the slightest danger of that, monseigneur," said Ambroise. "But gashed you will be, from the huge cicatrice—"

"Scarred?" the duke cried. "Why that's nothing. In fact, for a soldier, a scar is a decoration. Let me then, from now on, be called scarface . . ."

And from that time on, both to his contemporaries and to history, the prince was known as the "balafré."

(*Balafré* is a Germanic word which can best be rendered by "ugly lip" or "split lip," but which in time came to refer to any deep and disfiguring scar.)

But to return to the question of whether Dumas owed his ability for vivid historical writing to his many exciting experiences. The answer of this compiler is: no. Vivid writing comes out of a powerful imagination, aided by a facility for verbal expression, and reinforced by long practice at the art of composition.

Gustave Flaubert, for example, kept away from all political activity. His life was fairly quiet. He did it is true make a voyage to the ruins of Carthage in preparation for writing his *Salammbô*, which appeared some fifteen years after Dumas's *La Reine Margot*, but that book was an event in the history of historical novels, in spite of the author's quiet life.

Arnold Bennett, after publishing his *The Old Wives' Tale*, had to deny that he had ever witnessed an execution, because his powerful description of one, in that book, had convinced readers that he could not but be writing directly from life. So much for the necessity of experience.

The writer is not a camera. Or at least he is not just a camera. What is so exciting or unusual in the life of Shakespeare? His story is like that of millions: a country boy come to the city to earn his living. Completely unsupported guesses have been made about supposed voyages to the Lowlands and to Italy, to explain, at least in part, the gift of this man. But it was his talent and not his experiences that led him from the farce of *The Comedy of Errors* to the sublimity of *King Lear*.

This is a subject we must touch on again, when we quote from

Dumas's introduction to his novel *The Companions of Jehu*, in order to show that no one denies the value of direct experience as the basic source of art. All art. But it is the ability to transmute life into art that really counts. And no piling up of experiences will give that ability to a writer, if he hasn't already got it, or won't work to acquire it.

Before we come to the introduction to *The Companions of Jehu*, here is another quote from the *Memoirs*, Volume VI. It will be noticed that this excerpt begins with the phrase: "In the midst of all this," a phrase that requires some explanation, since Dumas himself took many, many pages to tell in detail the very exciting story of the attempt of the Duchesse de Berry to regain the throne of France for the Bourbons.

It will be recalled that the July 1830 revolution had swept the Bourbons out and given the throne of France to the Duc d'Orléans, Dumas's former boss. The Duchesse de Berry had been married to a Bourbon, to one of the sons of Charles X, before that king had been forced to flee to England for his life. But by that time she was already a widow, her husband having been assassinated.

The Duchess followed her father-in-law into exile, and then began to dream of getting back the throne for herself. She "invaded" France, with a handful of followers, expecting vast numbers to spring to arms in her behalf. But just as happened in the 1961 "invasion" of Cuba, these vast numbers, anxious to risk their lives, turned out to be completely mythical.

Not only was this failure ludicrous, but it wasn't the end. The Duchess had managed to flee, had hid out from the police in a castle, had been betrayed, had managed to conceal herself in a secret chamber behind the chimney, but had been smoked out.

Then it was that the worst blow of all fell: this duchess, this widow of a prince dead for several years, this Bourbon, this woman who wanted to be queen of France, was discovered to be pregnant. And the new government, in order to reduce her and her Bourbons forever, took every means to publicize her condition. All Europe rang with her double disgrace.

Now that the reader understands something of this introductory clause, here is the extract:

In the midst of all this a great literary event took place. Victor Hugo had had his first prose drama, *Lucrezia Borgia*, performed at the Théâtre Porte-Saint-Martin. It is difficult to believe it, but it is a fact, that during this stormy atmosphere literature sprang to life, and grew and increased from flower to fruit.

The play was splendidly put on. Georges and Fréderick played the principal parts. It contained powerfully moving passages, and had an immense success. Let us state that we owe this glowing picture of a portion of the life of the Este duchess to the absence of the censorship.

From the night of February 2, 1833 began the real life of the author of *Lucrezia Borgia* and of *Orientales*, as it appeared in his representation of his beautiful drama, *Marion Delorme*. You, lovely Princess Negroni, know what we mean, you, in whom he discovered the love and devotion that blessed every hour of his life in this his natal land as also in foreign lands.

Ah! dear Comtesse Dash, you may rightly say that, unluckily, the most interesting facts of these Memoirs are those which I cannot write down!

I witnessed the fresh success of Victor Hugo with great delight—although *friends* had thrown some clouds across our early friendship—a joy all the greater as, having temporarily renounced the theater myself, Hugo at that period represented the whole school.

Why had I renounced it? One experiences moments of lassitude and of disgust in life, quite beyond one's own control. I was passing through such a period. I had been deeply hurt—not by failure of the *Fils de l'Emigré*, for the play was poor; it had justly failed. I acknowledge and submit to the hard lessons which the public gives an author—this simplicity, let us remark in passing, is a part of my strength—but, in the simplicity of my heart, I did not understand the fury of the press against me. They indeed knew one thing—or rather two—

First that I had fallen ill during the second or third act of the work; and further that I had left France in consequence of the troubles of June—namely, at the beginning of the rehearsals; that, finally, I was hardly responsible for a third of the work, and they attacked me concerning my five or six preceding successes.

No wonder I was staggered.

But, in other ways, this retiring into my shell, which I am not so presumptuous to compare with that of Achilles, was of great advantage with respect to my literary life, which it split into two divisions. Without the failure of the *Fils de l'Emigré*, and the explosion of hatred which followed it, I should probably never have done anything but theatrical work. On the contrary, during the year's silence which I kept with regard to the stage, I published my first impressions of my travels, which was very successful among the booksellers, and I prepared my volume entitled *Gaule et France*, an unfinished but wonderful book, wherein the double vision of the poet supplements the knowledge of the historian.

Then, too, this latter work, which absorbed me completely, by precipitating me into the intoxication of unknown matters, was of still greater advantage to me than to the public for which I intended it; it did not teach the public much, but it taught me a great deal. I was, I repeat, profoundly ignorant in history. When I began a historical drama, I did not investigate the whole century in which my heroes had lived, but merely the two or three years during which the action took place and the event which formed the catastrophe of the drama was accomplished. I made a hole after the fashion of well sinkers; I dived like fishermen.

True, by dint of digging, I sometimes brought up an ingot of gold; by diving, I at times came to the surface with a pearl; but it was merely chance. The studies I was compelled to make about the French Monarchy, from Caesar's invasion of the Gauls to the invasion of the French Republic in Europe, unfolded before my eyes that magnificent continuity of eighteen centuries, wrongly styled the history of France, under Charlemagne, Philippe-Auguste, François I, Louis XIV, and Napoleon, which has become the history of the world.

I viewed with amazement the marvelous advantage there was to be derived from these changes of dynasty and of morals and of customs. I made acquaintance with the men who summed up a reign, with the men who summed up a century, with those, also, who represented a period. I saw appear, like meteors lost to the vulgar gaze in the night of time, those rare chosen spirits of Providence which pass with fire on their brows, bearing the thoughts of God, unconscious themselves of what they carry and not realizing their mission until they go to render up their account to Him who bestowed it upon them.

I confess I was at first dazzled before this awful Sinai, its summit thundered upon by the superb trinity of the men we call Caesar, Charlemagne, and Napoleon. I then understood that there was still to be done for this great and beauteous France what Walter Scott had done for poor little Scotland, an illustrated, picturesque, and dramatic story of the past—a bringing to life again of all the great dead—a kind of last judgment of all those who had worn a crown, whether of laurels, of flowers, or of gold. But, I admit, if I had been dazzled by this historical revelation, I was overwhelmed by the work it imposed on the historian, and I fell prostrate, saying to myself: Happy indeed is the man who shall accomplish this gigantic mission! but God knows full well I have not the vanity to imagine it will be mine.

Yet I proceeded with my work with a growing courage, amidst the doubts and laughter of all my friends. When I meet someone whom I have not seen for some time, he will say to me:

"So it is you!"

"Yes, it is I. What is there surprising in that?"

"I thought you were dead."

"Why?"

"Because you have been doing nothing."

"Who told you that?"

"Why! nobody is talking of you."

"I have written a book."

"Ah, yes! your *Impressions de Voyages*. I read that, it was very funny; you've got something of a sense of humor."

"Ah?"

"Yes, you're a card, haha!"

"Why am I a card?"

"Would you have me believe that you have tasted bear's flesh and caught trout with a billhook?"

"Of course, there is absolutely nothing else in my *Impressions de Voyages*. But I am writing a history now."

"*You* write a history! What an idea!"

"Why so?"

"Stick to drama, my dear fellow; you're dramatic through and through."

"Does it therefore follow that because, as you say, I am dramatic before everything else I ought not to write drama? Is there nothing dramatic outside the stage, and could one not put drama into a novel?"

"A novel! You want to do a romance after the style of Walter Scott?"

"Why not?"

But my interlocutor shook his head. "You're not Walter Scott, that's all."

"Walter Scott has depicted localities, characters, manners; I intend to go beyond Walter Scott, and take the historical novel from his hands just as Raphael took art from Perugino's. I intend to add the passions."

"If I were you—though really I have no right to advise you—I would stick to the theater."

"I'm going to have a try at it."

"Oh! you're a free agent, you know."

Yes, I knew that, and my questioner left me with a shrug of his shoulders, as much as to say, "There goes another one headed for sure destruction!"

Well, have I lost, or did I indeed, as I said Raphael did to Perugino, take romance from the hands of Walter Scott to give the art a push forward? And have I not taught a little of the history of my country to my contemporaries by causing them to read *la Comtesse de Salysbury, le Bâtard de Mauléon, Isabeau de Bavière, Jehanne la Pucelle, Ascanio, la Reine Margot, la Dame de Monsoreau, les Quarante-Cinq, les Trois Mousquetaires, Vingt ans après, le Vicomte de Bragelonne, le Chevalier d'Harmental, la Fille du Régent, Balsamo, le Collier de la Reine, Ange Pitou, la Comtesse de Charny et le Chevalier de Maison-Rouge?* The future must decide. In any case, the metamorphosis of a dramatic poet into a romance writer dates from 1833, and the probable cause of it was the failure of my *Fils de l'Emigré.*

The passage we have given doesn't tell the full story of Dumas's change from dramatist to novelist.

In the first place, things didn't go quite that fast. From the failure of his *Fils de l'Emigré,* to his first great success as a novelist, to, let us say, his *Acté,* a romance of the time of Nero (from which Sienkiewicz inspired himself [by his own admission] for his world success *Quo Vadis* which was to appear thirty-six years later), Dumas consumed some seven years. And if we go from the failure of the *Fils de l'Emigré* to Dumas's first real success as a novelist, *The Three Musketeers* (1844), we must count twelve years.

But not twelve years of idleness!

Nor even twelve years of failures. Neither in the world of books nor in that of the theater.

For sixteen months subsequent to his *Fils de l'Emigré*, Dumas had the big hit of *Angèle*, which would have run over three hundred performances, but was stopped at that point by the censors, and not permitted back on the stage for six years.

The failure of the *Fils de l'Emigré* had certainly been resounding enough. Dumas had been in Switzerland at the time, but he had heard from friends, how the public hooted it, how they bellowed insults, picked up their seats and threw them on to the stage. An inferno.

And the critics of Paris taking the occasion to rub it in. With that special joy that critics reserve for an opportunity to tear an altogether too successful author to pieces.

But then came Dumas's *Angèle*, and restored him. And then came his essay on the history of France, called *Gaule et France*, which appeared in the United States under the title of *The Progress of Democracy*.

In 1834 came his first important travel book, of the series which he called: *Travel Impressions*. The first one on Switzerland. Then a play drawn from Walter Scott's *Quentin Durward*. And another about Cromwell and Charles I. Then a play about Don Juan. And in particular his fine play *Kean*, revived some years ago in New York under the title *The Royal Box*. And revived again recently in a version by Sartre. And now announced as a musical for New York production.

That doesn't sound like utter failure. Nor like the abandonment of the career as dramatist, to turn novelist.

And then a play about Caligula. And a novel about Paul Jones which he also made into a play, and which then had a fairly successful run. Then his series of "Celebrated Crimes." And another travel book: a scientific expedition to Egypt and Sinai (which Dumas never took, although he gave the impression that he had, and so well that he was congratulated by the Pacha of Egypt).

A play called *The Alchemist*. A play called *A Marriage in the Reign of Louis XV*. A play called *Lorenzino*. Another called *Les*

Demoiselles de Saint-Cyr, which was a great hit, and Queen Victoria's favorite.

And still other plays: *The Laird of Dumbicky, Louise Bernard,* etc.

And other novels: *The Chevalier d'Harmental, Sylvandire, Jehanne la Pucelle, The Master at Arms,* etc.

And more *Travel Impressions: The South of France,* and the first one of a series of three volumes dealing with Italy.

And no end of poetry. Plus a series of studies on Napoleon. And his *Captain Pamphile,* an adventure story for children. Etc., etc.

No. Idle he wasn't. But what is important is that Dumas, during these years published a lot of little items, which he called *Scènes Historiques.* These were rather short extracts from history, done in a vivid and dramatic style. And it is interesting to note that he had begun writing such material *before* the failure of his play, *The Son of the Emigré.*

Henri Clouard, the author of an excellent study on Alexandre Dumas, points out that several other writers were doing similar historical scenes. Vitet had done a *Death of Guise.* And a *Death of Henri III.* Merimée was doing scenes of the days of feudalism. Etc.

Nor did Dumas claim any absolute originality. In his *Memoirs* he would write: "There was at this period a genre of literature that was so to speak halfway between the novel and the theater, sharing the interest of the one with the excitement of the other, and where the dialogue alternated with the narrative. This form of writing was called: historical scenes."

We see thus that Dumas was gradually moving out of the theater and into the novel, but that the journey was being taken by stages, and that the two forms would overlap, and that from his big success as a dramatist, to his big success as a novelist, would take a round dozen years. Years of apprenticeship in one form, and years of mastery in the other. Never would the separation be total.

I have already quoted from the *Memoirs,* the passage in which Dumas tells of his study of how to be a dramatist:

I did not rest satisfied with a superficial study. One after the other, I took the works of men of genius, like Shakespeare, Molière, Corneille, Calderon, Goethe, and Schiller, laid them out as bodies on a dissecting table, and, scalpel in hand, I spent whole nights in probing them to the heart in order to find the sources of life and the secret of the circulation of their blood.

And after a while I discovered with what admirable science they galvanized nerve and muscle into life, and by what skill they modeled the differing types of flesh that were destined to cover the one unchangeable human framework of bone.

For man does not invent. God has only given the created world into man's hands, but left it to him to apply it to his needs. Progress simply means the daily, monthly, and everlasting conquest of man over matter. Each individual as he appears on the scene takes possession of the knowledge of his fathers, works it up in different ways, and then dies after he has added one ray more to the sum of human knowledge which he bequeaths to his sons—one star in the Milky Way!

I was thus not only trying to complete my dramatic work but also my dramatic education. But that is an error: one's work may be finished someday, but one's education never!

You may be sure that Dumas studied the writing of the historical novel with just as much determination and dedication. We know, for example, that he began by first learning by heart a rhymed history of France, which gave him, so to speak, a grid, a rough map, whereby he could thereafter orient himself and keep in mind all the finer details which he then began to acquire by a study of more scholarly works, and even of the sources themselves, as we shall see in this next excerpt.

It is of interest that just in the year when Dumas claims he decided to go into historical novels that Walter Scott died. His fame had been so great, that when old and suffering from the gout, the government of Britain had put a vessel of its navy at the author's disposal, that he might inhabit a less rigorous climate. Scott cruised about the Mediterranean for a year, before he died, visiting many places of interest and being acclaimed everywhere.

Is it possible that Dumas envied the glory of Scott? Certainly he knew of this generosity of the English government to its most celebrated writer of the time. For, when later, in 1846, Dumas was traveling in Spain and Algeria, and calmly went aboard a French naval vessel and sailed about in it—a piece of incredible crust, which went off successfully however—he recalled this matter of Scott, and cited it, when a storm broke out in the French Chamber, and the minister, Salvandy, had to submit to some rough questioning.

"Why shouldn't the French government do as much for me as

the British did for their Scott?" Dumas asked stoutly. "Have my services not been equal or greater? Have I not made millions familiar with our history, who formerly knew nothing about it?"

That was 1846, and by then he was indeed the Scott of France.

But of Scott, Dumas had this to say, as we have seen: "He was wonderful when it came to painting customs, styles of dress, and characters, but was incapable of handling human passions."

The trick then, in adapting Scott to France, was to add the passions: in particular that of sexual love. But others too.

Moreover for a writer like Dumas, who had made his mark first in the theater, there was still another addition he could make, or rather a rule which he could apply. Tell your story more in dialogue than in solid paragraphs of expository prose.

You only have to open a book by Scott to note the difference. See how the pages there are like dark impenetrable walls, one rising after the other. Open a novel by Dumas. How the light shines through those pages of rapid-fire dialogue, imitated from real life, and from the give and take of his theatrical pieces!

And still another difference, which Dumas, curiously, would point out in a book about animals, *History of My Pets*. There Dumas claims that Scott begins his novels by boring his readers while he slowly sets up his cast of characters, and only then starts to put them into action.

But Dumas was living in a different world from that of Scott. The competition for the attention of the public had reached a pitch in Paris that it still did not know in Edinburgh. In Paris dozens of newspapers carried on a circulation war that was like a death-struggle. And in this fight of the many political parties of France to draw readers to their paper, the *feuilleton*, the daily serial, was one of the best lures.

It was for these feuilletons that Dumas began writing his historical scenes. And for them that he would write his novels. And in that Paris of hustle and bustle, that Paris of revolts and turmoil, people would not stand still while an author took a hundred pages to set up his stage. They wanted to be gripped at once.

And it is in this sense that perhaps Dumas's direct experience with history may have helped him most. As it certainly disposed him against any and all of the dryasdusts who are always trying to dominate the field of historical writing.

"To what do you think I owe the success of my *History of the Girondins*?" Lamartine once asked Dumas.

Dumas replied: "Because you raised the writing of history up to the level of the novel."

In this connection then I give here the following bit that Dumas used as an introduction to his *The Companions of Jehu*, which first ran as a serial in the pages of the *Journal pour Tous*, during the year of 1857.

I believe this article appeared first separately, as part of one of Dumas's *Causeries*, his intimate chats, into which he threw all sorts of odd material. But it is now generally published as a foreword to the *Companions of Jehu*, under the title: *A Word to the Reader*.

Just about a year ago my old friend Jules Simon, author of *Devoir*, came to me with a request that I write a novel for the *Journal pour Tous*. I gave him the outline of a novel which I had in mind. The subject pleased him, and the contract was signed on the spot.

But, as impatient as the editor was for my story, I insisted on a fortnight in order to become acquainted with the locality, for that is one thing I have never been able to do: write a novel or a drama about regions with which I have not made myself familiar.

In order to write *Christine* I went to Fontainebleau; in writing *Henri III* I went to Blois; for *Les Trois Mousquetaires* I went to Boulogne and Bethune; for *Monte-Cristo* I returned to the Catalans and the Château d'If; while for *Isaac Laquedem* I revisited Rome. And while I did not go to Jerusalem and to Corinth, for that same book, I spent more time studying those cities from a distance than I would have taken up by making the actual trip.

It is this that gives the character of veracity to everything that I write, so much so that the personages I have created eventually become such integral parts of the places in which I have planted them, that many people end up by believing in their actual existence.

People will then insist that they knew my characters in life!

This next bit of information is whispered to you in confidence, dear reader, since I have no wish to deprive certain honest fathers of families of the little industry by which they make a living, but it is a fact that if you go to Marseilles you will be shown the house of Morel on the Cours, and the house of Mercedes at the Catalans, and the dungeons of Dantes and Faria at the Château d'If.

This matter has gone so far that an artist to whom I appealed—when I was staging my *Monte-Cristo* at the Théâtre-Historique—for a plan of the Château d'If, sent me back one along with a sketch, under which he wrote: "View of the Château d'If, from the side where Dantes was thrown into the sea."

And another worthy man who guides tourists to the Château d'If, sells pens which he swears were made from fishbone by the Abbé Faria himself.

As if Dantes and Faria were real personages instead of inventions of my imagination. As if they had ever actually lived at the Château d'If.

And so Dumas set out for Bourg, in Bresse, to study the neighborhood and consult with the inhabitants there who may have witnessed the execution of Leprêtre, Amiet, Guyon, and Hyvert, members of the secret bandit-organization known as the Companions of Jehu.

There are two roads to Bourg—from Paris, I mean. One can leave the railway at Macon and take the stage from Macon to Bourg, or one can go on as far as Lyons, and take the railway from there. I hesitated between these two roads, and was decided by one of the travelers who happened to be in the same carriage with me. He was going to Bourg, where, as he told me, he had frequent business. He was going by way of Lyons, therefore that was the better route. I resolved to do the same.

I slept in Lyons, and the next day at ten o'clock I was in Bourg.

I found there a Lyons newspaper, containing a sarcastic article about me. Lyons has never pardoned me since 1833, twenty-four years ago, when I said that it was not a literary town; but alas! at this date, 1857, I have still the same opinion of Lyons that I had in 1833. I do not change my opinions easily.

There is another city in France which has almost as much of a grudge against me as Lyons, and that is Rouen. Rouen has hissed all my pieces, even *Count Hermann*.

One day a Neapolitan boasted to me that he had hissed Rossini and Malibran in both the *Barbiere* and *Desdemona*.

I replied: "That must be true, for Rossini and Malibran, they also are proud of having been hissed by the Neapolitans."

I too am proud of having been hissed by the people of Rouen.

Nevertheless, meeting one day a full-blooded son of Rouen, I resolved to discover why they hissed me. I like to understand these little matters.

My Rouenese replied: "We hiss you because we don't like you."

A good answer. After all Rouen didn't like Joan of Arc. And they burnt her. Could it be for the same reason?

I asked the man of Rouen why he and his compatriots did not like me. I had never said anything bad about them; I pretended to like their cooking, I was nice to M. Barbet, their mayor; and when I had been sent as a delegate from the Society of Men of Letters to the inauguration of the statue of the great Corneille, I was the only one who had thought to bow before making my speech.

It seemed to me there was no reason at all why the people of Rouen should hate me. Therefore to the reply, "We hissed you because we don't like you," I humbly asked:

"And why do you not like me?"

"Oh, you know well enough," he replied.

"I?" I asked.

"Yes, you."

"Never mind; pretend I do not."

"You remember the dinner which the town gave you at the time of Corneille's statue?"

"Perfectly; were you annoyed that I have never returned the courtesy?"

"No, it is not that."

"What is it?"

"While at this dinner, we said to you: 'Monsieur Dumas, you ought to write a play for the city of Rouen, upon a subject taken from its history.'"

"Yes," I said. "And I replied: 'Nothing more easy. I will come at your first summons, and stay a fortnight in Rouen. You will give me a subject, and during that fortnight I will write a play, the proceeds of which will be for the poor.'"

"That is true, you said so."

"I do not see any insult in that for the people of Rouen."

"Oh, but we also asked: 'Will you do it in prose?' To which you replied—do you remember what you replied?"

"No, indeed."

"You replied: 'I will do it in verse. I can do it more quickly.'"

"Very likely I did."

"Well!"

"What of it?"

"It is an insult for Corneille, Monsieur Dumas. That is why the people of Rouen do not like you, and have not liked you for a long time."

Word for word!

O worthy people of Rouen! I hope you will never do me the ill turn to pardon and applaud me!

The *Journal* said that M. Dumas had stayed only one night in Lyons, doubtless because a place which cared so little for literature was not worthy of keeping him any longer. M. Dumas had not thought anything about it. He had stayed only one night in Lyons because he was in a hurry to get to Bourg; and when he arrived there he went straight to the *Journal* office of the department. He knew that it was directed by a distinguished archaeologist, the editor of the work of my friend Baux on the church of Brou.

I also sent for M. Milliet. He hastened to me. We shook hands, and I told him the object of my journey.

"I know just the man for you," he said to me. "I will take you to the magistrate here, who is writing the history of the province."

"How far has he got?"

"As far as 1822."

"That is all right, then; as the events which I wish to relate date from 1799, and as my heroes were executed in 1800, he will have gone past that date, and can give me my information. Let us go to your magistrate."

On the way M. Milliet told me that this same magistrate and historian was a connoisseur in wines. A gourmet. We were taken to his private office. I found him a man with a ruddy face and a cheerful smile. He welcomed me with that protecting air which historians deign to extend to poets.

"Well, sir," he said, "so you are coming to look for a subject for a story in our poor country?"

"No, sir; my subject is already selected. I have only come to get historical facts."

"Oh, I did not suppose romance writers needed to take so much trouble!"

"You are wrong, sir, at least so far as I am concerned. I am in the habit of making serious researches when treating of historical subjects."

"You could have sent someone else."

"Any one whom I could have sent, sir, would not have been penetrated with my subject, and might have overlooked important facts. Besides, I am aided very much by localities, and I cannot describe them without having seen them."

"Oh! So this is a story which you are thinking of doing yourself?"

"Eh? Yes, sir. I had my last one done by my valet, but as it was very successful, the rogue asked such exorbitant wages that to my great regret I was not able to keep him."

The magistrate bit his lip; then, after a moment of silence he said: "Be good enough to tell me, sir, in what way I can aid you in this important work."

"You can direct my researches, sir. Having made a history of the department, none of the important facts which took place in its principal town can be unknown to you."

"Well, sir, I think that in this particular field I am very well informed."

"Well, to begin. Your department was the center of the operations of the companions of Jehu."

"I have heard of the companions of Jesus," replied the magistrate, beaming up at me with a smile that was nothing less than a jeer.

"You mean the Jesuits, do you not? That is not what I am looking for, sir."

"Neither is it of them I am speaking. I refer to those robbers of diligences who infested the roads from 1797 to 1800."

"Well, sir, permit me to say to you that those very people are the ones I have come to Bourg about. But they called themselves companions of Jehu, not companions of Jesus."

"Why should they call themselves 'Companions of Jehu'? What does that mean? I would like to understand that."

"I like to understand things also. That is why I did not wish to confound the highway robbers with the apostles."

"That certainly would not be very orthodox."

"That is what you, however, would have done, sir, if I, a poet, had not come to correct your judgment as a historian."

"I am waiting for your explanation, sir," said the magistrate, compressing his lips.

"It will be short and simple. Jehu was a king of Israel, consecrated by Elisha for the extermination of the House of Ahab. Elisha stands for Louis XVIII, Jehu is Cadoudal, and the House of Ahab was the Revolution. That is why the robbers of diligences who stole government money to carry on the war of la Vendée called themselves Companions of Jehu."

"Sir, I am happy to learn something at my age."

"Oh, one is always learning at all times and all ages. During this life one learns men, and after death one learns God."

"But," he returned, with a movement of impatience, "may I know in what way I can serve you?"

"In this way, sir. Four of these young men, the principal ones among the companions of Jehu, were executed at Bourg, on the Place du Bastion."

"In the first place, sir, at Bourg they do not execute on the Place du Bastion; the executions take place on the fairgrounds."

"Yes, within the last fifteen or twenty years that is true; but formerly, and particularly at the time of the Revolution, they took place as I have said."

"It is possible."

"It is true. These four young men were named Guyon, Leprêtre, Amiet, and Hyvert."

"That is the first time I ever heard those names."

"They are, however, not without a certain renown, particularly in Bourg."

"And you are sure, sir, that these people were executed here?"

"I am sure of it."

"Where did you get your information?"

"From a man whose uncle commanded the armed police, and was present at the execution."

"Can you name this man?"

"Charles Nodier."

"What! the novelist, the poet?"

"If he were a historian I should not be so sure of his facts, sir. I recently learned, on a trip to Varennes, what to think of historians; but just because he is a poet and a romance writer, I do trust him."

"That is your affair. But I dare say that if you came to Bourg only to get information about the execution of these gentlemen—what do you call them?"

"Guyon, Leprêtre, Amiet, and Hyvert."

"—that you have had your trouble for nothing. For twenty years, sir, I have been compiling the archives of this town, and I have never seen such a thing mentioned."

"The archives of the town are not those of the registrar's office. Perhaps in these latter I can find what I seek."

"Ah, sir, if you find anything in the archives of the registrar's office you will be very keen. It is chaos, sir! veritable chaos! You will have to stay here a month, and then—"

"I intend to stay here only one day, sir; but if in that day I find what I want, you will permit me to share it with you?"

"Yes, sir! yes, sir! yes! And you will do me a great service."

"No greater than that which I have just asked of you. I will tell you something that you did not know—that is all."

You may imagine that when I came away from my magistrate's my pride was piqued, and I was determined at all costs to get some information about the companions of Jehu. I went again to Milliet.

"Listen," he said, "I have a brother-in-law who is an advocate."

"That is the man for me. Let us go to the brother-in-law."

"He is at the palace now."

"Then let us go to the palace."

"Your presence there will create a sensation, let me warn you."

"Then go there yourself, alone, and tell him what I want. Let him make his researches; and I at the same time will go and look about the town and get an idea of the localities. We will meet at four o'clock, on the Place du Bastion, if you like."

"Very well."

"It seems to me that I saw a forest when I was on the way here."

"The forest of Seillon."

"Bravo!"

"Do you need a forest in your book."

"I must have one."

"Then allow me—"

"What?"

"I am going to take you to one of my friends, Monsieur Leduc, a poet, who at odd moments is an inspector."

"An inspector of what?"

"Of that forest."

"I suppose there are no ruins in the forest?"

"There is the Chartreuse monastery, which is not in the forest, but which is only a hundred feet from it."

"Anything in the forest?"

"There is a sort of building called the Correrie, which belongs to the monastery, and which communicates with it by a subterranean passage."

"Good! Very good! Now if you could only offer me a cave, you would fill my cup to the brim."

"We have the cave of Ceyzeriat, but it is on the other side of the Reyssouse."

"Never mind; if the cave will not come to me, I, like Mahomet, must go to the cave. In the meantime, let us go and see Monsieur Leduc."

Five minutes afterward we were with M. Leduc, who, when he learned my errand, put himself and his horse and carriage at my disposal. I accepted them all. There are some men who offer things in such a way that they put you at ease at once.

We visited the monastery first. If it had been built expressly for me, it could not have suited me better. The cloister was deserted and the garden gone to waste. Chance, I thank thee! From there we went to the Correrie. It was in the same condition as the monastery. I did not know yet what I should do with it, but it was evident that I could make it useful.

"Now, sir," I said to my obliging guide, "I want a pretty situation, rather gloomy, under tall trees, near the river. Have you got such a thing around here?"

"What do you want to do with it?"

"I want to build a château on it."

"What château?"

"A castle in the air. I want a place to put a family—a model mother, a melancholy young girl, a lively brother, and a poaching gardener."

"We have a place called Noires Fontaines."

"That is a charming name, to begin with."

"But there is no château on it."

"So much the better, for I should have been obliged to tear it down."

"Would you like to go there?"

We started, and a quarter of an hour afterward we arrived at the guard house.

"Let us take this little path," said M. Leduc to me. "It will take us where you want to go."

It did, in face, conduct us to a place filled with tall trees, which overshadowed three or four springs.

"This is what they call Noires Fontaines," said M. Leduc to me.

"This is the place where Madame de Montrevel, Amelie, and little Edward will live. And now what are those villages over there?"

"The nearest one is Montagnac. Yonder in the mountain is Ceyzeriat."

"Is that where the cave is?"

"Yes. How did you know there was one?"

"Oh, I heard of it; and now give me the names of those other villages, if you please."

"Saint-Just, Tréconnas, Ramasse, and Villereversure."

"Very well."

"Is that enough?"

"Yes."

I took out my memorandum book, made a plan of the localities, and wrote down as nearly as I could in their proper places the names of the villages which M. Leduc had just told me.

"That is done," I said.

"Now where are we going?"

"Is the Church of Brou on our way?"

"In our direct path."

"Let us visit the Church of Brou."

"Do you want that also in your story?"

"Certainly. Do you suppose I would put the scene of my story in a country which possesses one of the most beautiful pieces of architecture of the sixteenth century without utilizing it?"

"Then come to the Church of Brou."

A quarter of an hour afterward the sacristan opened for us this grand jewel-box, which contains the three marble jewels called the tombs of Marquerite of Austria, of Marguerite de Bourbon, and of Philibert le Beau.

"How did it happen," I asked, "that all these masterpieces were not leveled with the dust at the time of the Revolution?"

"Ah, sir," replied the sacristan, "the government had an idea."

"What was it?"

"It was to make the church a storehouse for fodder."

"And so the hay saved the marble? You are right, my friend—that was an idea."

"Does that idea give you one?" asked M. Leduc.

"Yes, indeed; it will go hard with me if I cannot make something out of it." I drew out my watch. "Three o'clock; let us go to the prison. I must meet Monsieur Milliet at four o'clock, on the Place du Bastion."

"Wait! one more thing."

"What is it?"

"Have you seen the motto of Marguerite of Austria?"

"No; where is it?"

"Here on her tomb."

" 'Fortune, infortune, fort'une?' "

"Exactly."

"Well, what does that play on words mean?"

"Learned men explain it thus: 'Destiny persecutes a woman.' "

"Really?"

"In the first place you must suppose the motto to have been Latin originally."

"Yes, it probably was."

"Well; 'Fortuna infortunat—' " my guide explained.

"Oh, oh! 'infortunat'!"

"Well?"

"That sounds like a barbarism."

"What do you want?"

"An explanation."

"Have you any of your own?"

"Here is mine: 'Fortuna, infortuna, forti una—fortune and misfortune are all alike to the strong.' "

"Do you know, that may possibly be the true translation!"

"That is what comes of not being a scholar, my dear friend. With common sense one can often see more correctly than with science. You have nothing else to tell me?"

"No."

"Then let us go to the prison."

We got into the carriage again, went back to the city, and stopped at the prison door. I put my head out of the window.

"Ah," I said, "they have spoiled it for me!"

"What! they have spoiled it for you?"

"Certainly; it was not like this in the time of my prisoners. Can we speak to the jailer?"

"Certainly."

"Let us do so, then."

We knocked at the gate, and a man about forty years old came and opened it for us. He recognized M. Leduc.

"My man," said M. Leduc, "here is one of my learned friends—"

"Come, now," I said, interrupting him, "no poor jokes, if you please."

"—who pretends," continued M. Leduc, "that the prison is no longer as it was in the last century."

"That is true, Monsieur Leduc. It was torn down and rebuilt in 1816."

"Then the inside arrangements are not the same?"

"Oh no, sir! everything has been changed!"

"Is there a plan of the old building?"

"Well, perhaps Monsieur Martin, the architect, can find one for us."

"Is he a relative of Monsieur Martin the lawyer?"

"He is his brother."

"Very well; then I will get my plan."

"Then there is no need of staying here?" asked M. Leduc.

"None at all."

"I can go home again?"

"Except for the sorrow of parting with you, there is nothing to prevent."

"You can find your way to the Place du Bastion without me?"

"Yes; it is only a few steps from here."

"What are you going to do with your evening?"

"I will come and spend it with you, if you like."

"Very well! at nine o'clock a cup of tea will be waiting for you."

"I will come and take it."

I thanked M. Leduc and we shook hands and parted. I went down through the Rue des Lisses (or Lices, meaning arena, because of a tournament which must have taken place on the square to which it leads), and going past the garden of Montburon I found myself at the Place du Bastion. It is a semicircle, on which the town markets are held at the present day. In the midst of the circle rises the statue of Bichat by David (d'Angers)—Bichat in a frock coat (why this exaggeration of realism?), standing with one hand on the heart of a naked child of nine or ten years (why this excess of idealism?), while at Bichat's feet is extended a corpse. It is Bichat's book, *Life and Death*, translated into bronze.

I was looking at the statue, which contains both the excellences and the defects of David, when I felt some one touch me on the shoulder. It was M. Milliet. He held a paper in his hand.

"Well?" I said.

"Well?"

"What have you there?"

"The report of the execution."

"Of whom?"

"Of your men."

"Of Guyon, Leprêtre, Amiet, and Hyvert?"

"Yes."

"Give it to me."

"Here it is."

I took it and read:

Official Report of the Death and Execution of Laurent Guyon, Etienne Hyvert, François Amiet, and Antoine Leprêtre. Condemned on the 20 Thermidor, in the year VIII, and executed on the 23 Vendemiaire, in the year IX.

On this day, the 23 Vendemiaire, in the year IX, the government commissioner at the tribunal, who received, at eleven o'clock in the evening, a packet from the minister of justice, containing the suit and judgment which condemned to death Laurent Guyon, Etienne Hyvert, François Amiet, and Antoine Leprêtre—being the judgment of the Court of Appeal of the sixth, which rejected the appeal against the judgment of the 21 Thermidor, in the year VIII.— gave notice, by letter, between seven and eight o'clock in the morning, to the four accused men that their death sentence would be executed today at eleven o'clock.

In the interval before eleven o'clock these four men shot themselves with pistols and stabbed themselves with daggers, in the prison. Leprêtre and Guyon, according to public report, were dead; Hyvert mortally wounded and expiring; and Amiet mortally wounded, but preserving consciousness. All four, in this state, were conducted to the guillotine, and, dead or alive, were guillotined.

At half past eleven, officer Colin sent the report of their execution to the municipal records, to have it written upon the book of the dead. The captain of police sent to the justice of the peace the report of what passed in the prison, where he was present.

I was not there, but I certify to what public report has told me.

BOURG, 23 Vendemiaire, in the year IX.

[Signed]

DUBOST, *Clerk.*

Ah, so the poet was more correct than the historian! The captain of police, who sent to the justice of the peace the report of what had passed in prison, *where he had been present,* was Nodier's uncle. This report sent to the justice of the peace was the story which was engraved upon the mind of the young man—a story which after forty years saw the light again, without alteration, in his masterpiece entitled *Souvenirs of the Revolution.* The whole account of the matter was in the archives of the registrar's office. M. Martin had offered to have it copied for me. I had in my pocket Nodier's *Souvenirs of the Revolution.* I held in my hand the official report of the execution, which confirmed the facts advanced by him.

"Now let us go and see our magistrate," I said to M. Milliet.

"Yes," he repeated after me, "now let us go and see our magistrate."

The magistrate had not a word to say for himself; and I left him convinced that poets knew history as well as historians, if not better.

It's the pride of the man that is exciting. He fights whole cities. Lyons despises him because he once said that it was not a literary town. Rouen hates him because he once said that he would write a play about some event of their municipality, just as soon as he could spare a "fortnight." "The proceeds will be for the poor."

How insulting! To Rouen, the proud birthplace of France's great playwright, Corneille. And the impudence of the man to say that he would do it in verse because he could write verse faster than prose. (Nearly a hundred years later, George Bernard Shaw would write a play in verse, excusing himself that he did not have the time to do it in prose.)

And in Bourg he would make a fool out of their magistrate, who was also their local historian, and then publish an introduction to a novel, in which he would say concerning his talks with this historian: "I left him convinced that poets knew history as well as historians, if not better."

Not that Bourg hadn't tried to insult him too. When he spoke of writing a novel about an event that had taken place in their city, and saying that he had therefore come to Bourg to look over the territory and become familiar with its landmarks, the following remark was elicited:

"Oh! So this is a story which you are thinking of doing yourself?"

Dumas's reply is a gem: "Eh? Yes, sir. I had my last one done by my valet, but as it was very successful, the rogue asked such exorbitant wages that to my great regret I was not able to keep him."

Dumas continues: "The magistrate bit his lip . . ." Naturally, because Dumas's novels were world-wide successes. And the magistrate, with his local history, would never sell more than a thousand copies, if that many. And Dumas well understood the envy that is in the heart of every writer, that yearning for the big sale, that dream of writing the book that will sell a million copies.

Dumas had achieved that. The magistrate simply couldn't.

And there's more to Dumas's little dig. Because these envious souls were comforting themselves with the thought, that after all Dumas was a fraud. He didn't write his books. He used collaborators. Thus Dumas's little barb woke them up to the fact that if Dumas hadn't written his successes, then someone else had! And that someone else was then the man to envy, the man to despise, the man to accuse of fraud. But as for the million-copy sale, that couldn't be wiped out.

So he gave them his valet. To envy!

And the ridiculous aspect of these charges thus was made crystal-clear. This valet, whom Dumas had had to discharge because he asked for exorbitant wages, must now produce another best-seller like *Monte-Cristo*, or *The Three Musketeers*. Why not? Hadn't he done it once? Why couldn't he do it again?

There's the heart of the matter which has agitated literary historians so often. Yes, Dumas had collaborators. Here's a small list of them:

The Countess Dash. Auguste Maquet. Anicet Bourgeois. Paul Meurice. De Leuven. Jules Lacroix. Théaulon. Fiorentino. Paul Bocage. Joseph Méry.

Obviously none of these names will mean anything to the average reader of the United States today. And indeed even to the average reader of France. They could be collaborators, but as independent writers they failed to make the sensation that they could make when they worked with Dumas.

But the cream of the jest, in the matter of this introduction to Dumas's *Companions of Jehu*, is that there seems good reason to believe that Dumas had a collaborator for this novel too! Edmond About, an author of the same period as Dumas, but some twenty years younger, claims that he saw on Dumas's worktable, while he was writing his *Jehu* novel, a pile of sheets in the handwriting of some other person. Richard Garnett made the guess that the original writer on the material may have been the Count de Cherville.

In his foreword to another novel *Le Chasseur de Sauvagine*, Dumas would not only admit that the Count de Cherville had sent him the manuscript to this story, but would add that it was complete . . .

". . . except for the dots on the i's. I put those in. And that's all that's mine in this work. You'll have to confess, dear readers, that no one could possibly be more modest than that."

The whole business of who wrote what was thus turned into a kind of mystification. Nowadays, on Broadway, or in Hollywood, Dumas might be highly in demand as a "play-doctor," or a script-polisher. He would be far more than that of course, being independently creative. But he would have that touch of genius that could turn something routine into something exciting, and something exciting into a work of art.

To speak of "theft," "plagiarism," "fraud," etc., is sheer nonsense. For in that case Dumas would have had endless trouble with those whom he defrauded. With those from whom he stole his works.

But his relations with his collaborators was in general harmonious—considering all the collaborations he engaged in.

And there might never have been any lack of harmony whatsoever, if so much fuss had not been made by outsiders, so that the collaborators were stirred up about these supposed frauds, and made to feel that they had been dupes, so that finally the most important one of all, Auguste Maquet, did finally sue Dumas.

That was too bad, for these two had done some mighty work together, of which the story has been written up in a book by Gustave Simon, called *Histoire d'une collaboration*.

Auguste Maquet was the son of wealthy parents. He was something of a martinet to himself. Severe, hard-working, a perpetual student, a professor of history at Collège Charlemagne, and constantly trying his hand at writing plays and novels.

His plays were rejected time and again. No one wanted them. But one day Maquet brought to Gérard de Nerval (that half-madman, half-genius, who had translated Goethe's *Faust*, and who was to make a suicide that would shock Paris) the manuscript of another one of this plays. Gérard, who had himself done a collaboration with Dumas, *Piquillo*, a comic opera, and who was soon to appear on the Paris stage in another piece done with Dumas: *The Alchemist*, wrote to Maquet: "First act and a half: good. Second act and a half: bad. Needs redoing."

Maquet was so upset by this verdict that Gérard suggested that Dumas should be brought into the situation to revise the play. But Dumas was too busy, and Gérard de Nerval had to nag him until finally Dumas consented.

The result was the play *Bathilde*. It was not much of a success. But it brought together Maquet and Dumas. Still it was three years before Maquet brought anything else to Dumas. One day he showed a manuscript novel to the publisher Dumont. It was called *Le Bonhomme Buvat*, and Dumont rather liked it. But it did seem far too short.

Dumont took the volume to Dumas. "How about swelling this up so that it will fill two or three volumes?" he asked. (In those days books were cut up into as many volumes as possible so that lending libraries, who charged by the volume, could make more money.)

Dumas read it, and a few days later, asked Dumont: "How much are you thinking of paying the author if you buy this story?"

"If I buy it—well, three or four hundred francs."

Dumas said: "Then if I were to offer the writer two thousand for it, wouldn't he be doing well to turn the rights over to me?"

And thus Dumas got hold of the basic material for his *Chevalier d'Harmental*, which concerned the Conspiracy of Cellamare of 1718, when an attempt was made to overthrow the Regency.

But note that Maquet too did not work his material out of thin air. As an avid reader in French history, he had come across two works: *Journal de la Régence* and Jean Buvat's *Mémoires*. Each man, Maquet and Dumas, worked on someone else's material.

Everybody was benefited by the entry of Dumas—including, naturally Dumas himself. But who had a better right to the profit? As conditions stood when Dumas entered the picture, Maquet did not have a very publishable book, nor did Dumont have a very salable novel. The *Siècle* did not have a serial, nor the lending libraries a very lucrative item.

But with Maquet's one-volume novel turned into Dumas's four-volume *Chevalier d'Harmental*, the whole situation became profitable for all concerned.

Of course Dumas alone signed the finished book.

Why? Because as Henri Clouard points out in his recent excellent study on Alexandre Dumas, and as Émile de Girardin had already said in Dumas's own time: "A novel signed by Dumas is worth 3 francs a line. One signed by both Maquet and Dumas is worth only 1½ francs a line."

And it might be added that one signed by Maquet alone was worth even less.

This payment by the line led Dumas to a style of writing about which we have already spoken, full of dialogue, breaking up the solid wall of Walter Scott's novels. It was a style not only suited to the modern times, but also better paid. Obviously.

But Dumas did not merely do it for greater gain. The style itself led him into a narrative of delicate wit, full of charm and subtle chuckles. Full of interesting nuances and enriching asides.

Here, to illustrate, is a bit from one of his series of *Travel Impressions*, the one called *The Corricolo*, the third of three books concerned with a trip to Italy and Sicily:

"My dear host," I said, "I have just come to a decision, dictated to me by my wisdom. I shall visit Naples riding in a corricolo."

"Wonderful!" Mr. Martin exclaimed. "The corricolo is one of our national vehicles. Its origin lies in the depths of antiquity. The

Romans knew it as the *biga*. I'm really pleased to see that you appreciate our corricolo."

"Very much so, my dear host. But first I would like to know: how much does it cost to rent a corricolo by the month."

"A corricolo is not rented by the month," Mr. Martin replied.

"Then by the week."

"Nor by the week."

"Well then, by the day."

"A corricolo is not even rented by the day."

"Well then how does one get the services of a corricolo?"

"You just hop into one when you see one passing, and you say to the driver: 'For a carlin!' And the coachman will drive you as far as that one carlin will take you. When the carlin is used up, you get off. But if you want more, you stay on, and say: 'For another carlin!' And your corricolo will take off again. And that's how it goes."

"And thus for one carlin or more you go wherever you want?"

"Oh no, sir. Not wherever you want, but wherever the horse wants. The corricolo is something like a balloon. No one has yet discovered how to steer it."

"Then why do people ride in corricolos?"

"For the fun of it."

Whether Maquet could write dialogue like that, I don't know. But I doubt it. For if he had been able, it would have been Dumas who would have come to him with an unpublishable novel, and not the other way around.

But what a flood of successful works poured from the pens of these collaborators! Until one day there came a man named Jacquot, who wrote under the pen name of Eugène de Mirecourt, and who had often tried to get Dumas to rewrite some of his stuff, but had failed, and who in revenge, and to give himself notoriety, got out a pamphlet called: *Fabrique de Romans—Alexandre Dumas et Compagnie.*

This pamphlet was a sensation. It tore through Europe, and for over half a century it tagged Dumas with the word "fraud."

Eventually Maquet even sued Dumas for a share of the profits. Hitherto he had felt himself well-compensated by a rising share of two to five hundred francs a volume. A whole series of notes have been printed showing how Dumas would keep urging Maquet to give him this bit of information, or to come to dinner and talk over this or that chapter, or send him some pages on this or that story which they were writing.

Maquet felt later that he had been cheated. But it certainly took years for him to discover that. And when the two men split, what happened? Dumas may have passed his prime, but he still turned out some wonderful works, whereas Maquet, left to himself, failed to make a single durable impression.

But he ruined Dumas financially. Helped of course by Dumas himself, who spent his huge earnings at a fantastic rate.

Dumas could only wonder that people would credit the stories of Eugène de Mirecourt.

"Are you really willing to believe that there exist, anywhere, men so giving and so discreet, that they would write such novels as *d'Harmental*, *The Musketeers*, *Twenty Years Later*, *Monte-Cristo* etc., and leave both honor and profit to someone else?" So Dumas wrote to the poet Béranger. And he went on:

"My collaborator is my own left hand, which holds open my history books, while my right hand labors twelve hours a day."

Maquet's first impulse had been to deny that he had been defrauded. He willingly signed a disclaimer. But then he demanded some sort of financial settlement. And in 1848 he accepted a contract in which Dumas was to pay him nearly 150,000 francs for whatever rights he may have thought himself entitled to.

Dumas however was by then plunging into bankruptcy. Maquet never got much of the money promised him. He sued Dumas in 1858 and 1859. And even as late as 1922, the heirs of Maquet were demanding justice in the French courts, demanding that the heirs of Dumas should not have the right to all the royalties that were still accruing from Dumas's works. And a part of these royalties was awarded to them. But their wish to have Maquet's name put beside Dumas's was denied.

Thus the great friendship and the beautiful collaboration of rough worker, and genius, was terminated. In his old age Maquet would speak of Dumas as "that perpetual scoundrel," and Dumas would call Maquet "nothing but a thief."

But for all that the two men continued to have a certain respect for each other. And Maquet would confess to a friend: "If the gossip of false friends had not broken up the warmest, the most solid and productive friendship that ever existed, we would be forty novels and forty plays ahead."

One imagines he must have wept as he said it. And the world might well weep too.

Chapter IV

THE FOURTH MUSKETEER

Edmond About, speaking at the time when the monument to Dumas was being unveiled, Place Malesherbes in Paris, gave a vivid picture of the "colossus" who suddenly picked him up bodily at the railroad station in Marseilles.

About had been about to take the train to Italy. Dumas had just arrived from Paris to watch over the production of a play he had recently made out of one of his stories, *Catherine Blum*. Dumas had written the story in a week, the play in three days.

As usual, Dumas took immediate charge of the situation. About would not go to Italy, but come to his hotel, where Dumas would cook him a bouillabaisse that would be the best About had ever tasted. Then they would go to the opening of his play.

The play was a great success. The delighted crowd escorted the author to his hotel. The theater orchestra serenaded the great man who came out on his balcony and gave a speech, etc., etc. Then came a big dinner . . .

At three o'clock in the morning About was ready to fall asleep standing up, while Dumas was fresh as a daisy. And while About went to sleep in Dumas's room, Dumas lit two candles and said: "I still have three installments to write for the papers I have contracts with. They must be ready tomorrow—I mean today, since it is already three in the morning. So you go to sleep. I'll stay up. And if I have any time left tonight, there's a playlet that's been buzzing around in my head, and I may jot it down."

Was he joking? No. When About awoke in the morning, Dumas was shaving. And on the table where the candles had burnt down, were three envelopes, addressed respectively to *La Patrie*, to *Le Journal pour Tous*, and some other paper that About could not remember. There was also the playlet that Dumas had spoken about.

It was rolled up, and addressed to the actor Montigny in Paris. . . .

And like Dumas himself were the heroes of his novels: they were tireless. As the following extracts from Dumas's greatest success: *The Three Musketeers*. The first episode tells of how D'Artagnan started out for Paris, from his little country home, in order to join the Musketeers.

On the first Monday of the month of April, 1626, the market town of Meung, in which the author of the *Romance of the Rose* was born, appeared to be in as perfect a state of revolution as if the Huguenots had just made a second Rochelle of it.

Many citizens, seeing the women flying toward the Grand Street, leaving their children crying at the open doors, hastened to don a cuirass, and supporting their somewhat uncertain courage with a musket or a partisan, directed their steps toward the hostelry of the Jolly Miller, before which was gathered, increasing every minute, a compact group, vociferous and full of curiosity.

In those times panics were common, and few days passed without some city or other setting forth in its archives some event of this kind. There were nobles, who made war against each other; there was the king, who made war against the cardinal; there was Spain, which made war against the king. Then, in addition to these concealed or public, secret or open, wars, there were robbers, mendicants, Huguenots, wolves, and scoundrels, who made war upon everybody.

The citizens always took up arms readily against thieves, wolves, or scoundrels, often against nobles or Huguenots, sometimes against the king, but never against the cardinal or Spain.

It resulted, then, from this habit that on the said first Monday of the month of April, 1626, the citizens, on hearing the clamor, and seeing neither the red-and-yellow standard nor the livery of the Duc de Richelieu, rushed toward the hostel of the Jolly Miller. When arrived there, the cause of this hubbub was apparent to all.

A young man—we can sketch his portrait at a dash. Imagine to yourself a Don Quixote of eighteen; a Don Quixote without his corselet, without his coat-of-mail, without his cuisses; a Don Quixote clothed in a woolen doublet, the blue color of which had faded into a nameless shade between lees of wine and a heavenly azure; face long and brown; high cheekbones, a sign of sagacity; the maxillary muscles enormously developed, an infallible sign by which a Gascon may always be detected, even without his cap—and our young man wore a cap set off with a sort of feather; the eye open and intelligent; the nose hooked, but finely chiseled.

Too big for a youth, too small for a grown man, an experienced eye might have taken him for a farmer's son upon a journey, had it not been for the long sword which, dangling from a leathern baldric, hit against the calves of its owner as he walked, and against the rough side of his steed when he was on horseback.

For our young man had a steed which was observed by all observers. It was a Béarn pony, from twelve to fourteen years old, yellow in his hide, without a hair in his tail, but not without windgalls on his legs, which, though going with his head lower than his knees (rendering a martingale quite unnecessary), contrived nevertheless to perform his eight leagues a day. Unfortunately, the qualities of this horse were so well concealed under his strange-colored hide and his unaccountable gait, that at a time when everybody was a connoisseur in horseflesh, the appearance of the aforesaid pony at Meung—which place he had entered about a quarter of an hour before, by the gate of Beaugency—produced an unfavorable feeling, which extended to his rider.

And this feeling had been the more painfully perceived by young D'Artagnan—for so was the Don Quixote of this second Rosinante named—from his not being able to conceal from himself the ridiculous appearance that such a steed gave him, good horseman as he was. He had sighed deeply, therefore, when accepting the gift of the pony from M. d'Artagnan the elder. He was not ignorant that such a beast was worth at least twenty livres; while the words which accompanied the present were above all price.

"My son," said the old Gascon gentleman, in that pure Béarn *patois* of which Henry IV could never rid himself, "my son, this horse was born in the house of your father about thirteen years ago, and has remained in it ever since—which ought to make you love it. Never sell it; allow it to die tranquilly and honorably of old age, and if you make a campaign with it, take as much care of it as you would of an old servant.

"At court, provided you have ever the honor to go there," continued M. d'Artagnan the elder, "an honor to which, remember, your ancient nobility gives you the right—sustain worthily your name of *gentleman*, which has been worthily borne by your ancestors for five hundred years, both for your own sake and for the sake of those who belong to you. By the latter I mean your relatives and friends. Endure nothing from anyone except Monsieur the Cardinal and the king. It is by his courage, please to observe— by his courage alone—that a gentleman can make his way nowadays. Whoever hesitates for a second perhaps allows the bait to escape which during that exact second, fortune held out to him.

"You are young. You ought to be brave for two reasons: the first is, that you are a Gascon; and the second is, that you are my son. Never fear quarrels, but seek adventures. I have taught you how to handle a sword; you have thews of iron, a wrist of steel. Fight on all occasions. Fight the more for duels being forbidden; since, consequently, there is twice as much courage in fighting.

"I have nothing to give you, my son, but fifteen crowns, my horse, and the counsels you have just heard. Your mother will add to them a recipe for a certain balsam, which she had from a Bohemian, and which has the miraculous virtue of curing all wounds that do not reach the heart. Take advantage of all, and live happily and long.

"I have but one word to add, and that is to propose an example to you—not mine, for I myself have never appeared at court, and have only taken part in religious wars as a volunteer; I speak of Monsieur de Tréville, who was formerly my neighbor, and who had the honor to be, as a child, the playfellow of our king, Louis XIII, whom God preserve! Sometimes their play degenerated into battles, and in these battles the king was not always the stronger. But the blows which the king received increased greatly his esteem and friendship for Monsieur de Tréville.

"Afterward, Monsieur de Tréville fought with others: in his first journey to Paris, five times; from the death of the late king till the young one came of age, without reckoning wars and sieges, seven times; and from that date up to the present day, a hundred times, perhaps! So that in spite of edicts, ordinances, and decrees, there he is now, captain of the Musketeers; that is to say, chief of a legion of Caesars, whom the king holds in great esteem, and whom the cardinal dreads—he who dreads nothing, as it is said. Still further, Monsieur de Tréville gains ten thousand crowns a year; he is therefore a great noble. He began as you begin. Go to him with this letter; and make him your model in order that you may do as he has done."

Upon which M. d'Artagnan the elder girded his own sword around his son, kissed him tenderly on both cheeks, and gave him his benediction.

On leaving the parental chamber, the young man found his mother, who was waiting for him with the famous recipe of which the counsels we have just repeated would necessitate frequent employment. The adieux were on this side longer and more tender than they had been on the other—not that M. d'Artagnan did not love his son, who was his only offspring, but M. d'Artagnan was a man, and he would have considered it unworthy of a man to give way to his feelings; whereas Madame d'Artagnan was a woman, and, still more, a mother. She wept abundantly; and—let us speak it to the praise of M. d'Artagnan the younger—notwithstanding the efforts he made to remain firm, as a future musketeer ought, nature prevailed, and he shed many tears, of which he succeeded with great difficulty in concealing the half.

The same day the young man set forward on his journey, furnished with the three paternal gifts, which consisted, as we have said, of fifteen crowns, the horse, and the letter for M. de Tréville—the counsels being thrown into the bargain.

With such a *vade mecum* D'Artagnan was morally and physically an exact copy of the hero of Cervantes, to whom we so happily compared him when our duty of a historian placed us under the necessity of sketching his portrait. Don Quixote took windmills for giants, and sheep for armies; D'Artagnan took every smile for an insult, and every look as a provocation—whence it resulted that from Tarbes to Meung his fist was constantly doubled, or his hand on the hilt of his sword; and yet the fist did not descend upon anv iaw, nor did the sword issue from its scabbard. It was not that the sight of the wretched pony did not excite numerous smiles on the countenances of passers-by; but as against the side of this pony rattled a sword of respectable length, and as over this sword gleamed an eye rather ferocious than haughty, these passers-by repressed their hilarity, or if hilarity prevailed over prudence, they endeavored to laugh only on one side, like the masks of the ancients. D'Artagnan, then, remained majestic and intact in his susceptibility, till he came to this unlucky city of Meung.

But there, as he was alighting from his horse at the gate of the Jolly Miller, without anyone—host, waiter, or hostler—coming to hold his stirrup or take his horse, D'Artagnan spied, through an open window on the ground floor, a gentleman, well-made and of good carriage, although of rather a stern countenance, talking with two persons who appeared to listen to him with respect. D'Artagnan fancied quite naturally, according to his custom, that he must be the object of their conversation, and listened.

This time D'Artagnan was only in part mistaken; he himself was not in question, but his horse was. The gentleman appeared to be enumerating all his qualities to his auditors; and, as I have said, the auditors seeming to have great deference for the narrator, they every moment burst into fits of laughter. Now, as a half-smile was sufficient to awaken the irascibility of the young man, the effect produced upon him by this vociferous mirth may be easily imagined.

Nevertheless, D'Artagnan was desirous of examining the appearance of this impertinent personage who ridiculed him. He fixed his haughty eye upon the stranger, and perceived a man of from forty to forty-five years of age, with black and piercing eyes, pale complexion, a strongly marked nose, and a black and well-shaped mustache. He was dressed in a doublet and hose of a violet color, with aiguillettes of the same, without any other ornaments than the customary slashes, through which the shirt appeared. This doublet and hose, though new, were creased, like traveling clothes packed for a long time in a portmanteau. D'Artagnan made all these remarks with the rapidity of a most minute observer, and doubtless from an instinctive feeling that this unknown was destined to have a great influence over his future life.

Now, as at the moment in which D'Artagnan fixed his eyes upon the gentleman in the violet doublet, the gentleman made one of his most knowing and profound remarks respecting the Béarnese pony, his two auditors laughed even louder than before, and he himself, though contrary to his custom, allowed a pale smile (if I may be allowed to use such an expression) to stray over his countenance.

This time there could be no doubt: D'Artagnan was really insulted. Full, then, of this conviction, he pulled his cap down over his eyes, and endeavoring to copy some of the court airs he had picked up in Gascony among young traveling nobles, he advanced with one hand on the hilt of his sword and the other resting on his hip. Unfortunately, as he advanced, his anger increased at every step; and instead of the proper and lofty speech he had prepared as a prelude to his challenge, he found nothing at the tip of his tongue but a gross personality, which he accompanied with a furious gesture.

"I say, sir, you, sir, who are hiding yourself behind that shutter—yes, you, sir, tell me what you are laughing at, and we will laugh together!"

The gentleman raised his eyes slowly from the nag to his cavalier, as if he required some time to ascertain whether it could be to him that such strange reproaches were addressed; then, when he could not possibly entertain any doubt of the matter, his eyebrows slightly bent, and with an accent of irony and insolence impossible to be described, he replied to D'Artagnan: "I was not speaking to you, sir."

"But as for me—I am speaking to you!" replied the young man, additionally exasperated with this mixture of insolence and good manners, of politeness and scorn.

The unknown looked at him again with a slight smile, and retiring from the window, came out of the hostelry with a slow step, and placed himself before the horse within two paces of D'Artagnan. His quiet manner and the ironical expression of his countenance redoubled the mirth of the persons with whom he had been talking, and who still remained at the window.

D'Artagnan, seeing him approach, drew his sword a foot out of the scabbard.

"This horse is decidedly, or rather has been in his youth, a buttercup," resumed the unknown, continuing the remarks he had begun, and addressing himself to his auditors at the window, without paying the least attention to the exasperation of D'Artagnan, who, however, placed himself between him and them. "It is a color very well known in botany, but until the present time very rare among horses."

"There are people who laugh at the horse that would not dare to laugh at the master," cried the young emulator of the furious Tréville.

"I do not often laugh, sir," replied the unknown, "as you may perceive by the expression of my countenance; but nevertheless I retain the privilege of laughing when I please."

"And I," cried D'Artagnan, "will allow no man to laugh when it displeases me!"

"Indeed, sir," continued the unknown, more calm than ever; "Well, that is perfectly right!" and turning on his heel, was about to re-enter the hostelry by the front gate, beneath which D'Artagnan on arriving had observed a saddled horse.

But D'Artagnan was not of a character to allow a man to escape him thus who had had the insolence to ridicule him. He drew his sword entirely from the scabbard, and followed him, crying:

"Turn, turn, Master Joker, or I'll have to strike you from behind!"

"Strike me!" said the other, turning on his heels, and surveying the young man with as much astonishment as contempt. "Why, my good fellow, you must be mad!" Then, in a suppressed tone, as if speaking to himself: "This is annoying." Continued he, "What a godsend this would be for His Majesty, who is seeking everywhere for brave fellows to recruit his musketeers!"

He had scarcely finished, when D'Artagnan made such a furious lunge at him that if he had not sprung nimbly backward, it is probable he would have jested for the last time. The unknown, then perceiving that the matter went beyond raillery, drew his sword, saluted his adversary, and seriously placed himself on guard. But at the same moment his two auditors, accompanied by the host, fell upon D'Artagnan with sticks, shovels, and tongs. This caused so rapid and complete a diversion from the attack, that D'Artagnan's adversary, while the latter turned around to face this shower of blows, sheathed his sword with the same precision, and instead of an actor, which he had nearly been, became a spectator of the fight —a part in which he acquitted himself with his usual impassibility, muttering, nevertheless: "A plague upon these Gascons! Replace him on his orange horse, and let him begone!"

"Not before I have killed you, poltroon!" cried D'Artagnan, making the best face possible, and never retreating one step before his three assailants, who continued to shower blows upon him.

"Another gasconade!" murmured the gentleman. "By my honor, these Gascons are incorrigible! Keep up the dance, then, since he will have it so. When he is tired, he will perhaps tell us that he has had enough of it."

But the unknown did not know what a headstrong personage he had to do with; D'Artagnan was not the man ever to cry for quarter. The fight was therefore prolonged for some seconds; but at length D'Artagnan dropped his sword, which was broken in two pieces by the blow of a stick. Another blow full upon his forehead at the same moment brought him to the ground, covered with blood and almost fainting.

It was at this moment that people came flocking to the scene of action from all sides. The host, fearful of consequences, with the help of his servants carried the wounded man into the kitchen, where some trifling attentions were bestowed upon him.

As to the gentleman, he resumed his place at the window, and surveyed the crowd with a certain impatience, evidently annoyed by their remaining undispersed.

"Well, how is it with this madman?" exclaimed he, turning around as the noise at the door announced the entrance of the host, who came to inquire if he was unhurt.

"Your Excellency is safe and sound?" asked the host.

"Oh yes! perfectly safe and sound, my good host; and I wish to know what is become of our young man."

"He is better," said the host; "he fainted quite away."

"Indeed!" said the gentleman.

"But before he fainted, he collected all his strength to challenge you, and to defy you while challenging you."

"Why, this fellow must be the Devil in person!" cried the unknown.

"Oh no, Your Excellency, he is not the Devil," replied the host, with a grin of contempt. "For while he was unconscious we rummaged his valise, and found nothing but a clean shirt, and twelve crowns—which, however, did not prevent his saying, as he was fainting, that if such a thing had happened in Paris you should have instantly repented of it, while here you would only have cause to repent of it at a later period."

"Then," said the unknown coolly, "he must be some prince in disguise."

"I have told you this, good sir," resumed the host, "in order that you may be on your guard."

"Did he name no one in his passion?"

"Yes; he struck his pocket and said, 'We shall see what Monsieur de Tréville will think of this insult offered to his *protégé.*'"

"Monsieur de Tréville?" said the unknown, becoming attentive. "He put his hand upon his pocket while pronouncing the name of Monsieur de Tréville? Now, my dear host, while your young man was insensible, you did not fail, I am quite sure, to ascertain what that pocket contained. What was there in it?"

"A letter addressed to Monsieur de Tréville, captain of the Musketeers."

"Indeed!"

"Exactly as I have the honor to tell Your Excellency."

The host, who was not endowed with great perspicacity, did not observe the expression which his words had given to the physiognomy of the unknown. The latter rose from the front of the window, upon the sill of which he had leaned with his elbow, and knitted his brows like a man disquieted.

"The devil!" murmured he, between his teeth. "Can Tréville have set this Gascon upon me? He is very young; but a sword thrust is a sword thrust, whatever the age of him who gives it, and a youth is less to be suspected than an older man," and the unknown fell into a reverie which lasted some minutes. "A weak obstacle is sometimes sufficient to overthrow a great design."

"Host," said he, "could you not contrive to get rid of this frantic boy for me? In conscience, I cannot kill him; and yet," added he, with a coldly menacing expression, "and yet he annoys me. Where is he?"

"In my wife's chamber, on the first flight, where they are dressing his wounds."

"His things and his bag are with him? Has he taken off his doublet?"

"On the contrary, everything is in the kitchen. But if he annoys you, this young fool—"

"To be sure he does. He causes a disturbance in your hostelry, which respectable people cannot put up with. Go; make out my bill, and notify my servant."

"What, monsieur, will you leave us so soon?"

"You know that very well, since I gave the order to saddle my horse. Haven't I been obeyed?"

"It is done; as Your Excellency may have observed, your horse is in the great gateway, saddled for your departure."

"That is well; do as I have directed you, then."

"What the devil!" said the host to himself. "Can he be afraid of this boy?" But an imperious glance from the unknown stopped him short; he bowed humbly, and retired.

"It is not necessary for Milady[1] to be seen by this fellow," continued the stranger. "She will soon pass; she is already late. I had better get on horseback, and go and meet her. I should like, however, to know what this letter addressed to Tréville contains." And the unknown, muttering to himself, directed his steps toward the kitchen.

In the meantime the host, who entertained no doubt that it was the presence of the young man that drove the unknown from his hostelry, reascended to his wife's chamber, and found D'Artagnan just recovering his senses. Giving him to understand that the police would deal with him pretty severely for having sought a quarrel with a great lord—for in the opinion of the host the unknown could be nothing less than a great lord—he insisted that notwithstanding his weakness D'Artagnan should get up and depart as quickly as possible. D'Artagnan, half-stupefied, without his doublet, and with his head bound up in a linen cloth, arose then, and urged by the host, began to descend the stairs; but on arriving at the kitchen, the first thing he saw was his antagonist talking calmly at the step of a heavy carriage, drawn by two large Norman horses.

His interlocutor, whose head appeared through the carriage win-

---

[1] We are well aware that this term, *milady*, is only properly used when followed by a family name. But we find it thus in the manuscript, and we do not choose to take upon ourselves to alter it.

dow, was a woman of from twenty to two-and-twenty years. We have already observed with what rapidity D'Artagnan seized the expression of a countenance. He perceived then, at a glance, that this woman was young and beautiful; and her style of beauty struck him the more forcibly from its being totally different from that of the southern countries in which D'Artagnan had hitherto resided. She was pale and fair, with long curls falling in profusion over her shoulders, had large blue, languishing eyes, rosy lips, and hands of alabaster. She was talking with great animation with the unknown.

"His Eminence, then, orders me—" said the lady.

"To return instantly to England, and to inform him as soon as the duke leaves London."

"And as to my other instructions?" asked the fair traveler.

"They are contained in this box, which you will not open until you are on the other side of the Channel."

"Very well; and you—what will you do?"

"I?—I return to Paris."

"What, without chastising this insolent boy?" asked the lady.

The unknown was about to reply; but at the moment he opened his mouth, D'Artagnan, who had heard all, precipitated himself over the threshold of the door.

"This insolent boy chastises others," cried he, "and I hope that this time he whom he ought to chastise will not escape him as before."

"Will not escape him?" replied the unknown, knitting his brow.

"No; before a woman you would not dare to fly, I presume?"

"Remember," said Milady, seeing the unknown lay his hand on his sword, "remember that the least delay may ruin everything."

"You are right," cried the gentleman; "begone then, on your part, and I will depart as quickly on mine." And bowing to the lady, he sprang into his saddle, while her coachman applied his whip vigorously to his horses. The two interlocutors thus separated, taking opposite directions, at full gallop.

"Your reckoning!" vociferated the host, whose regard for the traveler was changed into profound contempt on seeing him depart without settling his account.

"Pay him, booby!" cried the unknown to his servant, without checking the speed of his horse; and the man, after throwing two or three silver pieces at the foot of mine host, galloped after his master.

"You low coward! You false gentleman!" cried D'Artagnan, springing forward, in his turn, after the servant. But his wound had rendered him too weak to support such an exertion. Scarcely had he gone ten steps when his ears began to tingle, a faintness seized him, a cloud of blood passed over his eyes, and he fell in the middle of the street, crying still: "Coward! coward! coward!"

"He is a coward indeed," grumbled the host, drawing near to D'Artagnan, and endeavoring by this little flattery to make up matters with the young man, as the heron of the fable did with the snail he had despised the evening before.

"Yes, a base coward," murmured D'Artagnan; "but she—she was very beautiful."

"What *she?*" demanded the host.

"Milady," faltered D'Artagnan, and fainted a second time.

"Ah! it's all one," said the host; "I have lost two customers, but this one remains, of whom I am pretty certain for some days to come. There will be eleven crowns gained."

It is to be remembered that eleven crowns was just the sum that remained in D'Artagnan's purse.

The host had reckoned upon eleven days of confinement at a crown a day, but he had reckoned without his guest. On the following morning, at five o'clock, D'Artagnan arose, and, descending to the kitchen without help, asked, among other ingredients the list of which has not come down to us, for some oil, some wine, and some rosemary, and with his mother's recipe in his hand composed a balsam, with which he anointed his numerous wounds, replacing his bandages, and positively refusing the assistance of any doctor. Thanks, no doubt, to the efficacy of the Bohemian salve, and perhaps also, thanks to the absence of any doctor, D'Artagnan walked about that same evening, and was almost cured by the morrow.

But when the time came to pay for this rosemary, this oil, and the wine, the only expense the master had incurred, as he had preserved a strict abstinence—while, on the contrary, the yellow horse, by the account of the hostler at least, had eaten three times as much as a horse of his size could reasonably be supposed to have done— D'Artagnan found nothing in his pocket but his little old velvet purse with the eleven crowns it contained; for as to the letter addressed to M. de Tréville, it had disappeared.

The young man commenced to search for the letter with the greatest patience, turning out his pockets of all kinds over and over again, rummaging and rerummaging in his valise, and opening and reopening his purse; but when he had come to the conviction that the letter was not to be found, he flew, for the third time, into such a rage as was near costing him a fresh consumption of wine, oil, and rosemary—for upon seeing this hotheaded youth become exasperated and threaten to destroy everything in the establishment if his letter were not found, the host seized a spit, his wife a broom handle, and the servants the same sticks they had used the day before.

"My letter of recommendation!" cried D'Artagnan, "my letter of recommendation! or, the holy blood, I will spit you all like ortolans!"

Unfortunately, there was one circumstance which created a powerful obstacle to the accomplishment of this threat; which was, as we have related, that his sword had been in the first conflict broken in two, and which he had entirely forgotten. Hence it resulted that when D'Artagnan proceeded to draw his sword in earnest, he found himself purely and simply armed with a stump of a sword about eight or ten inches in length, which the host had carefully placed in the scabbard. As to the rest of the blade, the master had slyly put that on one side to make himself a larding pin.

But this deception would probably not have stopped our fiery young man if the host had not reflected that the reclamation which his guest made was perfectly just.

"But after all," said he, lowering the point of the spit, "where is this letter?"

"Yes, where is this letter?" cried D'Artagnan. "In the first place, I warn you that that letter is for Monsieur de Tréville, and it must be found; and if not found, he will know how to find it."

The threat completed the intimidation of the host. After the king and the cardinal, M. de Tréville was the man whose name was perhaps most frequently repeated by the military, and even by citizens. There was, to be sure, Father Joseph, but his name was never pronounced with but a subdued voice, such was the terror inspired by his Gray Eminence, as the cardinal's familiar was called.

Throwing down his spit, and ordering his wife to do the same with her broom handle, and the servants with their sticks, he set the first example of commencing an earnest search for the lost letter.

"Does the letter contain anything valuable?" demanded the host, after a few minutes of useless investigation.

"Zounds! I think it does, indeed!" cried the Gascon, who reckoned upon this letter for making his way at court. "It contained my fortune!"

"Bills upon Spain?" asked the disturbed host.

"Bills upon His Majesty's private treasury," answered D'Artagnan, who, reckoning upon entering into the king's service in consequence of this recommendation, believed he could make this somewhat hazardous reply without telling a falsehood.

"The devil!" cried the host, at his wit's end.

"But it's of no importance," continued D'Artagnan, with national assurance; "it's of no importance. The money is nothing; that letter was everything. I would rather have lost a thousand pistoles than have lost it." He would not have risked more if he had said twenty thousand; but a certain juvenile modesty restrained him.

A ray of light all at once broke upon the mind of the host as he was giving himself to the Devil upon finding nothing.

"That letter is not lost!" cried he.

"What!" said D'Artagnan.

"No; it has been stolen from you."

"Stolen! by whom?"

"By the gentleman who was here yesterday. He came down into the kitchen, where your doublet was. He remained there some time alone. I would lay a wager he has stolen it."

"Do you think so?" answered D'Artagnan, but little convinced, as he knew better than anyone else how entirely personal the value of this letter was, and said nothing in it likely to tempt cupidity. The fact was that none of the servants, none of the travelers present, could have gained anything by being possessed of this paper.

"Do you say," resumed D'Artagnan, "that you suspect that impertinent gentleman?"

"I tell you I am sure of it," continued the host. "When I informed him that your lordship was the *protégé* of Monsieur de Tréville, and that you even had a letter for that illustrious gentleman, he appeared to be very much disturbed, and asked me where that letter was, and immediately came down into the kitchen, where he knew your doublet was."

"Then that's my thief," replied D'Artagnan. "I will complain to Monsieur de Tréville, and Monsieur de Tréville will complain to the king."

He then drew two crowns majestically from his purse and gave them to the host, who accompanied him, cap in hand, to the gate.

And he remounted his yellow horse, which bore him without any further accident to the gate of St. Antoine at Paris, where his owner sold him for three crowns—which was a very good price, considering that D'Artagnan had ridden him hard during the last stage. As for the dealer to whom D'Artagnan sold him for the said nine livres, he did not conceal from the young man that he only gave that enormous sum for the beast on account of the originality of his color.

Thus D'Artagnan entered Paris on foot, carrying his little packet under his arm, and walked about till he found an apartment to be let on terms suited to the scantiness of his means. This chamber was a sort of garret, situated in the rue des Fossoyeurs, near the Luxembourg.

As soon as the earnest money was paid, D'Artagnan took possession of his lodging, and passed the remainder of the day sewing onto his doublet and hose some ornamental braiding which his mother had taken off from an almost new doublet of the elder M. d'Artagnan, and which she had given her son secretly. Next he went to the Quai de Ferraille to have a new blade put to his sword, and then returned toward the Louvre, inquiring of the first musketeer he met for the situation of the hotel of M. de Tréville, which proved to be in the rue du Vieux-Columbier; that is to say, in the immediate vicinity of the chamber hired by D'Artagnan—a circumstance which appeared to furnish a happy augury for the success of his journey.

After this, satisfied with the way in which he had conducted himself at Meung, without remorse for the past, confident in the present, and full of hope for the future, he retired to bed and slept the sleep of the brave.

This sleep, provincial as it was, brought him to nine o'clock in the morning; at which hour he rose, in order to repair to the residence of M. de Tréville, the third personage in the kingdom according to D'Artagnan's paternal estimation.

Skipping some pages we come to D'Artagnan's first sight of the body of men, the King's Musketeers, whom he was hoping to join. We are told that Paris is the city of levees, those morning calls of respect and business, which clients and those of lesser rank, make to the exalted of the town.

Of the more than two hundred levees of the city, only the king's and the cardinal's were more important than M. de Tréville's. At this levee, D'Artagnan meets the three musketeers who, with him as fourth, are the heroes of the romance: Athos, Aramis, and Porthos.

The court of M. de Tréville's hotel, on the rue du Vieux-Columbier, resembled a camp from by six o'clock in the morning in summer and eight o'clock in winter. From fifty to sixty musketeers, who appeared to replace one another in order always to present an imposing number, paraded constantly, armed to the teeth and ready for anything.

On one of those immense staircases, upon whose space modern civilization would build a whole house, ascended and descended the office seekers of Paris, who ran after any sort of favor—gentlemen from the provinces anxious to be enrolled, and servants in all sorts of liveries, bringing and carrying messages between their masters and M. de Tréville.

In the antechamber, upon long circular benches, reposed the elect; that is to say, those who were called. In this apartment a continued buzzing prevailed from morning till night, while M. de Tréville, in his office contiguous to this antechamber, received visits, listened to complaints, gave his orders, and like the king in his balcony at the Louvre, had only to place himself at the window to review both his men and arms.

The day on which D'Artagnan presented himself the assemblage was imposing, particularly for a provincial just arriving from his province. It is true that this provincial was a Gascon; and that, particularly at this period, the compatriots of D'Artagnan had the reputation of being not easily intimidated. When he had once passed the massive door covered with long square-headed nails, he fell into the midst of a troop of swordsmen, who crossed one another in their passage, calling out, quarreling, and playing tricks one with another. In order to make one's way amid these turbulent and conflicting waves, it was necessary to be an officer, a great noble, or a pretty woman.

It was, then, into the midst of this tumult and disorder that our young man advanced with a beating heart, ranging his long rapier up his lanky leg, and keeping one hand on the edge of his cap, with that half-smile of the embarrassed provincial who wishes to put on a good face. When he had passed one group he began to breathe more freely; but he could not help observing that they turned around to look at him, and for the first time in his life D'Artagnan, who had till that day entertained a very good opinion of himself, felt ridiculous.

Arrived at the staircase, it was still worse. There were four musketeers on the bottom steps, amusing themselves with the following exercise, while ten or twelve of their comrades waited upon the landing place to take their turn in the sport.

One of them, stationed upon the top stair, naked sword in hand, prevented, or at least endeavored to prevent, the three others from ascending.

These three others fenced against him with their agile swords. D'Artagnan at first took these weapons for foils, and believed them to be buttoned; but he soon perceived by certain scratches that every weapon was pointed and sharpened, and that at each of these scratches not only the spectators but even the actors themselves laughed like so many madmen.

He who at the moment occupied the upper step kept his adversaries marvelously in check. A circle was formed around them. The conditions required that at every hit the man touched should quit the game, yielding his turn for the benefit of the adversary who had hit him. In five minutes three were slightly wounded, one on the hand, another on the chin, and the third on the ear, by the defender of the stair, who himself remained intact—a piece of skill which was worth to him, according to the rules agreed upon, three turns of favor.

However difficult it might be, or rather as he pretended it was, to astonish our young traveler, this pastime really astonished him. He had seen in his province—that land in which heads become so easily heated—a few of the preliminaries of duels; but the daring of these four fencers appeared to him the strongest he had ever heard of, even in Gascony. He believed himself transported into that famous country of giants into which Gulliver afterward went and was so frightened; and yet he had not gained the goal, for there were still the landing place and the antechamber.

On the landing they were no longer fighting, but amused themselves with stories about women, and in the antechamber, with stories about the court. On the landing D'Artagnan blushed; in the antechamber he trembled. His warm and fickle imagination, which in Gascony had rendered him formidable to young chambermaids, and even sometimes to their mistresses, had never dreamed, even in moments of delirium, of half the amorous wonders, or a quarter of the feats of gallantry which were here set forth in connection with names the best known and with details the least concealed.

But if his morals were shocked on the landing, his respect for the cardinal was scandalized in the antechamber. There, to his great astonishment, D'Artagnan heard that policy which made all Europe tremble criticized aloud and openly, as well as the private life of the cardinal, which so many great nobles had been punished for trying to pry into. That great man who was so revered by D'Artagnan the elder served as an object of ridicule to the Musketeers of Tréville, who cracked their jokes upon his bandy legs and his crooked back. Some sang ballads about Madame d'Aiguillon, his mistress, and Madame Cambalet, his niece; while others formed parties and plans to annoy the pages and guards of the cardinal duke—all, things which appeared to D'Artagnan monstrous impossibilities.

Nevertheless, when the name of the king was now and then uttered unthinkingly amid all these cardinal jests, a sort of gag seemed to close for a moment all these jeering mouths. They looked hesitatingly around them, and appeared to doubt the thickness of the partition between them and the office of M. de Tréville; but a fresh allusion soon brought back the conversation to His Eminence, and then the laughter recovered its loudness, and the light was not withheld from any of his actions.

"Certes, these fellows will all be either imprisoned or hanged," thought the terrified D'Artagnan, "and I, no doubt, with them; for from the moment I have either listened to or heard them, I shall be held as an accomplice. What would my good father say, who so strongly pointed out to me the respect due to the cardinal, if he knew I was in the society of such pagans?"

We have no need, therefore, to say that D'Artagnan dared not join in the conversation, only he looked with all his eyes and listened with all his ears, stretching his five senses so as to lose nothing; and despite his confidence in the paternal monitions, he felt himself carried by his tastes and led by his instincts to praise rather than to blame the unheard-of things which were taking place.

Although he was a perfect stranger in the crowd of M. de Tréville's courtiers, and this moreover his first appearance in that place, he was at length noticed, and somebody came and asked him what he wanted. At this demand D'Artagnan gave his name very modestly, emphasized the title of compatriot, and begged the servant who had put the question to him to request a moment's audience of M. de Tréville—a request which the other, with an air of protection, promised to transmit in due season.

D'Artagnan, a little recovered from his first surprise, had now leisure to study costumes and physiognomy.

The center of the most animated group was a musketeer of great height, and haughty countenance, dressed in a costume so peculiar as to attract great attention. He did not wear the uniform cloak—which was not obligatory at that epoch of less liberty but more independence—but a cerulean blue doublet, a little faded and worn, and over this a magnificent baldric or belt, worked in gold, which shone like water-ripples in the sun. A long cloak of crimson velvet fell in graceful folds from his shoulders, disclosing in front the splendid baldric, from which was suspended a gigantic rapier.

This musketeer had just come off guard, complained of having a cold, and coughed from time to time affectedly. It was for this reason, as he said to those around him, that he had put on his cloak; and while he spoke with a lofty air, and twisted his mustache disdainfully, all admired his embroidered baldric, and D'Artagnan more than anyone.

"What would you have?" said the musketeer. "The fashion is

coming in. It is a folly, I admit, but still it is the fashion. Besides, one must lay out one's inheritance somehow."

"Ah, Porthos!" cried one of his companions, "don't try to make us believe you obtained that belt by paternal generosity. It was given to you by that veiled lady I met you with the other Sunday, near the gate St. Honoré."

"No; upon honor, and by the faith of a gentleman, I bought it with the contents of my own purse," answered he whom they designated by the name of Porthos.

"Yes; about in the same manner," said another musketeer, "that I bought this new purse with what my mistress put into the old one."

"It's true, though," said Porthos; "and the proof is that I paid twelve pistoles for it."

The wonder was increased, though the doubt continued to exist.

"Is it not true, Aramis?" said Porthos, turning towards another musketeer.

This other musketeer formed a perfect contrast to his interrogator, who had just designated him by the name of Aramis. He was a stout man, of about two or three and twenty, with an open, ingenuous countenance, a black, mild eye, and cheeks rosy and downy as an autumn peach. His delicate mustache marked a perfectly straight line upon his upper lip; he appeared to dread to lower his hands lest their veins should swell, and he pinched the tips of his ears from time to time to preserve their delicate pink transparency. Habitually he spoke little and slowly, bowed frequently, laughed without noise, showing his teeth, which were fine, and of which, as of the rest of his person, he appeared to take great care. He answered the appeal of his friend by an affirmative nod of the head.

This affirmation appeared to dispel all doubts with regard to the baldric. They continued to admire it, but said no more about it; and with a rapid change of thought, the conversation passed suddenly to another subject.

D'Artagnan finally has his interview with M. de Tréville. The latter will not of course accept a green boy from the country into his fine regiment of expert fighters. He wants D'Artagnan first to study in an academy of swordsmanship, and also first join some other company and get a few years of experience. One doesn't join such a noble body of fighting men fresh from the barn.

D'Artagnan had had to tell, of course, how he had come to lose the letter given to him by his father. M. de Tréville had listened attentively to this story about the man who had mocked D'Artagnan's horse, and the beautiful Milady to whom he had given a mysterious box.

But all this had only deepened a certain suspicion in M. de Tréville's mind that D'Artagnan was possibly a spy sent by the cardinal to worm his way into the musketeers.

"But wait a minute," said M. de Tréville, stopping him. "I promised you a letter for the director of the academy. Are you too proud to accept it, young gentleman?"

"No sir," said D'Artagnan; "and I will answer for it that this one shall not fare like the other. I will guard it so carefully that I will take an oath on its arriving at its address, and woe to him who shall attempt to take it from me!"

M. de Tréville smiled at this flourish; and leaving his young compatriot in the embrasure of the window, where they had talked together, he seated himself at a table in order to write the promised letter of recommendation. While he was doing this, D'Artagnan, having no better employment, amused himself with beating a march upon the window, and with looking at the musketeers, who were going away, one after another, and following them with his eyes until they disappeared at the turning of the street.

M. de Tréville, after having written the letter, sealed it, and, rising, approached the young man in order to give it to him. But at the very moment when D'Artagnan stretched out his hand to receive it, M. de Tréville was highly astonished to see his *protégé* make a sudden spring, become crimson with passion, and rush from the cabinet, crying, "S' blood, he shall not escape me this time!"

"And who?" asked M. de Tréville.

"He, my thief!" replied D'Artagnan. "Ah, the traitor!" and he disappeared.

"The devil take the madman!" murmured M. de Tréville. "Unless," added he, "this is a cunning mode of escaping, seeing that he has failed in his purpose!"

D'Artagnan, in a state of fury, crossed the antechamber at three bounds, and was darting towards the stairs, which he reckoned upon descending four at a time, when, in his heedless course, he ran head foremost against a musketeer who was coming out of one of M. de Tréville's private rooms, and, striking his shoulder violently, made him utter a cry, or rather a howl.

"Excuse me," said D'Artagnan, endeavoring to resume his course, "excuse me, but I am in a hurry."

Scarcely had he descended the first stair, when a hand of iron seized him by the belt and stopped him.

"You are in a hurry?" said the musketeer, as pale as a sheet. "Under that pretense you run against me! You say, 'Excuse me,' and you believe that is sufficient? Not at all, my young man. Do you fancy that because you have heard Monsieur de Tréville speak to us a little cavalierly today that other people are to treat us as he speaks to us? Undeceive yourself, comrade, you are not Monsieur de Tréville."

"My faith!" replied D'Artagnan, recognizing Athos, who, after the dressing performed by the doctor, was returning to his own apartment, "my faith! I did not do it intentionally, and not doing it intentionally, I said, 'Excuse me.' It appears to me that is quite enough. I repeat to you, however, and this time on my word of honor—I think, perhaps, too often—that I am in haste, great haste. Leave your hold then, I beg of you, and let me go where my business calls me."

"Monsieur," said Athos, letting him go, "you are not polite; it is easy to perceive that you come from a distance."

D'Artagnan had already strode down three or four stairs, but at Athos's last remark he stopped short.

"*Morbleu!* Monsieur!" said he, "however far I may come, it is not you who can give me a lesson in good manners, I warn you."

"Perhaps!" said Athos.

"Ah, if I were not in such haste, and if I were not running after someone," said D'Artagnan.

"Monsieur Man-in-a-hurry, you can find me without running— *me*, you understand?"

"And where, so please you?"

"Near the Carmes-Deschaux."

"At what hour?"

"About noon."

"About noon? That will do; I will be there."

"Endeavor not to make me wait, for at a quarter past twelve I will cut off your ears as you run."

"Good!" cried D'Artagnan, "I will be there ten minutes before twelve." And he set off running as if the Devil possessed him, hoping that he might yet find the unknown, whose slow pace could not have carried him far.

But at the street-gate Porthos was talking with the soldier on guard. Between the two talkers there was just room for a man to pass. D'Artagnan thought it would suffice for him, and he sprang forward like a dart between them. But D'Artagnan had reckoned without the wind. As he was about to pass, the wind blew out Porthos's long cloak, and D'Artagnan rushed straight into the middle of it. Without doubt, Porthos had reasons for not abandoning this part of his vestments, for instead of quitting his hold of the flap in his hand, he pulled it toward him, so that D'Artagnan rolled himself up in the velvet by a movement of rotation explained by the persistency of Porthos.

D'Artagnan, hearing the musketeer swear, wished to escape from the cloak, which blinded him, and sought to find his way from under the folds of it. He was particularly anxious to avoid marring the freshness of the magnificent baldric we are acquainted with; but on timidly opening his eyes, he found himself with his nose fixed between the two shoulders of Porthos—that is to say, exactly upon the baldric.

Alas, like most things in this world which have nothing in their favor but appearances, the baldric was glittering with gold in the front, but was nothing but simple buff behind. Vainglorious as he was, Porthos could not afford to have a baldric wholly of gold, but had at least the half. One could comprehend the necessity of the cold, and the urgency of the cloak.

"Bless me," cried Porthos, making strong efforts to disembarrass himself of D'Artagnan, who was wriggling about his back; "you must be mad to run against people in this manner."

"Excuse me," said D'Artagnan, reappearing under the shoulder of the giant, "but I am in such haste—I was running after someone, and—"

"And do you always shut your eyes when you run?" asked Porthos.

"No," replied D'Artagnan, piqued. "No, and thanks to my eyes, I can see what other people cannot see."

Whether Porthos understood him or did not understand him, giving way to his anger, "Monsieur," said he, "you stand a chance of getting your hide curried if you rub musketeers in this fashion."

"Curried, monsieur!" said D'Artagnan, "the expression is strong."

"It is one that becomes a man accustomed to look his enemies in the face."

"Ah, *pardieu!* I am in a position to know that you can't afford to turn your back to yours."

And the young man, delighted with his joke about Porthos's unfinished baldric, went away laughing somewhat louder than was proper.

Porthos, foaming with rage, made a movement to rush after D'Artagnan.

"Presently, presently," cried the latter, "when you haven't your cloak on."

"At one o'clock, then, behind the Luxembourg."

"Very well, at one o'clock, then," replied D'Artagnan, turning the angle of the street.

But neither in the street he had passed through, nor in the one which his eager glance pervaded, could he see anyone; however slowly the unknown had walked, he was gone on his way, or perhaps had entered some house. D'Artagnan inquired of everyone he met with, went down to the ferry, came up again by the rue de Seine and the Red Cross; but nothing; absolutely nothing! This chase was, however, advantageous to him in one sense, for in proportion as the perspiration broke from his forehead, his head began to cool.

He began to reflect upon the events that had passed; they were numerous and inauspicious. It was scarcely eleven o'clock in the morning, and yet this morning had already brought him into disgrace with M. de Tréville, who could not fail to think the manner in which D'Artagnan had left him a little cavalier.

Besides this, he had drawn upon himself two good duels with two men, each capable of killing three D'Artagnans—with two musketeers, in short, with two of those beings whom he esteemed so greatly that he placed them in his mind and heart above all other men.

The outlook was sad. Sure of being killed by Athos, it may easily be understood that the young man was not very uneasy about Porthos. As hope, however, is the last thing extinguished in the heart of man, he finished by hoping that he might survive, even though with terrible wounds, in both these duels; and in case of surviving, he made the following reprehensions upon his own conduct:

"What a madcap I was, and what a stupid fellow I am! That brave and unfortunate Athos was wounded on that very shoulder against which I had to run head foremost, like a ram. The only thing that astonishes me is that he did not strike me dead at once. He had good cause to do so; the pain I gave him must have been atrocious. As to Porthos—oh, as to Porthos, faith, that's a droll affair!"

And in spite of himself the young man began to laugh aloud, looking around carefully, however, to see if his solitary laugh, without a cause in the eyes of passers-by, offended no one.

"As to Porthos, that is certainly droll; but I am not the less a giddy fool. Are people to be run against without warning? No; and have I any right to go and peep under their cloaks to see what is not there? He would have pardoned me, he would certainly have pardoned me, if I had not said anything to him about that cursed belt of his—in ambiguous words, it is true, and funny too—but with a barb to it.

"Ah, cursed Gascon that I am, I get from one hobble into another. Friend D'Artagnan," continued he, addressing himself with all the civility that he thought due to himself, "if you escape, of which there is not much chance, I would advise you to practice perfect politeness for the future. You must henceforth be admired and quoted as a model of it. To be obliging and polite does not necessarily make a man a coward. Look at Aramis now; Aramis is mildness and grace personified. Well, did anybody ever dream of calling Aramis a coward? No, certainly not, and from this moment I will endeavor to model myself after him. Ah, here he is!"

D'Artagnan, walking and soliloquizing, had arrived within a few steps of the Hotel d'Aiguillon, and in front of that hotel perceived

Aramis, chatting gayly with three gentlemen of the king's guards. On his part Aramis perceived D'Artagnan; but as he had not forgotten that it was in the presence of this young man that M. de Tréville had been so angry in the morning, and that a witness of the rebuke the musketeers had received was not likely to be at all agreeable, he pretended not to see him. D'Artagnan, on the contrary, quite full of his plans of conciliation and courtesy, approached the young men with a profound bow, accompanied by a most gracious smile. Aramis bowed his head slightly, but did not smile. All four, besides, immediately broke off their conversation.

D'Artagnan was not so dull as not to perceive that he was one too many; but he was not sufficiently broken into the fashions of the gay world to know how to extricate himself gallantly from a false position, like that of a man who begins to mingle with people he is scarcely acquainted with, and in a conversation that does not concern him.

He was seeking in his mind, then, for the least awkward means of retreat, when he remarked that Aramis had let his handkerchief fall, and, by mistake, no doubt, had placed his foot upon it. This appeared a favorable opportunity to repair his intrusion. He stooped, and with the most gracious air he could assume, drew the handkerchief from under the foot of the musketeer in spite of the efforts the latter made to detain it, and, holding it out to him, said, "I believe, monsieur, that this is a handkerchief you would be sorry to lose?"

The handkerchief was indeed richly embroidered, and had a coronet and arms at one of its corners. Aramis blushed excessively, and snatched rather than took the handkerchief from the hands of the Gascon.

"Ah, ah!" cried one of the guards, "will you persist in saying, most discreet Aramis, that you are not on good terms with Madame de Bois-Tracy, when that gracious lady has the kindness to lend you one of her handkerchiefs?"

Aramis darted at D'Artagnan one of those looks which inform a man that he has acquired a mortal enemy. Then, resuming his mild air, "You are deceived, gentlemen," said he. "This handkerchief is not mine, and I cannot fancy why Monsieur has taken it into his head to offer it to me rather than to one of you; and as a proof of what I say, here is mine in my pocket."

So saying, he pulled out his own handkerchief, likewise a very elegant handkerchief, and of fine cambric—though cambric was dear at the period—but a handkerchief without embroidery and without arms, only ornamented with a single cipher, that of its proprietor.

This time D'Artagnan was not hasty. He perceived his mistake; but the friends of Aramis were not at all convinced by his denial, and one of them addressed the young musketeer with affected seriousness. "If it were as you pretend it is," said he, "I should be forced, my dear Aramis, to reclaim it myself; for, as you very well know, Bois-Tracy is an intimate friend of mine, and I cannot allow the property of his wife to be sported around as a trophy."

"You make the demand with bad grace," replied Aramis. "I will acknowledge the justice of your reclamation, but I must refuse compliance on account of the form."

"The fact is," hazarded D'Artagnan timidly, "I did not see the handkerchief fall from the pocket of Monsieur Aramis. He had his foot upon it, that is all; and I thought from his having his foot upon it the handkerchief was his."

"And you were deceived, my dear sir," replied Aramis, coldly, showing himself little sensible to the attempted reparation. Then turning towards that one of the guards who had declared himself the friend of Bois-Tracy: "Besides," continued he, "as much as you may be the intimate of Bois-Tracy, so am I, which means that I ought to wonder if perhaps this handkerchief hasn't perhaps fallen from your pocket."

"No, upon my honor!" cried His Majesty's guardsman.

"You are about to swear upon your honor and I upon my word, and then it will be pretty evident that one of us will have lied. Now, here, Montaran, we will do better than that, let each take a half."

"Of the handkerchief?"

"Yes."

"Perfectly just," cried the other two guardsmen. "The judgment of King Solomon! Aramis, you certainly are full of wisdom!"

The young men burst into a laugh, and, as may be supposed, the affair had no other sequel. In a moment or two the conversation ceased, and the three guardsmen and the musketeer, after having cordially shaken hands, separated, the guardsmen going one way, and Aramis another.

"Now is my time to make my peace with this gallant man," said D'Artagnan to himself, having stood on one side during the whole of the latter part of the conversation; and with this good feeling drawing near to Aramis, who was departing without paying any attention to him: "Monsieur," said he, "you will excuse me, I hope."

"Ah, monsieur!" interrupted Aramis, "permit me to observe to you, that you have not acted in this affair as a gallant man ought."

"What, monsieur!" cried D'Artagnan, "and do you suppose—"

"I suppose, monsieur, that you are not a fool, and that you knew very well, although coming from Gascony, that people do not tread upon handkerchiefs without a reason. What the devil! Paris is not paved with cambric!"

"Monsieur, you act wrongly in endeavoring to mortify me," said D'Artagnan, in whom the natural quarrelsome spirit began to speak more loudly than his pacific resolutions. "I am from Gascony; it is true; and since you know it, there is no occasion to tell you that Gascons are not very patient, so that when they have begged to be excused once, for no matter what folly, they are convinced that they have done about as much as the occasion demands."

"Monsieur, what I say to you about the matter," said Aramis, "is not for the sake of seeking a quarrel. Thank God, I am not a bravo! And being a musketeer but for a time, I only fight when I am forced to do so, and always with great repugnance; but this time the affair is serious, for here it is a matter of a lady compromised by you."

"By us, you mean," cried D'Artagnan.

"Why did you so maladroitly restore me the handkerchief?"

"Why did you so awkwardly let it fall?"

"I have said, monseiur, and I repeat, that the handkerchief did not fall from my pocket."

"And thereby you have lied twice, monsieur, for I saw it fall."

"Ah, you take it with that tone, do you, Master Gascon? Well, I will teach you how to behave yourself."

"And I will send you back to your Mass book, Master Abbé. Draw, if you please, and instantly—"

"Not so, if you please, my good friend—not here, at least. Can't you see that we are opposite the Hotel d'Aiguillon, which is full of the cardinal's creatures? How do I know that it is not His Eminence who has sent you here to provoke me to a duel that will cost me my head? Now, it happens that I entertain a ridiculous partiality for my head, it seems to suit my shoulders as if it grew there. I still intend to kill you, have no fears on that score, but I want to kill you quietly, in a snug, remote place, where you will not be able to boast of your death to anybody."

"I agree, monsieur; but do not be too confident. Take your handkerchief; whether it belongs to you or to another, you may perhaps stand in need of it."

"Monsieur is surely a Gascon?" asked Aramis.

"Yes. Monsieur doesn't happen to be trying to postpone our interview through caution?"

"Caution, monsieur? That is a virtue useless to musketeers. But indispensable to churchmen. So, as I am only a musketeer provisionally, I hold it good to be prudent. At two o'clock, I shall have the honor of expecting you at the hotel of Monsieur de Tréville. There I will indicate to you the best place and time."

The two young men bowed and separated, Aramis ascending the street which led to the Luxembourg, while D'Artagnan, perceiving the appointed hour was approaching, took the road to the Carmes-Deschaux, saying to himself: "Decidedly I can't draw back; but at least, if I am killed, I shall be killed by a musketeer."

D'Artagnan knew absolutely no one in Paris. He therefore had to go to his duel with Athos without a second, and be satisfied with whomever his adversary should choose. Anyhow, his intention was to make the brave musketeer all suitable apologies, but without betraying any sign of weakness. For what could result from this duel except that which generally results from an affair of this kind, where a young and vigorous man fights with an adversary who is wounded and weakened? If he is beaten, then his antagonist has all the greater triumph out of it, while if he wins, he gets no credit, but is, on the contrary, accused of a cowardly attack on a handicapped man.

Now we must have painted the character of our adventure-seeker very poorly if our readers have not already perceived something quite special about D'Artagnan. Killed he would be, that seemed fairly certain, but that was no reason why he should die quietly, or why he should not study the situation carefully. Meekness was no part of our Gascon.

He reflected upon the three men whom he would have to face. That is if he ever got that far. Athos, the wounded man, was his first combatant. Perhaps a genuine excuse, made in all sincerity would get him out of that, for he would have liked to make a friend of this man with the aristocratic appearance and the austere demeanor.

With Athos out of the way, he'd soon take care of Porthos. The trick would be to keep irritating him with the story of the unfinished baldric, and impress upon him that if he did not finish off D'Artagnan quickly, the story would soon be all over Paris, and turn him into a figure of ridicule. Porthos, thus disconcerted, would either kill or be killed with dispatch.

Then would come Aramis—if D'Artagnan could stay alive that long. To handle him, it would be necessary to threaten him with an attack against his features, frighten him with the thought of being disfigured (in the way Caesar used to recommend to his soldiers when they were fighting Pompey). The thought of his good looks being marred would upset a man as vain as Aramis.

In addition to this plan of conduct, D'Artagnan was further armed and strengthened by those firm resolutions that his father had implanted in his heart: "Endure nothing from anyone but the king, the cardinal, and Monsieur de Tréville."

So he flew, rather than walked, toward the convents of the barefoot carmelites, the Carmes-Deschaux, as it was called at that time, a sort of building without windows, surrounded by barren fields—an annex to the Pré-aux-Clercs, often used by men in a hurry to end a quarrel with blood.

When D'Artagnan arrived in sight of the bare spot of ground which extended along the foot of the monastery, Athos had been waiting some five minutes, and twelve o'clock was striking. For he was as punctual as the Samaritan woman, and the most rigorous casuist with regard to duels could have nothing to say.

Athos, who still suffered grievously from his wound, though it had been dressed anew by M. de Tréville's surgeon, was seated on a post and waiting for his adversary with that placid countenance and that noble air which never forsook him. At the sight of D'Artagnan, he arose and came politely a few steps to meet him. The latter, on his side, saluted his adversary with hat in hand, his feather even touching the ground.

"Monsieur," said Athos, "I have engaged two of my friends as seconds; but these two friends are not yet come, at which I am astonished, as it is not at all their custom."

"I have no seconds on my part, monsieur," said D'Artagnan; "for having only arrived yesterday in Paris, I as yet know no one but Monsieur de Tréville, to whom I was recommended by my father, who has the honor to be, in some degree, one of his friends."

Athos reflected for an instant. "You know no one but Monsieur de Tréville?" he asked.

"Yes, monsieur, I know only him."

"Well, but then," continued Athos, speaking half to himself, "—well, but then, if I kill you, I shall have the reputation of being a baby-killer."

"Not too much so," replied D'Artagnan, with a bow which was not deficient in dignity, "not too much so, since you do me the honor of fighting while still suffering from a wound which must be very inconvenient, to say the least."

"Very inconvenient, upon my word; and you hurt me devilishly, I can tell you. But I will take the left hand—it is my custom in such circumstances. Do not fancy that I do you a favor; I use either hand easily. And it will be even a disadvantage to you; a left-handed man is very troublesome to people who are not prepared for it. I regret I did not inform you sooner of this circumstance."

"You have truly, monsieur," said D'Artagnan, bowing again, "a courtesy, for which, I assure you, I am very grateful."

"You confuse me," replied Athos, with his gentlemanly air; "let us talk of something else, if you please. Ah, the devil! you really hurt me! my shoulder burns as if on fire!"

"If you would permit me—" said D'Artagnan, rather shyly.

"What, monsieur?"

"I happen to have a miraculous balsam for wounds—a salve given to me by my mother, and of which I have made a trial upon myself."

"Well?"

"Well, I am sure that in less than three days this salve would cure you; and at the end of three days, when you would be cured—well, sir, it would still be a great honor to me, to fight you."

D'Artagnan spoke these words with a simplicity that did honor to his courtesy, without throwing the least doubt upon his courage.

"*Pardieu*, monsieur!" said Athos, "that's a proposition that pleases me; not that I accept it, but it savors of the gentleman. Thus spoke and acted the gallant knights of the time of Charlemagne, in whom every cavalier ought to seek his model. Unfortunately, we do not live in the times of the great emperor, we live in the times of the cardinal; and three days hence, however well the secret might be guarded, it would be known that we intended to fight, and our combat would be prevented. Where can those lazy fellows be keeping themselves?"

"If you are in haste, monsieur," said D'Artagnan, with the same simplicity with which a moment before he had proposed to him to put off the duel for three days, "if you are in haste, and if it be your will to dispatch me at once, do not inconvenience yourself, I pray you."

"There again you have pleased me," cried Athos, with a gracious nod to D'Artagnan. "That did not come from a man without brains, and certainly not from a man without a heart. Monsieur, I love men of your kidney; and I foresee plainly that if we don't kill each other, I shall hereafter have much pleasure in your conversation. We will wait for these gentlemen, if you don't mind; I have plenty of time, and it will be more correct. Ah, here is one of them, I believe."

In fact, at the end of the rue Vaugirard the gigantic Porthos appeared.

"What!" cried D'Artagnan, "is your first witness Monsieur Porthos?"

"Yes. Does that disturb you?"

"By no means."

"And here is the second."

D'Artagnan turned in the direction pointed to by Athos, and perceived Aramis.

"What!" cried he, in an accent of greater astonishment than before, "your second witness is Monsieur Aramis?"

"Indeed! Don't you know that we are never seen one without the others, and that we are called among the musketeers and the guards, at court and in the city, Athos, Porthos, and Aramis, or the Three Inseparables? But of course you come from Dax or Pau—"

"From Tarbes," said D'Artagnan.

"So naturally you are ignorant of this little fact," said Athos.

"My faith!" replied D'Artagnan, "you are well named, gentlemen; and my adventure, if it should ever become known, will prove at least that your union is not founded upon contrasts."

In the meantime Porthos had come up, waved his hand to Athos, and then turning towards D'Artagnan, stood quite astonished.

Let us mention in passing that he had changed his belt, and relinquished his cloak.

"Ah, ah!" said he, "what is the meaning of this?"

"This is the gentleman I am going to fight with," said Athos, pointing to D'Artagnan with his hand, and saluting him with the same gesture.

"Why, it is with him I am also going to fight," said Porthos.

"But not before one o'clock," replied D'Artagnan.

"And I also am to fight with this gentleman," said Aramis, coming in his turn on to the place.

"But not till two o'clock," said D'Artagnan, with the same calmness.

"But what are you going to fight about, Athos?" asked Aramis.

"Faith! I'm not quite sure. He hurt my shoulder. Yes, that's it. And you, Porthos?"

"Faith! I am going to fight—because I am going to fight," answered Porthos. He blushed angrily.

Athos, whose keen eye lost nothing, perceived a faintly sly smile pass over the lips of the young Gascon, as he replied: "We had a short discussion about certain articles of men's dress."

"And you, Aramis?" asked Athos.

"Oh, ours is a theological quarrel," replied Aramis, making a sign to D'Artagnan to keep secret the cause of their duel.

Athos saw a second smile on the lips of D'Artagnan.

"Indeed?" said Athos.

"Yes; a passage of Saint Augustine, upon which we could not agree," said the Gascon.

"Decidedly, this is a clever fellow," murmured Athos.

"And now you are all assembled, gentlemen," said D'Artagnan, "permit me to offer you my apologies."

At this word *apologies*, a cloud passed over the brow of Athos, a haughty smile curled the lip of Porthos, and a negative sign was the reply of Aramis.

"You do not understand me, gentlemen," said D'Artagnan, throwing up his head, the sharp and bold lines of which were at the moment gilded by a bright ray of the sun. "I asked to be excused in case I should not be able to discharge my debt to all three; for Monsieur Athos has the right to kill me first, which must abate your valor in your own estimation, Monsieur Porthos, and render yours almost null, Monsieur Aramis. And now, gentlemen, I repeat, excuse me, but on that account only, and—on guard!"

At these words, with the most gallant air possible, D'Artagnan drew his sword.

The blood mounted to the head of D'Artagnan, and at that moment he would have drawn his sword against all the musketeers in the kingdom as willingly as now he did against Athos, Porthos, and Aramis.

It was a quarter past midday. The sun was in its zenith, and the spot chosen for the scene of the duel was exposed to its full ardor.

"It is very hot," said Athos, drawing his sword in his turn, "and yet I cannot take off my doublet; for I just now felt my wound begin to bleed again, and I should not like to annoy monsieur with the sight of blood which has not drawn from me himself."

"That is true, monsieur," replied D'Artagnan, "and whether drawn by myself or another, I assure you I shall always view with regret the blood of so brave a gentleman. I will therefore fight in my doublet, like yourself."

"Come, come, enough of such compliments," cried Porthos. "Remember, we are waiting for our turns."

"Speak for yourself when you are inclined to utter such incongruities," interrupted Aramis. "For my part, I think what they say is very well said, and quite worthy of two gentlemen."

"Just as soon as you please, monsieur," said Athos, putting himself on guard.

"I wait your orders," said D'Artagnan, crossing swords.

But scarcely had the two rapiers clashed, when a company of the Guards of His Eminence, commanded by M. de Jussac, turned the corner of the convent.

"The cardinal's guards!" cried Aramis and Porthos at the same time. "Sheathe your swords, gentlemen, sheathe your swords!"

But it was too late. The two combatants had been seen in a position which left no doubt of their intentions.

"Halloo!" cried Jussac, advancing towards them, and making a sign to his men to do so likewise, "halloo, musketeers! Fighting here, are you? And the edicts, what is become of them?"

"You are very generous, gentlemen of the guards," said Athos, full of rancor, for Jussac was one of the aggressors of the preceding day. "If we were to see you fighting, I can assure you that we would make no effort to prevent you. Leave us alone then, and you will enjoy a little amusement without cost to yourselves."

"Gentlemen," said Jussac, "it is with great regret that I pronounce the thing impossible. Duty before everything. Sheathe, then, if you please, and follow us."

"Monsieur," said Aramis, parodying Jussac, "it would afford us great pleasure to obey your polite invitation if it depended upon ourselves; but unfortunately the thing is impossible—Monsieur de Tréville has forbidden it. Pass on your way, then; it is the best thing to do."

This raillery exasperated Jussac. "We will charge upon you, then," said he, "if you disobey."

"There are five of them," said Athos, half-aloud, "and we are but three; we shall be beaten again, and must die on the spot, for, on my part, I declare I will never again appear before the captain as a conquered man."

Athos, Porthos, and Aramis instantly drew near one another, while Jussac drew up his soldiers.

This short interval was sufficient to determine D'Artagnan on the part he was to take. It was one of those events which decide the life of a man; it was a choice between the king and the cardinal—the choice made, it must be persisted in. To fight, that was to disobey the law, that was to risk his head, that was to make at one blow an enemy of a minister more powerful than the king himself. All this the young man perceived, and yet, to his praise, he did not hesitate a second. Turning toward Athos and his friends: "Gentle-men," said he, "allow me to correct your words, if you please. You said you were but three, but it appears to me we are four."

"But you are not one of us," said Porthos.

"That's true," replied D'Artagnan; "I have not the uniform, but I have the spirit. My heart is that of a musketeer; I feel it, monsieur, and that impels me on."

"Withdraw, young man," cried Jussac, who doubtless, by his ges-tures and the expression of his countenance, had guessed D'Arta-gnan's design. "You may retire; we consent to that. Save your skin; begone, but make it fast!"

D'Artagnan did not budge.

"Decidedly you are a brave fellow," said Athos, pressing the young man's hand.

"Come, come, choose your part," replied Jussac.

"Well," said Porthos to Aramis, "we must do something."

"Monsieur is full of generosity," said Athos.

But all three reflected upon the youth of D'Artagnan, and dreaded his inexperience.

"We should only be three, one of whom is wounded, with the ad-dition of a boy," resumed Athos; "and yet it will not be the less said we were four men."

"Yes, but to yield!" said Porthos.

D'Artagnan comprehended their irresolution.

"Try me, gentlemen," said he, "and I swear to you by my honor that I will not go hence if we are conquered."

"What is your name, my brave fellow?" said Athos.

"D'Artagnan, monsieur."

"Well, then, Athos, Porthos, Aramis, and D'Artagnan, forward!" cried Athos.

"Come, gentlemen, have you decided?" cried Jussac for the third time.

"It is done, gentlemen," said Athos.

"And what is your choice?" asked Jussac.

"We are about to have the honor of charging you," replied Aramis, lifting his hat with one hand and drawing his sword with the other.

"Ah, you resist, do you?" cried Jussac.

"*Sangdieu!* Does that astonish you?"

And the nine combatants rushed upon each other with a fury which, however, did not exclude a certain degree of method.

Athos fixed upon a certain Cahusac, a favorite of the cardinal's. Porthos had Bicarat, and Aramis found himself opposed to two adversaries. As to D'Artagnan, he found himself assailing Jussac himself.

The heart of the young Gascon beat as if it would burst through his side—not from fear, God be thanked, he had not the shade of it, but with emulation; he fought like a furious tiger, turning ten times around his adversary, and changing his ground and his guard twenty times. Jussac was, as was then said, a fine blade, and had had much practice; nevertheless, it required all his skill to defend himself against an adversary who, active and energetic, departed every instant from received rules, attacking him on all sides at once, and yet parrying like a man who had the greatest respect for his own epidermis.

This contest at length exhausted Jussac's patience. Furious at being held in check by one whom he had considered a boy, he became warm, and began to make mistakes. D'Artagnan, who though wanting in practice had a sound theory, redoubled his agility. Jussac, anxious to put an end to this, springing forward, aimed a terrible thrust at his adversary, but the latter parried it; and while Jussac was recovering himself, D'Artagnan glided like a serpent beneath his blade, and passed his sword through his body. Jussac fell like a dead mass.

D'Artagnan then cast an anxious and rapid glance over the field of battle.

Aramis had killed one of his adversaries, but the other pressed him warmly. Nevertheless, Aramis was in a good situation, and able to defend himself.

Bicarat and Porthos had just made counterhits. Porthos had received a thrust through his arm, and Bicarat one through his thigh. But neither of these two wounds was serious, and they only fought the more earnestly.

Athos, wounded anew by Cahusac, became evidently paler, but did not give way a foot. He only changed his sword hand, and fought with his left hand.

According to the laws of dueling at that period, D'Artagnan was at liberty to assist whom he pleased. While he was endeavoring to find out which of his companions stood in the greatest need, he caught a glance from Athos. This glance was of sublime eloquence. Athos would have died rather than appeal for help; but he could look, and with that look ask assistance. D'Artagnan understood. With a bound he sprang to the side of Cahusac, crying: "To me, Monsieur Guardsman; I will slay you!"

Cahusac turned. It was time; for Athos, whose great courage alone supported him, sank upon his knee.

"*Sangdieu!*" he cried to D'Artagnan, "do not kill him, young man, I beg you! I have an old affair to settle with him when I am cured and sound again. Disarm him only—make sure of his sword. That's it! Very well done!"

This exclamation was drawn from Athos by seeing the sword of Cahusac fly twenty paces from him. D'Artagnan and Cahusac sprang forward at the same instant, the one to recover, the other to obtain, the sword; but D'Artagnan, being the more active, reached it first, and placed his foot upon it.

Cahusac immediately ran to the guardsman whom Aramis had killed, seized his rapier, and returned toward D'Artagnan; but on his way he met Athos, who during this relief which D'Artagnan had procured him had recovered his breath, and who, for fear that D'Artagnan would kill his enemy, wished to resume the fight.

D'Artagnan perceived that it would be disobliging Athos not to leave him alone; and in a few minutes Cahusac fell, with a sword thrust through his throat.

At the same instant Aramis placed his sword point on the breast of his fallen enemy, and forced him to ask for mercy.

There only then remained Porthos and Bicarat. Porthos made a thousand flourishes, asking Bicarat what o'clock it could be, and offering him his compliments upon his brother's having just obtained a company in the regiment of Navarre; but, jest as he might, he gained nothing. Bicarat was one of those iron men who never fall dead.

Nevertheless, it was necessary to finish. The watch might come up and take all the combatants, wounded or not, royalists or cardinalists. Athos, Aramis, and D'Artagnan surrounded Bicarat, and required him to surrender. Though alone against all, and with a wound in his thigh, Bicarat wished to hold out; but Jussac, who had risen upon his elbow, cried out to him to yield. Bicarat was a Gascon, as

D'Artagnan was; he turned a deaf ear, and contended himself with laughing, and between two parries finding time to point to a spot of earth with his sword: "Here," cried he, parodying a verse of the Bible, "here will Bicarat die; for I only am left, and they seek my life."

"But there are four against you; leave off, I command you."

"Ah, if you command me, that's another thing," said Bicarat. "As you are my commander, it is my duty to obey." And springing backward, he broke his sword across his knee to avoid the necessity of surrendering it, threw the pieces over the convent wall, and crossed his arms, whistling a cardinalist air.

Bravery is always respected, even in an enemy. The musketeers saluted Bicarat with their swords, and returned them to their sheaths. D'Artagnan did the same. Then, assisted by Bicarat, the only one left standing, he bore Jussac, Cahusac, and one of Aramis's adversaries who was only wounded, under the porch of the convent. The fourth, as we have said, was dead. Then they rang the bell, and carrying away four swords out of five, they took their road, intoxicated with joy, toward the hotel of M. de Tréville.

They walked arm in arm, occupying the whole width of the street, and taking in every musketeer they met, so that in the end it became a triumphal march. The heart of D'Artagnan swam in delirium; he marched between Athos and Porthos, pressing them tenderly.

"If I am not yet a musketeer," said he to his new friends, as he passed through the gateway of M. de Tréville's hotel, "at least I have entered upon my apprenticeship, haven't I?"

We now know the four characters of this great masterpiece of the cloak and dagger school of romance. Athos, the aristocrat, really the Count de la Fère, is the finest type of the French nobleman. Porthos, or Monsieur du Vallon, is the embodiment of physical strength, the powerful mounting sap of the French soil. Aramis, the Chevalier d'Herblay, represents another aspect of France, its mysticism and Jesuitical learning and reasoning power. He is only temporarily a fighter: his aim is to enter the Church.

As for D'Artagnan, he represents the people of France, the common fiber, which is clever and rugged, like Henry IV.

And how good this conception was for the times in which Dumas was writing, to make these four elements of France united in a fine friendship unto death! France which has always been its own worst enemy. So that it is as if Dumas were pointing out to the French people what prodigies of valor and of astuteness four men such as these could accomplish, when truly they were "one for all, and all for one."

No sense in trying to give a resumé of the long novel. But the main theme is this: Richelieu would like to destroy the Queen of France, Anne of Austria. This queen, in a moment of weakness for the Duke of Buckingham, has given him a pledge of her affection: a valuable set of diamond studs.

Richelieu so works on King Louis XIII, that the latter projects a ball, and orders the queen to wear the diamonds to that ball.

There is no time to be lost if the queen's honor is to be saved. The four musketeers are off to England to get the jewelry and bring it back. Richelieu through his secret and treacherous henchmen, and particularly his wily and unscrupulous but beautiful female assistant, Milady, puts every obstacle in the way of this expedition to England to reach the Duke of Buckingham in time.

D'Artagnan alone succeeds, secures the jewelry and brings it back to save the queen.

While there are many wonderful incidents in this novel, three stand out in particular: and two of them concern Milady. It was Maquet, the professor of history, who brought to Dumas's attention an old forgotten book, the *Memoirs of d'Artagnan*, which suggested the main characters, and indeed many of the incidents of the book, for example the sorry nag on which D'Artagnan rides to Paris, the theft of his letter at the inn, the quadruple duel near the monastery of the unshod carmelites, and the terrible character of Milady.

Gratien de Courtilz, the author of the original work, was a sort of Dumas himself. Born in Paris in 1646, he entered a long military career, and probably met the real D'Artagnan before the latter died in 1676. After his years of warfare, in which he reached a captaincy, he settled in Holland and from there issued some sharply satirical volumes concerning life at the French court. Though anonymously printed, the author was recognized during a journey to France and shut up in the Bastille for six years. Apparently he hadn't learned his lesson, for upon his release he resumed his career as author and eventually landed in the Bastille again. He had been married three times before death took him in Paris in 1712.

But though Gratien de Courtilz' work furnished Maquet with a basis, it was Dumas who gave the work life, as a reading of both books will show. It was also Dumas who gave the book breadth and meaning. It was he who insisted that the book should bring in the figures of Louis XIII, Anne of Austria, Richelieu, the Duke of Buckingham, and thus be more than just an exciting piece of fiction.

And when the *Siècle* began to print the installments, the work caught on with such furore that circulation multiplied itself four-fold in a matter of weeks. The musketeers became the rage of France, and then of the world.

The first of the three extracts shows with what ingenuity and sangfroid the four friends operated in order to assure themselves of a conference to plan their future moves against Milady. With Richelieu's spies everywhere, and death threatening on all sides, this was no mean problem to be solved.

Milady is one of the most perverse creatures ever depicted in literature. She is not only the secret agent of the cardinal, she is also the wife of one of the musketeers, Athos, though D'Artagnan doesn't know of this tragedy of his friend. She is ready to prostitute herself for the furtherance of her plans. She uses poison and the dagger without pity.

Here, in a section called "The Bastion of Saint-Gervais," is the first of the three portions that are the best of the book.

On arriving at the lodgings of his three friends D'Artagnan found them assembled in the same chamber. Athos was meditating; Porthos was twisting his mustaches, Aramis was saying his prayers from a charming little Book of Hours, bound in blue velvet.

"*Pardieu*, gentlemen," said he. "I hope what you have to tell me is worth the trouble, or else, I warn you, I will not pardon you for making me come here instead of letting me have my little rest after a night spent in taking and dismantling a bastion. Ah, why were you not there, gentlemen? It was warm work."

"We too were in a place where it was not very cold," replied Porthos, giving his mustache a twist which was peculiar to him.

"Hush!" said Athos. "Stop bragging."

"Oh, oh!" said D'Artagnan, comprehending the slight frown of the musketeer. "It appears there is something fresh abroad."

"Aramis," said Athos, "you went to breakfast the day before yesterday at the inn of the Parpaillot, I believe?"

"Yes."

"How did you fare?"

"For my part, I ate but little. The day before yesterday was a fish day, and yet they served nothing but meat. I couldn't touch a bite."

"What," said Athos, "no fish at a seaport?"

"They say," said Aramis, resuming his pious reading, "that the dike which the cardinal is making drives them all out into the open sea."

"But that is not quite what I meant to ask you, Aramis," replied Athos. "I want to know if you were left alone, and nobody interrupted you."

"Why, I think there were not many intruders. Yes, Athos, I know what you mean: we shall do very comfortably at the Parpaillot."

"Let us go to the Parpaillot, then, for here the walls are like sheets of paper."

D'Artagnan, who was accustomed to his friend's manner of acting, and who perceived immediately, by a word, a gesture, or a sign from him, that the circumstances were serious, took Athos's arm, and went out without saying anything. Porthos followed, chatting with Aramis.

On their way they met Athos's servant, Grimaud. Athos made him a sign to come with them. Grimaud, according to custom, obeyed in silence; the poor lad had nearly come to the pass of forgetting how to speak.

They arrived at the drinking room of the Parpaillot. It was seven o'clock in the morning, and daylight began to appear. The four friends ordered breakfast, and went into a room in which the host said they would not be disturbed.

Unfortunately, the hour was badly chosen for a private conference. The morning drum had just been beaten and everyone was trying to shake off the drowsiness of night, and to dispel the humid morning air, by taking a drop at the inn. Dragoons, Swiss, guardsmen, musketeers, light-horsemen, succeeded one another with a rapidity which might answer the purpose of the host very well, but agreed badly with the views of the four friends. Thus they replied very curtly to the salutations, healths, and jokes of their friends.

"I see how it will be," said Athos; "we shall get into some petty quarrel or other, and that's the last thing we want right now. D'Artagnan, tell us what sort of a night you have had, and we will describe ours afterward."

"Ah, yes," said a light-horseman, with a glass of brandy in his hand, "ah, yes. I hear you gentlemen of the guards were in the trenches tonight, and that the Rochellais gave you quite a time."

D'Artagnan looked at Athos to know if he ought to reply to this intruder who thus mixed unasked in their conversation.

"Well," said Athos, "don't you hear Monsieur de Busigny, who does you the honor to ask you a question? Why don't you tell him what happened during the night, since these gentlemen seem to be so anxious to find out."

"You took a bastion, didn't you?" asked a Swiss, who was drinking rum out of a beer glass.

"Yes, monsieur," said D'Artagnan, bowing, "we had that honor. We even have, as you may have heard, introduced a barrel of powder under one of the angles, which in blowing up made a very pretty breach. Without reckoning that as the bastion was built yesterday all the rest of the building was badly shaken."

"And what bastion was that?" asked a dragoon, brandishing a saber run through a goose which he was taking to be cooked.

"The bastion St. Gervais," replied D'Artagnan, "from behind which the Rochellais annoyed our workmen."

"Was the affair hot?"

"Yes, moderately so. We lost five men, and the Rochellais eight or ten."

"*Balzempleu!*" said the Swiss, who, notwithstanding the admirable collection of oaths possessed by the German language, had acquired the habit of swearing in French.

"But it is probable," said the light-horseman, "that they will send pioneers this morning to repair the bastion."

"Yes, that's probable," said D'Artagnan.

"Gentlemen," said Athos, "a wager!"

"Ah, *wooi*, a vager!" cried the Swiss.

"What is it?" said the light-horseman.

"Stop a bit," said the dragoon, placing his saber like a spit upon the two large iron dogs which held the firebrands in the chimney, "stop a bit, I am in it. You cursed host! a dripping pan immediately, that I may not lose a drop of the fat of this estimable bird."

"You was right," said the Swiss; "goose-grease is kood with basdry."

"There!" said the dragoon. "Now for the wager! We listen, Monsieur Athos."

"Yes, the wager!" said the light-horseman.

"Well, Monsieur de Busigny, I will bet you," said Athos, "that my three companions, Messieurs Porthos, Aramis, and D'Artagnan, and myself, will go and breakfast in the bastion St. Gervais, and we will remain there an hour, by the watch, whatever the enemy may do to dislodge us."

Porthos and Aramis looked at each other; they began to comprehend.

"But," said D'Artagnan, in the ear of Athos, "you are going to get us all killed without mercy."

"We are much more likely to be killed," said Athos, "if we do not go."

"My faith, gentlemen," said Porthos, turning around upon his chair, and twisting his mustache, "that's a fair bet, I hope."

"I accept," said M. de Busigny; "so let us fix the stake."

"You are four, gentlemen," said Athos, "and we are four; an unlimited dinner for eight. Will that do?"

"Capitally," replied M. de Busigny.

"That shoots me," said the Swiss.

"Perfectly," said the dragoon.

The fourth auditor, who, during all this conversation had played a mute part, made a sign of the head in proof that he acquiesced in the proposition.

"The breakfast of these gentlemen is ready," said the host.

"Well, bring it," said Athos.

The host obeyed. Athos called Grimaud, pointed to a large basket which lay in a corner, and made a sign to him to wrap the food up in the napkins.

Grimaud understood that it was to be a breakfast on the grass, took the basket, packed up the viands, added the bottles, and then took the basket on his arm.

"But where are you going to eat my breakfast?" asked the host.

"What matter, if you are paid for it?" said Athos, and he threw two pistoles majestically on the table.

"Shall I give you the change, my officer?" said the host.

"No, only add two bottles of champagne, and the difference will be for the napkins."

The host had not quite so good a bargain as he at first hoped for, but he made amends by slipping in two bottles of Anjou wine instead of two bottles of champagne.

"Monsieur de Busigny," said Athos, "will you be so kind as to set your watch with mine, or permit me to regulate mine by yours?"

"Whichever you please, monsieur!" said the light-horseman, drawing from his fob a very handsome watch, studded with diamonds; "half-past seven."

"Thirty-five minutes after seven," said Athos, "by which you perceive I am five minutes faster than you."

And bowing to all the astonished persons present, the young men took the road to the bastion St. Gervais, followed by Grimaud, who carried the basket, ignorant of where he was going, but in his passive obedience drilled into him by his master, Athos, not even thinking of asking.

As long as they were within the circle of the camp, the four friends did not exchange one word; besides, they were followed by the curious, who, hearing of the wager, were anxious to know how they would come out of it. But when once they had passed the line of circumvallation, and found themselves in the open plain, D'Artagnan, who was completely ignorant of what was going forward, thought it was time to demand an explanation.

"And now, my dear Athos," said he, "do me the kindness to tell me where we are going?"

"Why, you see plainly enough we are going to the bastion."

"But what are we going to do there?"

"You know well that we go to breakfast there."

"But why did we not breakfast at the Parpaillot?"

"Because we have some very important matters to communicate to one another, and it was impossible to talk five minutes in that inn without being annoyed by all those importunate fellows, who keep coming in, saluting you, and addressing you. Here at least," said Athos, pointing to the bastion, "they will not come and disturb us."

"It appears to me," said D'Artagnan, with that prudence which allied itself in him so naturally with excessive bravery, "it appears to

me that we could have found some retired place on the downs or
the seashore."

"Where we should have been seen all four conferring together, so
that at the end of an hour the cardinal would have been informed
by his spies that we were holding a council."

"Yes," said Aramis, "Athos is right: *Animadvertuntur in desertis.*"

"A desert would not have been amiss," said Porthos; "but it be-
hooved us to find it."

"There is no desert where a bird cannot pass over one's head,
where a fish cannot leap out of the water, where a rabbit cannot
come out of its burrow, and I believe that bird, fish, and rabbit each
becomes a spy of the cardinal. Better then, pursue our enterprise;
from which, besides, we cannot retreat without shame. We have
made a wager—a wager which could not have been foreseen, and of
which I defy anyone to divine the true cause. We are going, in order
to win it, to remain an hour in the bastion. Either we shall be attacked or not. If we are not, we shall have all the time to talk, and
nobody will hear us—for I guarantee the walls of the bastion have
no ears; if we are, we will talk of our affairs just the same. Moreover,
in defending ourselves, we shall cover ourselves with glory. You see
that everything is to our advantage."

"Yes," said D'Artagnan; "but we shall indubitably attract a ball of
lead or two."

"Well, my dear friend," replied Athos, "you know well that the
balls most to be dreaded are not from the enemy."

"But for such an expedition we surely ought to have brought our
muskets."

"You are stupid, friend Porthos. Why should we load ourselves
with a useless burden?"

"I don't find a good musket, twelve cartridges, and a powder flask
very useless in face of an enemy."

"Well," replied Athos, "have you not heard what D'Artagnan
said?"

"What did he say?" demanded Porthos.

"D'Artagnan said that in the attack of last night eight or ten
Frenchmen were killed, and as many Rochellais."

"What then?"

"The bodies were not plundered, were they? It appears the conquerors had something else to do."

"Well?"

"Well, we shall find their muskets, their cartridges, and their flasks; and instead of four musketoons and twelve balls, we shall have fifteen guns and a hundred charges to fire."

"Oh, Athos!" said Aramis, "truly you are a great man."

Porthos nodded in sign of agreement. D'Artagnan alone did not seem convinced.

Grimaud no doubt shared the misgivings of the young man, for seeing that they continued to advance towards the bastion—something he had till then doubted—he pulled his master by the skirt of his coat.

"Where are we going?" asked he, by a gesture.

Athos pointed to the bastion.

"But," said Grimaud, in the same silent dialect, "we shall leave our skins there."

Athos raised his eyes and his finger towards heaven. "If it be God's will."

Grimaud put his basket on the ground and sat down with a shake of the head.

Athos took a pistol from his belt, looked to see if it was properly primed, cocked it, and placed the muzzle close to Grimaud's ear.

Grimaud was on his legs again as if launched by a spring. Athos then made him a sign to take up the basket and to walk on first. Grimaud obeyed. All that Grimaud gained by this momentary pantomime was to pass from the rear guard to the vanguard.

Arrived at the bastion, the four friends turned around.

More than three hundred soldiers of all kinds were assembled at the gate of the camp; and in a separate group might be distinguished M. de Busigny, the dragoon, the Swiss, and the fourth bettor.

Athos took off his hat, placed it on the end of his sword, and waved it in the air.

All the spectators returned him his salute, accompanying this courtesy with a loud hurrah which was audible to the four; after which all four disappeared in the bastion, whither Grimaud had preceded them.

As Athos had foreseen, the bastion was only occupied by a dozen corpses, French and Rochellais.

"Gentlemen," said Athos, who had assumed the command of the expedition, "while Grimaud spreads the table, let us begin by collecting the guns and cartridges together. We can talk while performing the necessary task. These gentlemen," added he, pointing to the bodies, "cannot hear us."

"But we could throw them into the ditch," said Porthos, "after having assured ourselves they have nothing in their pockets."

"Yes," said Athos, "that's Grimaud's business."

"Well, then," cried D'Artagnan, "pray let Grimaud search them and throw them over the walls."

"Heaven forfend!" said Athos; "they may serve us."

"These bodies serve us?" said Porthos. "You are mad, dear friend."

"Judge not rashly, say both the Gospel and the cardinal," replied Athos. "How many guns, gentlemen?"

"Twelve," replied Aramis.

"How many shots?"

"A hundred."

"That's quite as many as we shall want. Let us load the guns."

The four musketeers went to work; and as they were loading the last musket, Grimaud announced that the breakfast was ready.

Athos replied, always by gestures, that that was well, and indicated to Grimaud, by pointing to a kind of pepper caster, that he was to stand as sentinel. Only, to alleviate the tediousness of the duty, Athos allowed him to take a loaf, two cutlets, and a bottle of wine.

"And now, to table," said Athos.

The four friends seated themselves on the ground with their legs crossed. Like Turks, or tailors.

"And now," said D'Artagnan, "as there is no longer any fear of being overheard, I hope you are going to let me into your secret."

"I hope to procure for you at one and the same time amusement and glory, gentlemen," said Athos. "I have induced you to take a charming promenade; here is a delicious breakfast; and yonder are five hundred persons, as you may see through the loopholes, taking us for heroes or madmen—two classes of imbeciles greatly resembling each other."

"But the secret!" said D'Artagnan.

"The secret is," said Athos, "that I saw Milady last night."

D'Artagnan was lifting a glass to his lips; but at the name of Milady, his hand trembled so that he was obliged to put the glass on the ground again for fear of spilling the contents.

"You saw your wi——"

"Hush!" interrupted Athos. "You forget, my dear, you forget that these gentlemen are not initiated into my family affairs like yourself. I have seen Milady."

"Where?" demanded D'Artagnan.

"Within two leagues of this place, at the inn of the Red Dovecot."

"In that case I am lost," said D'Artagnan.

"Not so bad yet," replied Athos; "for by this time she must have quitted the shores of France."

D'Artagnan breathed again.

"But after all," asked Porthos, "who is Milady?"

"A charming woman!" said Athos, sipping a glass of sparkling wine. "Villainous host!" cried he, "he has given us Anjou wine instead of champagne, and fancies we know no better! Yes," continued he, "a charming woman, who entertained kind views toward our friend D'Artagnan, who, on his part, has given her some offense for which she tried to revenge herself a month ago by having him killed by two musket shots, a week ago by trying to poison him, and yesterday by demanding his head of the cardinal."

"What! by demanding my head of the cardinal?" cried D'Artagnan, pale with terror.

"Yes, that is as true as the Gospel," said Porthos; "I heard her with my own ears."

"I also," said Aramis.

"Then," said D'Artagnan, letting his arm fall with discouragement, "it is useless to struggle longer. I may as well blow my brains out, and all will be over."

"That's the last folly to be committed," said Athos, "seeing it is the only one for which there is no remedy."

"But I can never escape," said D'Artagnan, "with such enemies. First, my unknown man of Meung; then De Wardes, to whom I have given three sword wounds; next Milady, whose secret I have discovered; finally, the cardinal, whose vengeance I have balked."

"Well," said Athos, "that only makes four; and we are four—one for one. *Pardieu!* if we may believe the signs Grimaud is making, we are about to have to do with a very different number of people. What is it, Grimaud? Considering the gravity of the occasion, I permit you to speak, my friend; but be laconic, I beg. What do you see?"

"A troop."

"Of how many persons?"

"Twenty men."

"What sort of men?"

"Sixteen pioneers, four soldiers."

"How far distant?"

"Five hundred paces."

"Good, we have just time to finish this fowl, and to drink one glass of wine to your health, D'Artagnan!"

"To your health!" repeated Porthos and Aramis.

"Well, then, to my health; although I am very much afraid that your good wishes will not be of great service to me."

"Bah!" said Athos, "God is great, as say the followers of Mahomet, and the future is in his hands."

Then, swallowing the contents of the glass, which he put down close to him, Athos arose carelessly, took the musket next to him, and drew near to one of the loopholes.

Porthos, Aramis, and D'Artagnan followed his example. As to Grimaud, he received orders to place himself behind the four friends, in order to reload their weapons.

At the expiration of a minute the troop appeared. They advanced along a sort of narrow channel of the trench which made a means of communication between the bastion and the city.

"*Pardieu!*" said Athos, "it was hardly worth while to disturb ourselves for twenty fellows, armed with pickaxes, mattocks, and shovels. Grimaud had only to make them a sign to go away, and I am convinced they would have left us in peace."

"I doubt that," replied D'Artagnan, "for they are advancing very resolutely. Besides, in addition to the pioneers, there are four soldiers and a brigadier, armed with muskets."

"That's because they don't see us," said Athos.

"My faith," said Aramis, "I must confess I feel a great repugnance to fire on these poor devils of civilians."

"He is a bad priest," said Porthos, "who has pity for heretics!"

"In truth," said Athos, "Aramis is right. I will warn them."

"What the devil are you going to do?" cried D'Artagnan. "You will be shot, my dear fellow."

But Athos heeded not his advice. Mounting on the breach, with his musket in one hand, and his hat in the other, he bowed courteously, and addressed himself to the soldiers and the pioneers, who, astonished at this apparition, stopped fifty paces from the bastion: "Gentlemen, a few friends and myself are about to breakfast in this bastion. Now, you know nothing is more disagreeable than being disturbed when one is at breakfast. We request you, then, if you really have business here, to wait till we have finished our repast, or to come again a short time hence; unless, which would be far better, you form the salutary resolution to quit the side of the rebels, and come and drink with us to the health of the King of France."

"Take care, Athos!" cried D'Artagnan; "don't you see they are aiming?"

"Yes, yes," said Athos; "but they are only civilians—very bad marksmen, who will be sure not to hit me."

In fact, at the same instant four shots were fired, and the balls were flattened against the wall around Athos, but not one touched him.

Four shots replied to them almost instantaneously, but much better aimed than those of the aggressors; three soldiers fell dead, and one of the pioneers was wounded.

"Grimaud," said Athos, still on the breach, "another musket!"

Grimaud obeyed immediately. On their part, the three friends had reloaded their arms; a second discharge followed the first. The brigadier and two pioneers fell dead; the rest of the troop took to flight.

"Now, gentlemen, a *sortie!*" cried Athos.

And the four friends rushed out of the fort, gained the field of battle, picked up the four muskets of the privates and the half-pike of the brigadier, and, convinced that the fugitives would not stop till they reached the city, turned again towards the bastion, bearing with them the trophies of their victory.

"Reload the muskets, Grimaud," said Athos, "and we, gentlemen, will go on with our breakfast, and resume our conversation. Where were we?"

"I recollect you were saying," said D'Artagnan, "that after having demanded my head of the cardinal, Milady had quitted the shores of France. But you didn't say in what direction," he added.

"She goes to England," said Athos.

"With what view?"

"With the view of assassinating, or causing to be assassinated, the Duke of Buckingham."

D'Artagnan uttered an exclamation of surprise and indignation.

"But this is infamous!" cried he.

"As to that," said Athos, "I beg you to believe that I care very little about it. Now you have done Grimaud, take our brigadier's half-pike, tie a napkin to it, and plant it at the top of our bastion, that these rebels of Rochellais may see that they have to deal with brave and loyal soldiers of the king."

Grimaud obeyed without replying. An instant afterward, the white flag was floating over the heads of the four friends. A thunder of applause saluted its appearance; half the camp was at the barrier.

"What is this?" D'Artagnan cried. "You care little if she kills Buckingham or causes him to be killed? But the duke is our friend."

"The duke is English; the duke fights against us. Let her do what she likes with the duke; I care no more about him than about this empty bottle." And Athos threw fifteen paces from him an empty bottle from which he had poured the last drop into his glass.

"One moment," said D'Artagnan. "I will not abandon Buckingham. He gave us some very fine horses."

"And moreover, very handsome saddles," said Porthos, who at the moment wore on his cloak the lace of his own.

"Besides," said Aramis, "God desires the conversion and not the death of a sinner."

"Amen!" said Athos. "We must return to that subject later, if such be your pleasure; but what for the moment engaged my attention most earnestly, and I am sure you will follow me, D'Artagnan, was the fact that this woman managed to extort from the cardinal a kind of *carte blanche* by means of which she can with impunity get rid of you. And perhaps of all of us."

"But this creature must be a demon!" said Porthos, holding out his plate to Aramis, who was cutting up a fowl. "Some more please."

"And this *carte blanche*," said D'Artagnan, "this *carte blanche*, does it remain in her hands?"

"No, it passed into mine; I will not say without trouble, for if I did I should tell a lie."

"My dear Athos, I shall no longer count the number of times I am indebted to you for my life."

"Then it was to go to her that you left us?" said Aramis.

"Exactly."

"And you have that letter of the cardinal?" said D'Artagnan.

"Here it is," said Athos; and he took the invaluable paper from the pocket of his uniform. D'Artagnan unfolded it with one hand, whose trembling he did not even attempt to conceal, and read:

Dec. 3, 1627

It is by my order and for the good of the state that the bearer has done what he has done.

RICHELIEU.

"This," said Aramis, "is nothing less than an absolution to do anything whatsoever!"

"That paper must be torn to pieces," said D'Artagnan, who fancied he read in it his sentence of death, and reached for it eagerly.

"On the contrary," said Athos, "it must be preserved carefully. I would not give up this paper if it were covered with as many gold pieces."

"But what will she do now?" asked the young man.

"Why," replied Athos, carelessly, "she is probably going to write to the cardinal that a damned musketeer, named Athos, has taken her safe-conduct from her by force; she will advise him in the same letter to get rid of his two friends, Aramis and Porthos, at the same time. The cardinal will remember that these are the same men who have so often crossed his path; and then some fine morning he will arrest D'Artagnan, and for fear he should feel lonely, he will send us to keep him company in the Bastille."

"Stop it! I don't appreciate your dull jokes, my friend," said Porthos.

"I do not jest," said Athos.

"Do you know," said Porthos, "that to twist that damned Milady's neck would be a smaller sin than to twist those of these poor devils of Huguenots, who have committed no other crime than singing in French the psalms we sing in Latin?"

"What says the abbé?" asked Athos, quietly.

"I say I am entirely of Porthos's opinion," replied Aramis.

"And I too," said D'Artagnan.

"Fortunately, she is far off," said Porthos, "for I confess she would worry me if she were here."

"She worries me in England as well as in France," said Athos.

"She worries me everywhere," said D'Artagnan.

"But when you held her in your power, why did you not drown her, strangle her, hang her?" said Porthos. "It is only the dead who do not return."

"You think so, Porthos?" replied the musketeer, with a sad smile which D'Artagnan alone understood.

"I have an idea," said D'Artagnan.

"What is it?" said the musketeers.

"To arms!" cried Grimaud.

The young men sprang up, and seized their muskets.

This time a small troop advanced, consisting of from twenty to twenty-five men; but they were not pioneers, they were soldiers of the garrison.

"Shall we return to the camp?" said Porthos. "I don't think the sides are equal."

"Impossible, for three reasons," replied Athos. "The first, that we have not finished breakfast; the second, that we have still some very important things to say; and the third, that it yet wants ten minutes before the lapse of the hour."

"Well, then," said Aramis, "we must form a plan of battle."

"That's very simple," replied Athos. "As soon as the enemy are within musket-shot, we must fire upon them. If they continue to advance, we must fire again. We must fire as long as we have loaded guns. If those who remain of the troop persist in coming to the assault, we will allow the besiegers to get as far as the ditch, and then we will push down upon their heads that strip of wall which keeps its perpendicular by a miracle."

"Bravo!" cried Porthos. "Decidedly, Athos, you were born to be a general, and the cardinal, who fancies himself a great soldier, is nothing beside you."

"Gentlemen," said Athos, "no divided attention, I beg; let each one pick out his man."

"I cover mine," said D'Artagnan.

"And I mine," said Porthos.

"And I *idem*," said Aramis.

"Fire, then," said Athos.

The four muskets made but one report, but four men fell.

The drum immediately beat, and the little troop advanced at a charging pace.

Then the shots were repeated without regularity, but always aimed with the same accuracy. Nevertheless, as if they had been aware of the numerical weakness of the friends, the Rochellais continued to advance in quick time.

With every three shots at least two men fell; but the march of those who remained was not slackened.

Arrived at the foot of the bastion, there was still more than a dozen of the enemy. A last discharge welcomed them, but did not stop them; they jumped into the ditch, and prepared to scale the breach.

"Now, my friends," said Athos, "finish them at a blow. To the wall; to the wall!"

And the four friends, seconded by Grimaud, pushed with the barrels of their muskets an enormous sheet of the wall, which bent as if pushed by the wind, and, detaching itself from its base, fell with a horrible crash into the ditch. Then a fearful cry was heard; a cloud of dust mounted toward the sky—and all was over!

"Can we have destroyed them all, from the first to the last?" said Athos.

"My faith, it appears so!" said D'Artagnan.

"No," cried Porthos; "there go three or four, limping away."

In fact, three or four of these unfortunate men, covered with dirt and blood, fled along the hollow way, and at length regained the city. These were all who were left of the little troop.

Athos looked at his watch.

"Gentlemen," said he, "we have been here an hour, and our wager is won; but we will be fair players. Besides, D'Artagnan has not told us his idea yet."

And the musketeer, with his usual coolness, reseated himself before the remains of the breakfast.

"My idea?" said D'Artagnan.

"Yes; you said you had an idea," said Athos.

"Oh, I remember," said D'Artagnan. "Well, I will go to England a second time; I will go and find Buckingham."

"You shall not do that, D'Artagnan," said Athos, coolly.

"And why not? Have I not been there once?"

"Yes; but at that period we were not at war. At that period Buckingham was an ally, and not an enemy. What you would now do amounts to treason."

D'Artagnan perceived the force of this reasoning, and was silent.

"But," said Porthos, "I think I have an idea, in my turn."

"Silence for Monsieur Porthos's idea!" said Aramis.

"I will ask leave of absence of Monsieur de Tréville, on some pretext or other which you must invent; I am not very clever at pretexts. Milady does not know me; I will get access to her without her suspecting me, and when I catch my beauty, I will strangle her."

"Well," replied Athos, "I am not far from approving the idea of Monsieur Porthos."

"For shame!" said Aramis. "Kill a woman? No, listen to me; I have the true idea."

"Let us hear your idea, Aramis," said Athos, who felt considerable deference for the young musketeer.

"We must inform the queen."

"Ah, my faith, yes!" said Porthos and D'Artagnan, at the same time; "we are coming nearer to it now."

"Inform the queen!" said Athos; "and how? Have we relations with the court? Could we send anyone to Paris without its being known in the camp? From here to Paris it is a hundred and forty leagues; before our letter got to Angers we should all be in a dungeon."

"As to remitting a letter with safety to Her Majesty," said Aramis, coloring, "I will take that upon myself. I know a clever person at Tours—"

Aramis stopped on seeing Athos smile.

"Well, do you not adopt this means, Athos?" said D'Artagnan.

"I do not reject it altogether," said Athos; "but I wish to remind Aramis that he cannot quit the camp, and that nobody but one of ourselves is trustworthy; that two hours after the messenger has set out, all the capuchins, all the police, all the black caps of the cardinal, will know your letter by heart, and you and your clever person will be arrested."

"Without reckoning," objected Porthos, "that the queen would save Monsieur de Buckingham, but would take no heed of us."

"Gentlemen," said D'Artagnan, "what Porthos says is full of sense."

"Ah, ah! but what's going on in the city yonder?" said Athos.

"They are beating the general alarm."

The four friends listened, and the sound of the drum plainly reached them.

"You see, they are going to send a whole regiment against us," said Athos.

"You don't think of holding out against a whole regiment, do you?" said Porthos.

"Why not?" said the musketeer. "I feel myself quite in a humor for it; and I would hold out before an army if we had taken the precaution to bring a dozen more bottles of wine."

"Upon my word, the drum draws near," said D'Artagnan.

"Let it come," said Athos. "It is a quarter of an hour's journey from here to the city, consequently a quarter of an hour's journey from the city hither. That is more than time enough for us to devise a plan. If we go from this place we shall never find another so suitable. Ah, stop! I have it, gentlemen; the right idea has just occurred to me."

"Tell us."

"Allow me to give Grimaud some indispensable orders."

Athos made a sign for his lackey to approach.

"Grimaud," said Athos, pointing to the bodies which lay under the wall of the bastion, "take those gentlemen, set them up against the wall, put their hats upon their heads, and their guns in their hands."

"Oh, the great man!" cried D'Artagnan. "I comprehend now."

"You comprehend?" said Porthos.

"And do you comprehend, Grimaud?" said Aramis.

Grimaud made a sign in the affirmative.

"That's all that is necessary," said Athos; "now for my idea."

"I should like, however, to comprehend," said Porthos.

"That is useless."

"Yes, yes! Athos's idea!" cried Aramis and D'Artagnan, at the same time.

"This Milady, this woman, this creature, this demon, has a brother-in-law, as I think you told me, D'Artagnan?"

"Yes, I know him very well; and I also believe that he has not a very warm affection for his sister-in-law."

"There is no harm in that. If he detested her it would be all the better," replied Athos.

"In that case we are as well off as we wish."

"And yet," said Porthos, "I would like to know what Grimaud is about."

"Silence, Porthos!" said Aramis.

"What is her brother-in-law's name?"

"Lord de Winter."

"Where is he now?"

"He returned to London at the first sound of war."

"Well, there's just the man we want," said Athos. "It is he whom we must warn. We will have him informed that his sister-in-law is on the point of having someone assassinated, and beg him not to lose sight of her. There is in London, I hope, some establishment like that of the Magdalens, or of the Repentant Daughters. He must place his sister in one of these, and we shall be in peace."

"Yes," said D'Artagnan, "till she comes out."

"Ah, my faith!" said Athos, "you require too much, D'Artagnan. I have given you all I have, and I beg leave to tell you that this is the bottom of my sack."

"But I think it would be still better," said Aramis, "to inform the queen and Lord de Winter at the same time."

"Yes; but who is to carry the letter to Tours, and who to London?"

"I answer for Bazin," said Aramis of his man.

"And I for Planchet," said D'Artagnan, speaking of his servant.

"Ay," said Porthos, "if we cannot leave the camp, our lackeys may."

"To be sure, they may; and this very day we will write the letters," said Aramis. "Give the lackeys money, and they will start."

"We will give them money?" replied Athos. "Have you any money?"

The four friends looked at one another, and a cloud came over the brows which but lately had been so cheerful.

"Look out!" cried D'Artagnan, "I see black points and red points moving yonder. Why did you talk of a regiment, Athos? It is a veritable army!"

"My faith, yes," said Athos; "there they are. See the sneaks come, without drum or trumpet. Ah, ah! have you finished, Grimaud?"

Grimaud made a sign in the affirmative, and pointed to a dozen bodies which he had set up in the most picturesque attitudes. Some carried arms, others seemed to be taking aim, and the remainder appeared merely to be sword in hand.

"Bravo!" cried Athos; "that does honor to your imagination."

"All very well," said Porthos, "but I should like to understand."

"Let us decamp first, and you will understand afterward."

"A moment, gentlemen; a moment; give Grimaud time to clear away the breakfast."

"Ah, ah!" said Aramis, "the black points and the red points are visibly enlarging. I am of D'Artagnan's opinion; we have no time to lose in regaining our camp."

"My faith," said Athos, "I have nothing more to say against a retreat. We betted upon one hour, and we have stayed an hour and a half. Nothing can be said; let us be off, gentlemen, let us be off!"

Grimaud was already ahead, with the basket and the dessert. The four friends followed, ten paces behind him.

"What the devil shall we do now, gentlemen?" cried Athos.

"Have you forgotten anything?" said Aramis.

"The white flag, *morbleu!* We must not leave a flag in the hands of the enemy, even if that flag be but a napkin."

And Athos ran back to the bastion, mounted the platform, and bore off the flag; but as the Rochellais had arrived within musket range, they opened a terrible fire upon this man, who appeared to expose himself for pleasure's sake.

But Athos might be said to bear a charmed life. The balls passed and whistled all around him; not one struck him.

Athos waved his flag, turning his back on the guards of the city, and saluting those of the camp. On both sides loud cries arose—on the one side cries of anger, on the other cries of enthusiasm.

A second discharge followed the first, and three balls, by passing through it, made the napkin really a flag. Cries were heard from the camp: "Come down! come down!"

Athos came down; his friends, who anxiously awaited him, saw him return with joy.

"Come along, Athos, come along!" cried D'Artagnan; "now we have found everything except money, it would be stupid to be killed."

But Athos continued to march majestically, whatever remarks his companions made; and they, finding their remarks useless, regulated their pace by his.

Grimaud and his basket were far in advance, out of the range of the balls.

At the end of an instant they heard a furious fusillade.

"What's that?" asked Porthos, "what are they firing at now? I hear no balls whistle, and I see nobody!"

"They are firing at the corpses," replied Athos.

"But the dead cannot return their fire."

"Certainly not! They will then fancy it is an ambuscade, they will deliberate; and by the time they have found out the pleasantry, we shall be out of the range of their balls. That renders it useless to get a pleurisy by too much haste."

"Oh, I comprehend now," said the astonished Porthos.

"That's lucky," said Athos, shrugging his shoulders.

On their part, the French, on seeing the four friends return at such a step, uttered cries of enthusiasm.

At length a fresh discharge was heard, and this time the balls came rattling among the stones around the four friends, and whistling sharply in their ears. The Rochellais had at last taken possession of the bastion.

"These Rochellais are bungling fellows," said Athos; "how many have we killed of them—a dozen?"

"Or fifteen."

"How many did we crush under the wall?"

"Eight or ten."

"And in exchange for all that not even a scratch! Ah, but what is the matter with your hand, D'Artagnan? It bleeds, seemingly."

"Oh, it's nothing," said D'Artagnan.

"A spent ball?"

"Not even that."

"What is it, then?"

We have said that Athos loved D'Artagnan like a child, and his somber and inflexible personage felt the anxiety of a parent for the young man.

"Only grazed a little," replied D'Artagnan; "my fingers were caught between two stones—that of the wall and that of my ring—and the skin was broken."

"That comes of wearing diamonds, my master," said Athos, disdainfully.

"Ah, to be sure," cried Porthos, "there is a diamond. Why the devil, then, do we plague ourselves about money, when there is a diamond?"

"Stop a bit!" said Aramis.

"Well thought of, Porthos; this time you have an idea."

"Undoubtedly," said Porthos, drawing himself up at Athos's compliment; "as there is a diamond, let us sell it."

"But," said D'Artagnan, "it is the queen's diamond."

"The stronger reason why it should be sold," replied Athos. "The queen saving Monsieur de Buckingham, her lover; nothing more just. The queen saving us, her friends; nothing more moral. Let us sell the diamond. What says Monsieur l'Abbé? I don't ask Porthos; his opinion has been given."

"Why, I think," said Aramis, blushing as usual, "that his ring not coming from a mistress, and consequently not being a love token, D'Artagnan may sell it."

"My dear Aramis, you speak like theology personified. Your advice, then, is—"

"To sell the diamond," replied Aramis.

"Well, then," said D'Artagnan gayly, "let us sell the diamond, and say no more about it."

The fusillade continued; but the friends were out of reach, and the Rochellais only fired to appease their consciences.

"My faith, it was time that idea came into Porthos's head. Here we are at the camp; therefore, gentlemen, not a word more of this affair. We are observed; they are coming to meet us. We shall be carried in triumph."

In fact, as we have said, the whole camp was in motion. More than two thousand persons had assisted, as at a spectacle, in this fortunate but wild undertaking of the four friends—an undertaking of which they were far from suspecting the real motive. Nothing was heard but cries of "Long live the musketeers! Long live the guards!"

M. de Busigny was the first to come and shake Athos by the hand, and acknowledge that the wager was lost. The dragoon and the Swiss followed him, and all their comrades followed the dragoon and the Swiss. There was nothing but felicitations, pressures of the hand, and embraces; there was no end to the inextinguishable laughter at the Rochellais. The tumult at length became so great that the cardinal fancied there must be some riot, and sent La Houdinière, his captain of the guards, to inquire what was going on.

The affair was described to the messenger with all the effervescence of enthusiasm.

"Well?" asked the cardinal, on seeing La Houdinière return.

"Well, Monseigneur," replied the latter, "three musketeers and a guardsman laid a wager with Monsieur de Busigny that they would go and breakfast in the bastion St. Gervais; and while breakfasting, they held it for two hours against the enemy, and killed I don't know how many Rochellais."

"Did you inquire the names of those three musketeers?"

"Yes, Monseigneur."

"What are their names?"

"Messieurs Athos, Porthos, and Aramis."

"Still my three brave fellows!" murmured the cardinal. "And the guardsman?"

"D'Artagnan."

"Still my young scapegrace. Positively, these four men must be on my side."

That same evening the cardinal spoke to M. de Tréville of the exploit of the morning, which was the talk of the whole camp. M. de Tréville, who had received the account of the adventure from the mouths of the heroes of it, related it in all its details to His Eminence, not forgetting the episode of the napkin.

"That's well, Monsieur de Tréville," said the cardinal; "pray let that napkin be sent to me. I will have three *fleurs-de-lis* embroidered on it in gold, and will give it to your company as a standard."

"Monseigneur," said M. de Tréville, "that will be unjust to the guardsmen. Monsieur d'Artagnan is not with me; he serves under Monsieur d'Essart."

"Well, then, take him," said the cardinal; "when four men are so much attached to one another, it is only fair that they should serve in the same company."

That very evening, M. de Tréville announced this good news to the three musketeers and D'Artagnan, at the same time inviting all four to breakfast with him next morning.

D'Artagnan was beside himself with joy. We know that the dream of his life had been to become a musketeer. The three friends were likewise greatly delighted.

"My faith," said D'Artagnan to Athos, "you had a triumphant idea! As you said, we have acquired glory, and were enabled to carry on a conversation of the highest importance."

"Which we can resume now without anybody suspecting us, for, with the help of God, we shall henceforth pass for cardinalists."

That evening D'Artagnan went to present his respects to M. d'Essart, and to inform him of his promotion.

M. d'Essart, who esteemed D'Artagnan, made him offers of help, as this change would entail expenses for equipment.

D'Artagnan refused; but thinking the opportunity a good one, he begged him to have the diamond he put into his hand valued, as he wished to turn it into money.

The next day, by two o'clock, M. d'Essart's valet came to D'Artagnan's lodging, and gave him a bag containing seven thousand livres.

This was the price of the queen's diamond.

Chapter V

THE INCOMPARABLE MILADY

THE plan concocted by the four men at the bastion is executed and Lord de Winter imprisons Milady. That story is told in this excellent portion which might easily stand alone as a short and fascinating novel.

The First Day of Captivity

Let us now return to Milady, whom we lost sight of for an instant while occupied with details of the other members of our story.

We shall discover her just as we left her, plunged in despair at her imprisonment, brooding with dismal reflections on her condition —trapped in a dark hell, with all hope abandoned, because for the first time she knew doubt; for the first time she knew fear.

Twice now fortune had failed her. Twice she had seen herself discovered and betrayed. And both times it was D'Artagnan who had been her fatal genius—a devil, sent no doubt by God Himself, to be the power of evil that should defeat her.

In her love he had come to deceive her. In her pride he had come to humble her. In her ambition he had come to thwart her. And now he was ruining not only her fortune, but depriving her of her liberty, and threatening her very life! And worse than that: he had penetrated her disguise—not altogether, no, that far he hadn't succeeded, but far enough to shake her strength, which would fail her if ever she were deprived of her mask.

And just when she had obtained from Richelieu that *carte blanche* by which she held D'Artagnan's life in her hands, the paper had been snatched from her—and instead it was she who was the prisoner of D'Artagnan, she who was about to be sent off to some hellhole of a Botany Bay, some infamous Tyburn of the Indian Ocean.

D'Artagnan! Everywhere it was D'Artagnan. D'Artagnan who turned aside from Buckingham (whom she hated as she had to hate everyone whom she had loved) the tempest that Richelieu had devised to shipwreck him along with the queen of France. D'Artagnan, who had passed himself off as De Wardes, and for whom she had conceived one of those tigerlike fancies common to women of her type.

D'Artagnan, finally, who had fathomed that terrible secret of hers, which she had sworn no one should ever know without dying. Yes, and therefore it could be no one else but D'Artagnan who had conveyed to Lord de Winter all that he knew about her, and thus brought her to her present condition.

What hatred she was now distilling, as she crouched in her prison, without stirring, but with an angry roar filling her chest and rising now and then like the surge of the breakers, from the depths of her being, rising and growling and roaring like angry waves dashing themselves uselessly against dark rocks. Not that any real sound escaped from her. But her burning eyes, her fixed stare, revealed the passion in her.

Like flashes of lightning in a black sky, dreams of revenge glowed and extinguished, one after the other, as she thought of Madame Bonacieux, of Buckingham, but above all as she thought of D'Artagnan.

But how ridiculous! In order to revenge herself she had to be free! And how does one pierce a wall? How does one detach a bar, cut through the floor, assault guards? These are operations for a strong and patient man, not for a woman shaken by feverish irritations. Besides what plan could hope to achieve success in the space of days? She needed months, years. And instead she had twelve days, just as Lord de Winter, her terrible jailer—and brother-in-law—had said.

And yet, were she a man, she would attempt it. She would attempt anything, no matter what the odds. And succeed too. God, that she should be a woman—when in her frail and delicate body there raged a soul that was male to the core. What a dreadful error!

But only the first moments of her captivity were spent in this useless raging against the inevitable. A few convulsions which she could not suppress, and she had paid her debt of feminine weakness to nature. Then the outbursts of her mad passion, her nervous tremblings which agitated her frame, began to diminish and disappear, and she remained as if folded within herself, like a fatigued serpent in repose.

"What nonsense! I must have been mad to let myself be carried away," she said, and gazed into a mirror that reflected back eyes so full of the flame of passion that she had to scold herself.

"Violence? Why should I dream of violence, when it is nothing but a proof of weakness. When have I ever succeeded in anything by means of violence? If I were struggling against another woman, yes then I might hope to find one that was weaker than I am, and thus win out. But here I must match myself against men. And all the more reason then why I should fight like a woman. For against men it is the weakness of women that is their strength."

Then, as if to draw up a column of figures in the bookkeeping of her resources, she began to place, one by one, upon her countenance that was so mobile and so expressive, those characteristics that could help her: substituting for her anger and her vindictiveness which had convulsed her features, the sweetest, the most affectionate, the most seductive of smiles.

She brushed and combed her hair, brought out all its curls, arranged it to add to the charms of her face. And soon she murmured: "Come, nothing is lost: I'm still beautiful." And she felt quite satisfied with herself.

It was now nearly eight o'clock in the evening. Milady noticed the bed. She calculated that a repose of a few hours would not only refresh her brains and give her new and clever ideas, but would do her complexion good too.

A better idea, however, came into her mind before going to bed. She had heard something said about supper. She had already been in this apartment for an hour. They could not delay very much longer before bringing her something to eat. Now was the time to make an attempt to ascertain the nature of the ground on which she had to work—by studying the characters of the various men into whose guardianship she was committed.

A light appeared under the door; this light announced the re-appearance of her jailers. Milady, who had risen, threw herself quickly into the armchair, her head thrown back, her beautiful hair unbound and disheveled, her bosom half bare beneath her crumpled lace, one hand on her heart, and the other hanging down.

The bolts were drawn; the door groaned upon its hinges; steps sounded in the chamber and drew near.

"Place that table there," said a voice which the prisoner recognized as that of Felton.

The order was executed.

"You will bring lights, and relieve the sentinel," continued Felton.

And this double order which the young lieutenant gave to the same individuals proved to Milady that her servants were the same men as her guards; that is to say, soldiers.

Felton's orders were, for the rest, executed with a silent rapidity that gave a good idea of the way in which he maintained discipline.

At length Felton, who had not yet looked at Milady, turned toward her.

"Ah, ah," said he, "she is asleep; that's well. When she wakes she can sup." And he made some steps toward the door.

"But, my lieutenant," said a soldier, less stoical than his chief, and who had approached Milady, "this woman is not asleep."

"What, not asleep!" said Felton; "what is she doing, then?"

"She has fainted. Her face is very pale, and I have listened in vain; I do not hear her breathe."

"You are right," said Felton, after having looked at Milady from the spot on which he stood without moving a step toward her. "Go and tell Lord de Winter that his prisoner has fainted—for I don't know what to do in this case."

The soldier went out to obey the orders of his officer. Felton sat down upon an armchair which happened to be near the door, and waited without speaking a word, without making a gesture. Milady possessed that great art, so much studied by women, of looking through her long eyelashes without appearing to open the lids. She perceived Felton, who sat with his back toward her. She continued to look at him for nearly ten minutes, and in these ten minutes the immovable guardian never turned around once.

She then thought that Lord de Winter would come, and by his

presence give fresh strength to her jailer. Her first trial was lost; she acted like a woman who reckons up her resources. As a result she raised her head, opened her eyes, and sighed deeply.

At this sign Felton turned around.

"Ah, you are awake, madame," he said; "then I have nothing more to do here. If you want anything you can ring."

"Oh, my God, my God! how I have suffered!" said Milady, in that harmonious voice which, like that of the ancient enchantresses, charmed all whom she wished to destroy.

And she assumed, upon sitting up in the armchair, a still more graceful and abandoned position than when she reclined.

Felton arose.

"You will be served, thus, madame, three times a day," said he. "In the morning at nine o'clock, in the day at one o'clock, and in the evening at eight. If that does not suit you, you can point out what other hours you prefer, and in this respect your wishes will be complied with."

"But am I to remain always alone in this vast and dismal chamber?" asked Milady.

"A woman of the neighborhood has been sent for, who will be tomorrow at the castle, and will return as often as you desire her presence."

"I thank you, sir," replied the prisoner, humbly.

Felton made a slight bow, and directed his steps toward the door. At the moment he was about to go out, Lord de Winter appeared in the corridor, followed by the soldier who had been sent to inform him of the swoon of Milady. He held a vial of salts in his hand.

"Well, what is it—what is going on here?" said he, in a jeering voice, on seeing the prisoner sitting up, and Felton about to go out. "Is this corpse come to life already? Felton, my lad, did you not perceive that you were taken for a novice, and that the first act was being performed of a comedy of which we shall doubtless have the pleasure of following out all the developments?"

"I thought so, my lord," said Felton; "but as the prisoner is a woman, after all, I wish to pay her the attention that every man of gentle birth owes a woman, if not on her account, at least on my own."

Milady shuddered through her whole system. These words of Felton's passed like ice through her veins.

"So," replied De Winter, laughing, "that beautiful hair so skillfully disheveled, that white skin, and that languishing look, have not yet seduced you, you heart of stone?"

"No, my lord," replied the impassible young man; "Your Lordship may be assured that it requires more than the tricks and coquetry of a woman to corrupt me."

"In that case, my brave lieutenant, let us leave Milady to find out something else, and go to supper. But be careful: she has a fruitful imagination, and the second act of the comedy will not delay its steps after the first."

And at these words Lord de Winter passed his arm through that of Felton, and led him out, laughing.

"Oh, I will be a match for you!" murmured Milady, between her teeth; "be assured of that, you poor spoiled monk, you poor converted soldier, who has cut his uniform out of a monk's frock!"

"By the way," resumed De Winter, stopping at the threshold of the door, "you must not, Milady, let this check take away your appetite. Taste that fowl and those fish. On my honor, they are not poisoned. I have a very good cook, and he is not to be my heir; I have full and perfect confidence in him. Do as I do. Adieu, dear sister, till your next swoon!"

This was all that Milady could endure. Her hands clutched her armchair; she ground her teeth inwardly; her eyes followed the motion of the door as it closed behind Lord de Winter and Felton, and the moment she was alone a fresh bit of despair seized her. She cast her eyes upon the table, saw the glittering of a knife, rushed toward it, and clutched it; but her disappointment was cruel. The blade was round, and of flexible silver.

A burst of laughter resounded from the other side of the ill-closed door, and the door reopened.

"Ha, ha!" cried Lord de Winter; "ha, ha! Don't you see, my brave Felton; don't you see what I told you? That knife was for you, my lad; she would have killed you. Observe, this is one of her peculiarities, to get rid thus, after one fashion or another, of all the people who bother her. If I had listened to you, the knife would have been pointed and of steel. Then no more of Felton; she would have cut your throat, and after that everybody else's. See, John, see how well she knows how to handle a knife."

In fact, Milady still held the harmless weapon in her clenched hand; but these last words, this supreme insult, relaxed her hands, her strength, and even her will. The knife fell to the ground.

"You were right, my lord, and I was wrong."

And both again left the room.

But this time Milady lent a more attentive ear than the first, and she heard their steps die away in the distance of the corridor.

"I am lost," murmured she; "I am lost! I am in the power of men upon whom I can have no more influence than upon statues of bronze or granite; they know me by heart, and are steeled against all my weapons. It is, however, impossible that this should end as they have decreed!"

In fact, as this last reflection indicated—this instinctive return to hope—sentiments of weakness or fear did not dwell long in her ardent spirit. Milady sat down to table, ate from several dishes, drank a little Spanish wine, and felt all her resolution return.

Before she went to bed she had pondered, analyzed, turned on all sides, examined on all points, the words, the steps, the gestures, the signs, and even the silence of her interlocutors; and of this profound, skillful, and anxious study the result was that Felton, everything considered, appeared the more vulnerable of her two persecutors.

One expression above all recurred to the mind of the prisoner: "If I had listened to you," Lord de Winter had said to Felton.

Felton then had spoken in her favor, since Lord de Winter had not been willing to listen to him.

"Weak or strong," repeated Milady, "that man has, then, a spark of pity in his soul; of that spark I will make a flame that shall devour him. As to the other, he knows me, he fears me, and knows what he has to expect of me if ever I escape from his hands. It is useless, then, to attempt anything with him. But Felton—that's another thing. He is a young, ingenuous, pure man who seems virtuous. There are ways of destroying that kind."

And Milady went to bed and fell asleep with a smile upon her lips. Anyone who had seen her sleeping might have said she was a young girl dreaming of the crown of flowers she was to wear on her brow at the next festival.

The Second Day of Captivity

Milady dreamed that she at length had D'Artagnan in her power, that she was present at his execution; and it was the sight of his odious blood, flowing beneath the ax of the headsman, which spread that charming smile upon her lips.

She slept as a prisoner sleeps, cradled by his first hope.

In the morning, when they entered her chamber, she was still in bed. Felton remained in the corridor. He brought with him the woman of whom he had spoken the evening before, and who had just arrived; this woman entered, and, approaching Milady's bed, offered her services.

Milady was habitually pale; her complexion might therefore deceive a person who saw her for the first time.

"I am in a fever," said she; "I have not slept a single instant during all this long night. I suffer horribly. Are you likely to be more humane to me than the others were yesterday? All I ask is permission to remain abed."

"Would you like to have a physician called?" said the woman.

Felton listened to this dialogue without speaking a word.

Milady reflected that the more people she had around her the more she would have to work upon, and Lord de Winter would redouble his watch. Besides, the physician might declare the ailment feigned; and Milady, after having lost the first trick, was not willing to lose the second.

"Go and fetch a physician?" said she. "What could be the good of that? These gentlemen declared yesterday that my illness was a comedy; it would just be the same today, no doubt—for since yesterday evening they have had plenty of time to send for a doctor."

"Then," said Felton, who became impatient, "say yourself, madam, what treatment you wish followed."

"How can I tell? My God! I know that I suffer, that's all. Give me anything you like, it is of little consequence."

"Go and fetch Lord de Winter," said Felton, tired of these eternal complaints.

"Oh no, no!" cried Milady; "no, sir, do not call him, I conjure you. I am well, I want nothing; do not call him."

She gave so much vehemence, such magnetic eloquence to this exclamation, that Felton in spite of himself advanced some steps into the room.

"He is come!" thought Milady.

"Meanwhile, madame, if you really suffer," said Felton, "a physician will be sent for; and if you deceive us—well, it will be the worse for you. But at least we shall not have to reproach ourselves with anything."

Milady made no reply, but turning her beautiful head round upon her pillow, she burst into tears, and uttered heartbreaking sobs.

Felton surveyed her for an instant with his usual impassibility; then, seeing that the crisis threatened to be prolonged, he went out. The woman followed him, and Lord de Winter did not appear.

"I fancy I begin to see my way," murmured Milady, with a savage joy, burying herself under the clothes to conceal from anybody who might be watching her this burst of inward satisfaction.

Two hours passed away.

"Now it is time that the malady should be over," said she; "let me rise, and obtain some success this very day. I have but ten days, and this evening two of them will be gone."

In the morning, when they entered Milady's chamber they had brought her breakfast. Now she thought they could not long delay coming to clear the table, and that Felton would then reappear.

Milady was not deceived. Felton reappeared, and, without observing whether Milady had or had not touched her repast, made a sign that the table should be carried out of the room, it having been brought in ready-spread.

Felton remained behind; he held a book in his hand.

Milady, reclining in an armchair near the chimney, beautiful, pale, and resigned, looked like a holy virgin awaiting martyrdom.

Felton approached her, and said: "Lord de Winter, who is a Catholic, like yourself, madame, thinking that the deprivation of the rites and ceremonies of your church might be painful to you, has consented that you should read every day the ordinary of your Mass; and here is a book which contains the ritual."

At the manner in which Felton laid the book upon the little table near which Milady was sitting, at the tone in which he pronounced the two words, *your Mass*, at the disdainful smile with which he accompanied them, Milady raised her head, and looked more attentively at the officer.

By that plain arrangement of the hair, by that costume of extreme simplicity, by the brow polished like marble and as hard and impenetrable, she recognized one of those gloomy Puritans she had so often encountered, not only in the court of King James, but in that of the king of France, where, in spite of the remembrance of the St. Bartholomew, they sometimes came to seek refuge.

Straightway she had one of those sudden inspirations which only people of genius receive in great crises, in those supreme moments which must decide their fortunes or their lives.

Those two words, *your Mass*, and a simple glance cast upon Felton, revealed to her all the importance of the reply she was about to make; but with that rapidity of intelligence which was peculiar to her, this reply, ready arranged, presented itself to her lips:

"I?" said she, with an accent of disdain in unison with that which she had remarked in the voice of the young officer. "I, sir? *My Mass?* Lord de Winter, the corrupted Catholic, knows very well that I am not of his religion, and this is a snare he wishes to lay for me!"

"And of what religion are you, then, madame?" asked Felton, with an astonishment which in spite of the empire he held over himself he could not entirely conceal.

"I will tell it," cried Milady, with a feigned exultation, "on the day when I shall have suffered sufficiently for my faith."

The look of Felton revealed to Milady the full extent of the space she had opened for herself by this single word.

The young officer, however, remained mute and motionless; his look alone had spoken.

"I am in the hands of my enemies," continued she, with that tone of enthusiasm which she knew was familiar to the Puritans. "Well, let my God save me, or let me perish for my God! That is the reply I beg you to make to Lord de Winter. And as to this book," added she, pointing to the manual with her finger, but without touching it, as if she must be contaminated by it, "you may carry it back and make use of it yourself, for doubtless you are doubly the accomplice of Lord de Winter—the accomplice in his persecutions, the accomplice in his heresies."

Felton made no reply, took the book with the same appearance of repugnance which he had before manifested, and retired pensively.

Lord de Winter came towards five o'clock in the evening. Milady had had time, during the whole day, to trace her plan of conduct. She received him like a woman who had already recovered all her advantages.

"It appears," said the baron, seating himself in the armchair opposite that occupied by Milady, and stretching out his legs carelessly upon the hearth; "it appears we have made a little apostasy!"

"What do you mean, sir?"

"I mean to say that since we last met you have changed your religion. You have not, by chance, married a Protestant for a third husband, have you?"

"Explain yourself, my lord," replied the prisoner, with majesty; "for though I hear your words I declare I do not understand them."

"Then you have no religion at all; I like that best," replied Lord de Winter, laughing.

"Certainly that is most in accord with your own principles," replied Milady, frigidly.

"Oh, I confess it is all the same to me."

"Oh, you need not avow this religious indifference, my lord; your debaucheries and crimes would vouch for it."

"What? You talk of debaucheries, Madame Messalina, Lady Macbeth! Either I misunderstand you, or you are shameless indeed!"

"You only speak thus because you are overheard," coolly replied Milady; "and you wish to interest your jailers and your hangmen against me."

"My jailers and my hangmen! Heyday, madame! you are taking a poetical tone, and the comedy of yesterday turns to a tragedy this evening. As to the rest, in eight days you will be where you ought to be, and my task will be completed."

"Infamous task! impious task!" cried Milady, with the exultation of a victim who provokes his judge.

"My word," said De Winter, rising, "I think the hussy is going mad! Come come, calm yourself, Madame Puritan, or I'll remove you to a dungeon. It's my Spanish wine that has got into your head, is it not? But never mind; that sort of intoxication is not dangerous, and will have no bad effects."

And Lord de Winter retired swearing, which at that period was a very knightly habit.

Felton was indeed behind the door, and had not lost one word of this scene. Milady had guessed aright.

"Yes, go, go!" said she to her "brother"; "the effects *are* drawing near, on the contrary; but you, weak fool, will not see them until it is too late to shun them."

Silence was re-established. Two hours passed away. Milady's supper was brought in, and she was found deeply engaged in saying her prayers aloud—prayers which she had learned of an old servant of her second husband, a most austere Puritan. She appeared to be in ecstasy, and did not pay the least attention to what was going on around her. Felton made a sign that she should not be disturbed; and when all was arranged, he went out quietly with the soldiers.

Milady knew she might be watched, so she continued her prayers to the end; and it appeared to her that the soldier who was on duty at her door did not march with the same step, and seemed to listen. For the moment she wished nothing better. She arose, went to the table, ate but little, and drank only water.

An hour after, her table was cleared; but Milady remarked that this time Felton did not accompany the soldiers. He feared, then, to see her too often.

She turned toward the wall to smile—for there was in this smile such an expression of triumph that this smile alone would have betrayed her.

She allowed, therefore, half an hour to pass away; and as at that moment all was silence in the old castle, as nothing was heard but the eternal murmur of the waves—that immense breaking of the ocean—with her pure, harmonious, and powerful voice, she began the first couplet of the psalm then in great favor with the Puritans:

> "Thou leavest thy servants, Lord,
>   To see if they be strong;
> But soon thou dost afford
>   Thy hand to lead them on."

These verses were not excellent—very far from it; but as it is well known, the Puritans did not pique themselves upon their poetry.

While singing, Milady listened. The soldier on guard at her door stopped, as if he had been changed into stone. Milady was then able to judge of the effect she had produced.

Then she continued her singing with inexpressible fervor and feeling. It appeared to her that the sounds spread to a distance beneath the vaulted roofs, and carried with them a magic charm to soften the hearts of her jailers. It however likewise appeared that the soldier on duty—a zealous Catholic no doubt—shook off the charm, for through the door he called: "Hold your tongue, madame! Your song is as dismal as a 'De profundis'; and if besides the pleasure of being in garrison here, we must hear such things as these, no mortal can hold out."

"Silence!" exclaimed another stern voice which Milady recognized as that of Felton. "What are you meddling with, stupid? Did anybody order you to prevent that woman from singing? No. You were told to guard her—to fire at her if she attempted to fly. Guard her! If she flies, kill her; but don't exceed your orders."

An expression of unspeakable joy lightened the countenance of Milady; but this expression was as fleeting as the reflection of lightning. Without appearing to have heard the dialogue, of which she had not lost a word, she began again, giving to her voice all the charm, all the power, all the seduction the demon had bestowed upon it:

> "For all my tears, my cares,
>   My exile, and my chains,
> I have my youth, my prayers,
>   And God, who counts my pains."

Her voice, of immense power and sublime expression, gave to the rude, unpolished poetry of these psalms a magic and an effect which the most exalted Puritans rarely found in the songs of their brethren, and which they were forced to ornament with all the resources of their imagination. Felton believed he heard the singing of the angel who consoled the three Hebrews in the furnace.

Milady continued:

> "One day our doors will ope,
>   With God come our desire;
> And if betrays that hope,
>   To death we can aspire."

This verse, into which the terrible enchantress threw her whole soul completed the trouble which had seized the heart of the young officer. He opened the door quickly; and Milady saw him appear, pale as usual, but with his eyes inflamed and almost wild.

"Why do you sing thus, and with such a voice?" said he.

"Your pardon, sir," said Milady, with mildness. "I forgot that my songs are out of place in this castle. I have perhaps offended you in your creed; but it was without wishing to do so, I swear. Pardon me, then, a fault which is perhaps great, but which certainly was involuntary."

Milady was so beautiful at this moment, the religious ecstasy in which she appeared to be plunged gave such an expression to her countenance, that Felton was so dazzled that he fancied he beheld the angel whom he had only just before heard.

"Yes, yes," said he; "you disturb, you agitate the people who live in the castle."

The poor senseless young man was not aware of the incoherence of his words, while Milady was reading with her lynx's eyes the very depths of his heart.

"I will be silent, then," said Milady, casting down her eyes with all the sweetness she could give to her voice, with all the resignation she could impress upon her manner.

"No, no, madame," said Felton; "only do not sing so loud, particularly at night."

And at these words Felton, feeling that he could not long maintain his severity towards his prisoner, rushed out of the room.

"You have done right, Lieutenant," said the soldier. "Such songs disturb the mind; and yet we become accustomed to them, her voice is so beautiful."

The Third Day of Captivity

Felton had fallen; but there was still another step to be taken. He must be retained, or rather he must be left quite alone; and Milady but obscurely perceived the means which could lead to this result.

Still more must be done. He must be made to speak, in order that he might be spoken to—for Milady very well knew that her greatest seduction was in her voice, which so skillfully ran over the whole gamut of tones from human speech to language celestial.

Yet in spite of all this seduction Milady might fail—Felton was forewarned, and that against the least chance. From that moment she watched all his actions, all his words, from the simplest glance of his eyes to his gestures—even to a breath that could be interpreted as a sigh. In short, she studied everything, as a skillful comedian does to whom a new part has been assigned in a line to which he is not accustomed.

Face to face with Lord de Winter, her plan of conduct was more easy. She had laid that down the preceding evening. To remain silent and dignified in his presence; from time to time to irritate him by affected disdain, by a contemptuous word; to provoke him to threats and violence which would produce a contrast with her own resignation—such was her plan. Felton would see all; perhaps he would say nothing, but he would see.

In the morning, Felton came as usual; but Milady allowed him to preside over all the preparations for breakfast without addressing a word to him. At the moment when he was about to retire, she was cheered with a ray of hope, for she thought he was about to speak; but his lips moved without any sound leaving his mouth, and, making a powerful effort to control himself, he sent back to his heart the words that were about to escape from his lips, and went out.

Toward midday, Lord de Winter entered.

It was a tolerably fine winter's day, and a ray of that pale English sun which lightens but does not warm came through the bars of her prison.

Milady was looking out at the window, and pretended not to hear the door as it opened.

"Ah, ah!" said Lord de Winter, "after having played comedy, after having played tragedy, we are now playing melancholy?"

The prisoner made no reply.

"Yes, yes," continued Lord de Winter, "I understand. You would like very well to be at liberty on that beach! You would like very well to be on a good ship dancing upon the waves of that emerald green sea; you would like very well, either on land or on the ocean, to lay for me one of those nice little ambuscades you are so skillful in planning. Patience, patience! In four days' time the shore will be beneath your foot, the sea will be open to you—more open than will perhaps be agreeable to you, for in four days England will be relieved of you."

Milady folded her hands, and raising her fine eyes toward heaven, "Lord, Lord," said she, with an angelic meekness of gesture and tone. "Pardon this man, as I myself pardon him."

"Yes, pray, accursed woman!" cried the baron; "your prayer is so much the more generous from your being, I swear to you, in the power of a man who will never pardon you!" And he went out.

At the moment he went out a piercing glance darted through the opening of the nearly closed door, and she perceived Felton, who drew quickly to one side to prevent being seen by her.

Then she threw herself upon her knees, and began to pray.

"My God, my God!" said she, "thou knowest in what holy cause I suffer; give me, then, strength to suffer."

The door opened gently; the beautiful supplicant pretended not to hear the noise, and in a voice broken by tears, she continued:

"God of vengeance! God of goodness! wilt thou allow the frightful projects of this man to be accomplished?"

Then only did she pretend to hear the sound of Felton's steps, and rising quick as thought, she blushed, as if ashamed of being surprised on her knees.

"I do not like to disturb those who pray, madame," said Felton, seriously; "do not disturb yourself on my account, I beseech you."

"How do you know I was praying, sir?" said Milady, in a voice broken by sobs. "You were deceived, sir; I was not praying."

"Do you think, then, madame," replied Felton, in the same serious voice, but with a milder tone, "do you think I assume the right of preventing a creature from prostrating herself before her Creator? God forbid! Besides, repentance becomes the guilty; whatever crimes they may have committed, for me the guilty are sacred when they are at the feet of God!"

"Guilty? I?" said Milady, with a smile which might have disarmed the angel of the last judgment. "Guilty? Oh, my God, Thou knowest whether I am guilty! Say I am condemned, sir, if you please; but you know that God, who loves martyrs, sometimes permits the innocent to be condemned."

"Were you condemned, were you innocent, or were you a martyr," replied Felton, "the greater would be the necessity for prayer; and I myself would aid you with my prayers."

"Oh, you are a just man!" cried Milady, throwing herself at his feet. "I can hold out no longer, for I fear I shall be wanting in strength at the moment when I shall be forced to undergo the struggle, and confess my faith. Listen, then, to the supplication of a despairing woman. You are abused, sir; but that is not the question. I only ask you one favor; and if you grant it me, I will bless you in this world and in the next."

"Speak to the master, madame," said Felton; "happily, I am neither charged with the power of pardoning nor punishing. It is upon one higher placed than I am that God has laid this responsibility."

"To you—no, to you alone! Listen to me, rather than add to my destruction, rather than add to my ignominy!"

"If you have merited this shame, madame, if you have incurred this ignominy, you must submit to it as an offering to God."

"What do you say? Oh, you do not understand me! When I speak of ignominy, you think I speak of some chastisement, of imprisonment or death. Would to Heaven! Of what consequence to me is imprisonment or death?"

"It is I who no longer understand you, madame," said Felton.

"Or, rather, who pretend not to understand me, sir!" replied the prisoner, with a smile of incredulity.

"No, madame, on the honor of a soldier, on the faith of a Christian."

"What, you are ignorant of Lord de Winter's designs upon me?"

"I am."

"Impossible; you are his confidant!"

"I never lie, madame."

"Oh, he conceals them too little for you not to divine them."

"I seek to divine nothing, madame; I wait till I am confided in, and apart from that which Lord de Winter has said to me before you, he has confided nothing to me."

"Why, then," cried Milady, with an incredible tone of truthfulness, "you are not his accomplice; you do not know that he destines me to a disgrace which all the punishments of the world cannot equal in horror?"

"You are deceived, madame," said Felton, blushing; "Lord de Winter is not capable of such a crime."

"Good," said Milady to herself; "without knowing what it is, he calls it a crime!" Then aloud: "The friend of that wretch is capable of everything."

"Whom do you call *that wretch?*" asked Felton.

"Are there, then, in England two men to whom such an epithet can be applied?"

"You mean George Villiers?" said Felton, whose looks became excited.

"Whom pagans and unbelieving gentiles call Duke of Buckingham," replied Milady. "I could not have thought that there was an Englishman in all England who would have required so long an explanation to make him understand of whom I was speaking."

"The hand of the Lord is stretched over him," said Felton; "he will not escape the chastisement he deserves."

Felton only expressed, with regard to the duke, the feeling of execration which all the English had declared toward him whom the Catholics themselves called the extortioner, the pillager, the debauchee, and whom the Puritans styled simply Satan.

"Oh, my God, my God!" cried Milady; "when I supplicate Thee to pour upon this man the chastisement which is his due, Thou knowest it is not my own vengeance I pursue, but the deliverance of a whole nation that I implore!"

"Do you know him, then?" asked Felton.

"At length he interrogates me!" said Milady to herself, at the height of joy at having obtained so quickly such a great result. "Oh, know him? Yes, yes! to my misfortune, to my eternal misfortune!" And Milady twisted her arms as if in a paroxysm of grief.

Felton no doubt felt within himself that his strength was abandoning him, and he made several steps toward the door; but the prisoner, whose eye never left him, sprang in pursuit of him, and stopped him.

"Sir," cried she, "be kind, be clement, listen to my prayer! That knife, which the fatal prudence of the baron deprived me of, because he knows the use I would make of it! Oh, hear me to the end! that knife, give it to me for a minute only, for mercy's, for pity's sake! I will embrace your knees! You shall shut the door that you may be certain I contemplate no injury to you! My God! to you—the only just, good, and compassionate being I have met with! To you—my preserver, perhaps! One minute that knife, one minute, a single minute, and I will restore it to you through the grating of the door. Only one minute, Mr. Felton, and you will have saved my honor!"

"To kill yourself?" cried Felton, with terror, forgetting to withdraw his hands from the hands of the prisoner—"to kill yourself?"

"I have told, sir," murmured Milady, lowering her voice, and allowing herself to sink overpowered to the ground; "I have told my secret! He knows all! My God. I am lost!"

Felton remained standing, motionless and undecided.

"He still doubts," thought Milady; "I have not been earnest enough."

Someone was heard in the corridor; Milady recognized the step of Lord de Winter.

Felton recognized it also, and made a step toward the door.

Milady sprang toward him. "Oh, not a word," said she, in a concentrated voice, "not a word of all that I have said to you to this man, or I am lost, and it would be you—you—"

Then as the steps drew near, she became silent for fear of being heard, applying, with a gesture of infinite terror, her beautiful hand to Felton's mouth.

Felton gently repulsed Milady, and she sank into a chair.

Lord de Winter passed before the door without stopping, and they heard the noise of his footsteps soon die away.

Felton, as pale as death, remained some moments with his ear bent and listening; then, when the sound was quite extinct, he breathed like a man awaking from a dream, and rushed out of the apartment.

"Ah!" said Milady, listening in her turn to the noise of Felton's steps, which withdrew in a direction opposite of those of Lord de Winter; "at length you are mine!"

Then her brow darkened. "If he tells the baron," said she, "I am lost—for the baron, who knows very well that I shall not kill myself, will place me before him with a knife in my hand, and he will discover that all this despair is just acting."

She placed herself before her mirror, and regarded herself attentively; never had she appeared more beautiful.

"Oh yes," said she, smiling, "but he won't tell him!"

In the evening Lord de Winter accompanied the supper.

"Sir," said Milady, "is your presence an indispensable accessory of my captivity? Could you not spare me the increase of torture which your visits cause me?"

"How, dear sister!" said Lord de Winter. "Did you not yourself with that pretty mouth of yours, inform me that you came to England solely for the pleasure of seeing me at your ease, an enjoyment of which you told me you so sensibly felt the deprivation that you had risked everything for it—seasickness, tempest, captivity? Well, here I am; be satisfied. Besides, this time, my visit has a motive."

Milady trembled; she thought Felton had told all. Perhaps never in her life had this woman, who had experienced so many opposite and powerful emotions, felt her heart beat so violently.

She was seated. Lord de Winter took a chair, drew it toward her, and sat down close beside her. Then taking a paper out of his pocket, he unfolded it slowly.

"Here," said he, "I want to show you the kind of passport which I have drawn up, and which will serve you henceforward as the rule of order in the life I consent to leave you."

Then turning his eyes from Milady to the paper, he read: "'Order to conduct to——' the name is blank," interrupted Lord de Winter. "If you have any preference you can point it out to me; and if it be not within a thousand leagues of London, attention will be paid to your wishes. I will begin again, then:

"'Order to conduct to—the person named Charlotte Backson, branded by justice of the kingdom of France, but liberated after chastisement. She is to dwell in this place without ever going more than three leagues from it. In case of any attempt to escape, the penalty of death is to be applied. She will receive five shillings per day for lodging and food.'"

"That order does not concern me," replied Milady, coldly, "since it bears another name than mine."

"A name? Have you a name, then?"

"I bear that of your brother."

"Ay, but you are mistaken. My brother is only your second husband; and your first is still living. Tell me his name, and I will put it in the place of the name of Charlotte Backson. No? You will not?

You are silent. Well, then you must be registered as Charlotte Backson."

Milady remained silent; only this time it was no longer from affectation, but from terror. She believed the order ready for execution. She thought that Lord de Winter had hastened her departure; she thought she was condemned to set off that very evening. Everything in her mind was lost for an instant; when all at once she perceived that no signature was attached to the order. The joy she felt at this discovery was so great she could not conceal it.

"Yes, yes," said Lord de Winter, who perceived what was passing in her mind; "yes, you look for the signature, and you say to yourself: 'All is not lost, for that order is not signed. It is only shown to me to terrify me, that's all.' You are mistaken. Tomorrow this order will be sent to the Duke of Buckingham. The day after tomorrow it will return signed by his hand and marked with his seal; and four-and-twenty hours afterward I will answer for its being carried into execution. Adieu, madame, that is all I had to say to you."

"And I reply to you, sir, that this abuse of power, this exile under a fictitious name, are infamous!"

"Would you like better to be hanged in your true name, Milady? You know that English justice is inexorable on the abuse of marriage. Speak freely. Although my name, or rather that of my brother, would be mixed up with the affair, I will risk the scandal of a public trial to make myself certain of getting rid of you."

Milady made no reply, but became pale as a corpse.

"Oh, I see you prefer peregrination. That's well, madame; and there is an old proverb that says, 'Traveling trains youth.' My faith! you are not wrong after all, and life is sweet. That's the reason why I take such care you shall not deprive me of mine. There only remains, then, the question of five shillings to be settled. You think me rather parsimonious, don't you? That's because I don't care to leave you the means of corrupting your jailers. Besides, you will always have your charms left to seduce them with. Employ them, if your check with regard to Felton has not disgusted you with attempts of that kind."

"Felton has not told him," Milady exulted to herself. "Nothing is lost! Nothing is lost!"

"And now, madame, till I see you again! Tomorrow I will come and announce to you the departure of my messenger."

Lord de Winter rose, saluted her ironically and went out.

Milady breathed again. She had still four days before her. Four days would quite suffice to complete the seduction of Felton.

A terrible idea, however, rushed into her mind. She thought that Lord de Winter would perhaps send Felton himself to get the order signed by the Duke of Buckingham. In that case, Felton would escape her—for in order to secure success, the magic of a continuous seduction was necessary. Nevertheless, as we have said, one circumstance reassured her. Felton had not spoken.

As she would not appear to be agitated by the threats of Lord de Winter, she placed herself at the table and ate.

Then, as she had done the evening before, she fell on her knees and repeated her prayers aloud. As on the evening before, the soldier stopped his march to listen to her.

Soon she heard lighter steps than those of the sentinel, which came from the end of the corridor and stopped before her door.

"It is he," said she. And she began the same religious chant which had so strongly excited Felton the evening before.

But although her voice—sweet, full, and sonorous—vibrated as harmoniously and as affectingly as ever, the door remained shut. It appeared, however, to Milady that in one of the furtive glances she darted from time to time at the grating of the door she thought she saw the ardent eyes of the young man through the narrow opening. But whether this was reality or vision, he had this time sufficient self-command not to enter.

However, a few moments after she had finished her religious song, Milady thought she heard a profound sigh. Then the same steps she had heard approach slowly withdrew, and as if with regret.

The Fourth Day of Captivity

The next day, when Felton entered Milady's apartment he found her standing, mounted upon a chair, holding in her hands a cord made by means of torn cambric handkerchiefs, twisted into a kind of rope one with another, and tied at the ends. At the noise Felton made in entering, Milady leaped lightly to the ground, and tried to conceal behind her the improvised cord she held in her hand.

The young man was more pale than usual, and his eyes, reddened by want of sleep, denoted that he had passed a feverish night. Nevertheless, his brow was armed with a severity more austere than ever.

He advanced slowly toward Milady, who had seated herself, and taking an end of the murderous rope which by neglect, or perhaps by design, she allowed to be seen, "What is this, madame?" he asked coldly.

"That? Nothing," said Milady, smiling with that painful expression which she knew so well how to give to her smile. "*Ennui* is the mortal enemy of prisoners; I had *ennui*, and I amused myself with twisting that rope."

Felton turned his eyes toward the part of the wall of the apartment before which he had found Milady standing in the armchair in which she was now seated, and over her head he perceived a gilt-headed screw, fixed in the wall for the purpose of hanging up clothes or weapons.

He started, and the prisoner saw that start—for though her eyes were cast down, nothing escaped her.

"What were you doing on that armchair?" asked he.

"What difference?" replied Milady.

"I wish to know," said Felton sternly.

"Do not question me," said the prisoner; "you know that we who are true Christians are forbidden to lie."

"Well, then," said Felton, "I will tell you what you were doing, or rather what you meant to do; you were going to complete the fatal project you cherish in your mind. Remember, madame, if our God forbids falsehood, he much more severely condemns suicide."

"When God sees one of his creatures persecuted unjustly, placed between suicide and dishonor, believe me, sir," replied Milady, in a tone of deep conviction, "God pardons suicide, for then suicide becomes martyrdom."

"You say either too much or too little. Speak, madame. In the name of Heaven, explain yourself."

"That I may relate my misfortunes to you to treat them as fables; that I may tell you my projects for you to go and betray them to my persecutor? No, sir. Besides, of what importance to you is the life or death of a condemned wretch? You are only responsible for my body, is it not so? And provided you produce a carcass that may be recognized as mine, they will require no more of you; nay, perhaps you will even have a double reward."

"I, madame, I?" cried Felton. "You suppose that I would ever accept the price of your life? Oh, you cannot believe what you say!"

"Let me act as I please, Felton, let me act as I please," said Milady, elated. "Every soldier must be ambitious, must he not? You are a lieutenant? Well, you will follow me to the grave with the rank of captain."

"What have I, then, done to you," Felton cried, "that you should load me with such a responsibility before God and before men? In a few days you will be away from this place; your life, madame, will then no longer be under my care, and," he added, with a sigh, "then you can do what you will with it."

"So," cried Milady, as if she could not resist giving utterance to a holy indignation, "you, a pious man, you who are called a just man, you ask but one thing—and that is that you may not be inculpated, annoyed, by my death!"

"It is my duty to watch over your life, madame, and I will watch."

"But do you understand the mission you are fulfilling? Cruel enough, if I am guilty; but what name can you give it, what name will the Lord give it, if I am innocent?"

"I am a soldier, madame, and fulfill the orders I have received."

"Do you believe, then, that at the day of the Last Judgment God will separate blind executioners from iniquitous judges? You are not willing that I should kill my body, but you make yourself the agent of him who would kill my soul."

"But I repeat it again to you," replied Felton, in great emotion, "no danger threatens you; I will answer for Lord de Winter as for myself."

"Dunce," cried Milady—"dunce! who dares to answer for another man, when the wisest, when those most after God's own heart, hesitate to answer for themselves, and who ranges himself on the side of the strongest and the most fortunate, to crush the weakest and the most unfortunate."

"Impossible, madame, impossible," murmured Felton, who felt to the bottom of his heart the justness of this argument. "A prisoner, you will not recover your liberty through me; living, you will not lose your life through me."

"Yes," cried Milady, "but I shall lose that which is much dearer to me than life, I shall lose my honor, Felton; and it is you, you whom I make responsible, before God and before men, for my shame and my infamy."

This time, Felton, immovable as he was, or as he appeared to be, could not resist the secret influence which had already taken possession of him. To see this woman, so beautiful, fair as the brightest vision, to see her by turns overcome with grief and threatening; to resist at once the ascendancy of her grief and her beauty—it was too much for a visionary; it was too much for a brain weakened by the ardent dreams of an ecstatic faith; it was too much for a heart furrowed by the love of heaven that burns, and by the hatred of men that devours.

Milady saw the trouble. She felt by intuition the flame of the opposing passions which seethed in the veins of the young fanatic. As a skillful general, seeing the enemy ready to surrender, marches toward him with a cry of victory, she rose, beautiful as an antique priestess, inspired like a Christian virgin, her arms extended, her throat uncovered, her hair disheveled, holding with one hand her robe modestly drawn over her breast, her look illumined by that fire which had already created such disorder in the blood of the young Puritan, and went toward him, crying out with a vehement air, and in her melodious voice to which on this occasion she communicated a terrible energy:

> "Let his victim to Baal be sent,
>   To the lions the martyr be thrown!
> Thy God shall teach thee to repent!
>   From th' abyss he'll give ear to my moan."

Felton stood before this strange apparition like one petrified.

"Who art thou? Who art thou?" cried he, clasping his hands. "Art thou a messenger from God; are thou a minister from hell; art thou an angel or a demon; callest thou thyself Eloa or Astarte?"

"Do you not know me, Felton? I am neither an angel nor a demon; I am a daughter of earth, I am a sister of thy faith, that is all."

"Yes, yes!" said Felton, "I doubted, but now I believe."

"You believe, and still you are an accomplice of that child of Belial who is called Lord de Winter! You believe, and yet you leave me in the hands of mine enemies, who are also the enemies of England, and the enemies of God! You believe, and yet you deliver me up to him who fills and defiles the world with his heresies and debaucheries—to that infamous Sardanapalus whom the blind call the Duke of Buckingham, and whom believers name Antichrist!"

"I deliver you up to Buckingham? I? What mean you by that?"

"They have eyes," cried Milady, "but they see not; ears have they, but they hear not."

"Yes, yes!" said Felton, passing his hands over his brow, covered with sweat, as if to remove his last doubt. "Yes, I recognize the voice which speaks to me in my dreams; yes, I recognize the features of the angel who appears to me every night, crying to my soul, which cannot sleep: 'Strike, save England, save thyself—for thou wilt die without having appeased God! Speak, speak!" cried Felton, "I can understand you now."

A flash of terrible joy, but rapid as thought, gleamed from the eyes of Milady.

However fugitive this homicide flash, Felton saw it, and started as if its light had revealed the abysses of this woman's heart. He recalled, all at once, the warnings of Lord de Winter, the seductions of Milady, her first attempts after her arrival. He drew back a step, and hung down his head, without, however, ceasing to look at her, as if, fascinated by this strange creature, he could not detach his eyes from her eyes.

Milady was not a woman to misunderstand the meaning of this hesitation. Under her apparent emotions her icy coolness never abandoned her. Before Felton replied, and before she could be forced to resume this conversation, so difficult to be sustained in the same exalted tone, she let her hands fall; and as if the weakness of the woman overpowered the enthusiasm of the inspired fanatic, she said: "But no, it is not for me to be the Judith to deliver Bethulia from this Holofernes. The sword of the eternal is too heavy for my arm. Allow me, then, to avoid dishonor by death; let me take refuge in martyrdom. I do not ask you for liberty, as a guilty one would, nor for vengeance, as would a pagan. Let me die; that is all. I supplicate you,

I implore you on my knees—let me die, and my last sigh shall be a blessing for my preserver."

Hearing that voice, so sweet and suppliant, seeing that look, so timid and downcast, Felton reproached himself. By degrees the enchantress had clothed herself with that magic adornment which she assumed and threw aside at will; that is to say, beauty, meekness, and tears—and above all, the irresistible attraction of mystical voluptuousness, the most devouring of all voluptuousness.

"Alas!" said Felton, "I can do but one thing, which is to pity you— if you should prove to me you are a victim! But Lord de Winter makes cruel accusations against you. You are a Christian; you are my sister in religion. I feel myself drawn toward you—I, who have never loved anyone but my benefactor—I who have met with nothing but traitors and impious men. But you, madame, so beautiful in reality, you, so pure in appearance, must have committed great iniquities for Lord de Winter to pursue you thus."

"They have eyes," repeated Milady, with an accent of indescribable grief, "but they see not; ears have they, but they hear not."

"But," cried the young officer, "speak, then, speak!"

"Confide my shame to you," cried Milady, with the blush of modesty upon her countenance—"for often the crime of one becomes the shame of another—confide my shame to you, a man, and I a woman? Oh," continued she, placing her hand modestly over her beautiful eyes, "never! never!—I could not!"

"To me, to a brother in faith?" said Felton.

Milady looked at him for some time with an expression which the young man took for doubt, but which, however, was nothing but observation, or rather the wish to fascinate.

Felton, in his turn a suppliant, clasped his hands.

"Well, then," said Milady, "I confide in my brother; I will dare to—"

At this moment the steps of Lord de Winter were heard; but this time the terrible brother-in-law of Milady did not content himself, as on the preceding day, with passing before the door and going away again. He paused, exchanged two words with the sentinel; then the door opened, and he appeared.

During the exchange of these two words Felton drew back quickly, and when Lord de Winter entered, he was several paces from the prisoner.

The baron entered slowly, sending a scrutinizing glance from Milady to the young officer.

"You have been here a very long time, John," said he. "Has this woman been relating her crimes to you? In that case I can comprehend the length of the conversation."

Felton started; and Milady felt she was lost if she did not come to the assistance of the disconcerted Puritan.

"Ah, you fear your prisoner should escape!" said she. "Well, ask your worthy jailer what favor I this instant solicited of him."

"You demanded a favor?" said the baron, suspiciously.

"Yes, my lord," replied the young man, confused.

"And what favor, pray?" asked Lord de Winter.

"A knife, which she would return to me through the grating of the door a minute after she had received it," replied Felton.

"There is someone, then, concealed here whose throat this amiable lady is desirous of cutting," said De Winter, in an ironical, contemptuous tone.

"There is myself," replied Milady.

"I have given you the choice between America and Tyburn," replied Lord de Winter. "Choose Tyburn, madame. Believe me, the cord is more certain than the knife."

Felton grew pale, and made a step forward, remembering that, at the moment he entered, Milady had a rope in her hand.

"You are right," said she, "I have often thought of it." Then she added in a low voice: "And I will think of it again."

Felton felt a shudder run to the marrow of his bones; probably Lord de Winter perceived this emotion.

"Mistrust yourself, John," said he. "I have placed reliance upon you, my friend. Beware! I have warned you! But be of good courage, my lad; in three days we shall be delivered from this creature, and where I shall send her she can harm nobody."

"You hear him!" cried Milady, with vehemence, so that the baron might believe she was addressing Heaven, and that Felton might understand she was addressing him.

Felton lowered his head and reflected.

The baron took the young officer by the arm, and led him out of the room, but without losing sight of Milady till he was gone out.

"Well," sighed the prisoner, when the door was shut, "I am not so far advanced as I believed. De Winter has changed his usual stupidity into a strange prudence. It is the desire of vengeance, and there is nothing like desire to mould a man! As to Felton, he hesitates. Ah, he is not a man like that cursed D'Artagnan. A Puritan only adores virgins, and he adores them by clasping his hands. A musketeer loves women, and he loves them by clasping his arms."

Milady waited, then, with much impatience, for she feared the day would pass away without her seeing Felton again. At last, in an hour after the scene we have just described, she heard someone speaking in a low voice at the door. Presently, the door opened, and she perceived Felton.

The young man advanced rapidly into the chamber, leaving the door open behind him, and making a sign to Milady to be silent; his face was much agitated.

"What do you want with me?" said she.

"Listen," replied Felton, in a low voice. "I have just sent away the sentinel that I might remain here without anybody knowing it, in order to speak to you without being overheard. The baron has just related a frightful history to me."

Milady assumed her smile of a resigned victim, and shook her head.

"Either you are a demon," continued Felton, "or the baron—my benefactor, 'my father'—is a monster. I have known you four days; I have loved him four years. I therefore may hesitate between you. Be not alarmed at what I say; I want to be convinced. Tonight, after twelve, I will come and see you, and you shall convince me."

"No, Felton, no, my Brother," said she; "the sacrifice is too great, and I feel what it must cost you. No, I am lost; do not be lost with me. My death will be much more eloquent than my life, and the silence of the corpse will convince you much better than the words of the prisoner."

"Be silent, madame," cried Felton, "and do not speak to me thus; I came to entreat you to promise me upon your honor, to swear to me by what you hold most sacred, that you will make no attempt upon your life."

"I will not promise," said Milady, "for no one has more respect

for a promise or an oath than I have; and if I make a promise I must,
I must keep it."

"Well," said Felton, "only promise till you have seen me again. If,
when you have seen me again, you still persist—well, then you shall
be free, and I myself will give you the weapon you desire."

"Well," said Milady, "for you I will wait."

"Swear."

"I swear it, by our God. Are you satisfied?"

"Yes," said Felton. "Till tonight."

And he darted out of the room, shut the door, and awaited in
the corridor, the soldier's half-pike in his hand, as if he had mounted
guard in his place.

The soldier returned, and Felton gave him back his weapon.

Then, through the grating to which she had drawn near, Milady
saw the young man make a sign with delirious fervor, and depart in
an apparent transport of joy.

As for her, she returned to her place with a smile of savage contempt upon her lips, and repeated, blaspheming, that terrible name
of God, by whom she had just sworn without ever having learned
to know him.

"My God," said she, "what a senseless fanatic! My God, it is I—I
—and this fellow who will help me to avenge myself."

The Fifth Day of Captivity

Milady had, however, achieved a half-triumph, and success doubled
her forces.

It was not difficult to conquer, as she had hitherto done, men who
were prompt to let themselves be seduced, and whom the gallant
education of a court led quickly into her net. Milady was handsome
enough not to find much resistance on the part of the flesh, and she
was sufficiently skillful to prevail over all the obstacles of the mind.

But this time she had to contend with an unpolished nature, concentrated and made insensible by force of austerity. Religion and its
observances had made Felton a man inaccessible to ordinary seductions. There fermented in that sublimated brain plans so vast, projects so tumultuous, that there remained no room for any capricious

or material love—that sentiment which is fed by leisure and grows with corruption. Yet, by her false virtue, Milady had managed to make a breach in the opinion of a man horribly prejudiced against her, and by her beauty in the heart of a man hitherto chaste and pure. In short, through this experiment, made upon the most rebellious subject that nature and religion could submit to her study, she had taken the measure of a character whose motives she had hitherto never encountered.

Many a time, nevertheless, during the evening she despaired of fate and of herself. She did not invoke God, as we well know, but she had a kind of faith in the genius of evil—and faith of whatever sort is still that immense sovereignty which reigns in all the details of human life, and by which, as in the Arabian fable, a single pomegranate seed is sufficient to reconstruct a ruined world.

Milady, being well prepared for the reception of Felton, was able to erect her batteries for the next day. She knew she had only two days left; that when once the order was signed by Buckingham—and Buckingham would sign it all the more readily because of its bearing a false name, which would give him no inkling of the woman in question—once signed, we say, the baron would make her embark immediately, and she knew very well that a woman condemned to exile employs arms much less powerful in their seductions than the pretendedly virtuous woman whose beauty is enlightened by the sun of the world, whose style the voice of fashion lauds, and whom a halo of aristocracy gilds with enchanting splendors.

To be a woman condemned to a painful and disgraceful punishment is no impediment to beauty, but it is an obstacle to the recovery of power. Like all persons of real genius, Milady knew what suited her nature and her means. Poverty was repugnant to her; degradation took away two-thirds of her greatness. Milady was only a queen while among queens. The pleasure of satisfied pride was necessary to her domination. To command inferior beings was rather a humiliation than a pleasure for her.

That she would eventually return from her exile—that she did not doubt for a single instant; but how long might this exile last? For an active, ambitious nature, like that of Milady, days not spent in climbing are inauspicious days. What word, then, can be found to describe the days which they occupy in descending? Imagine losing a year, two years, three years! Why that is to talk of an eternity! It might mean returning after the death or disgrace of the cardinal. Or returning when D'Artagnan and his friends, happy and triumphant, should have received from the queen the reward they had well acquired by the services they had rendered her—these were devouring ideas that a woman like Milady could not endure. But the storm which raged within her doubled her strength, and she would have burst the walls of her prison if her body had been able to take for a single instant the proportions of her mind.

That which now spurred her on additionally in the midst of all this was the remembrance of the cardinal. What must the mistrustful, restless, suspicious cardinal think of her silence—the cardinal, not merely her only support, her only prop, her only protector at present, but still further, the principal instrument of her future fortune and vengeance? She knew him; she knew that at her return from a fruitless journey it would be in vain to tell him of her imprisonment, in vain to enlarge upon the sufferings she had undergone. The cardinal would reply, with the sarcastic calmness of the sceptic, strong at once by power and genius: "You should not have allowed yourself to be taken."

Then Milady collected all her energies, murmuring in the depths of her soul the name of Felton—the only beam of light that penetrated to her in the hell into which she had fallen; and like a serpent which folds and unfolds its rings to ascertain its strength, she enveloped Felton beforehand in the thousand meshes of her inventive imagination.

Time, however, passed away; the hours, one after another, seemed to awaken the clock as they passed, and every blow of the brass hammer resounded upon the heart of the prisoner. At nine o'clock, Lord de Winter made his customary visit, examined the window and the bars, sounded the floor and the walls, looked to the chimney and the doors, without, during this long and minute examination, he or Milady pronouncing a single word.

Doubtless both of them understood that the situation had become too serious to lose time in useless words and aimless wrath.

"Well," said the baron, on leaving her, "you will not escape tonight!"

At ten o'clock Felton came and placed the sentinel. Milady recognized his step. She was as well acquainted with it now as a mistress is with that of the lover of her heart; and yet Milady at the same time detested and despised this weak fanatic.

It was not yet the appointed hour, and Felton did not enter.

Two hours after, as midnight sounded, the sentinel was relieved. This time it *was* the hour, and from this moment Milady waited with impatience. The new sentinel commenced his walk in the corridor. At the expiration of ten minutes Felton came.

Milady was all attention.

"Listen," said the young man to the sentinel, "on no pretense leave the door, for you know that last night my lord punished a soldier for having quitted his post for an instant, although I, during his absence, watched in his place."

"Yes, I know it," said the soldier.

"I recommend you therefore to keep the strictest watch. For my part I am going to pay a second visit to this woman, who I fear entertains sinister intentions upon her own life, and I have received orders to watch her."

"Good!" murmured Milady; "the austere Puritan lies."

As to the soldier, he only smiled.

"Zounds, Lieutenant!" said he; "you are not unlucky in being charged with such commissions, particularly if my lord has authorized you to look into her bed."

Felton blushed. Under any other circumstances he would have reprimanded the soldier for indulging in such pleasantry, but his conscience murmured too loud for his mouth to dare speak.

"If I call, come," said he. "If anyone comes, call me."

"I will, Lieutenant," said the soldier.

Felton entered Milady's apartment. Milady arose.

"You are here!" said she.

"I promised you to come," said Felton, "and I have come."

"You promised me something else."

"What, my God?" said the young man, who in spite of his self-command felt his knees tremble and the sweat start from his brow.

"You promised to bring a knife, and to leave it with me after our interview."

"Say no more of that, madame," said Felton. "There is no situation, however terrible it may be, which can authorize a creature of God to inflict death upon himself. I have reflected, and I cannot, must not, be guilty of such a sin."

"Ah, you have reflected!" said the prisoner, sitting down in her armchair, with a smile of disdain; "and I have also reflected."

"Upon what?"

"That I can have nothing to say to a man who does not keep his word."

"Oh, my God!" murmured Felton.

"You may retire," said Milady. "I will not talk."

"Here is the knife," said Felton, drawing from his pocket the weapon which he had brought, according to his promise, but which he hesitated to give to his prisoner.

"Let me see it," said Milady.

"For what purpose?"

"Upon my honor, I will instantly return it to you. You shall place it on that table, and you may remain between it and me."

Felton offered the weapon to Milady, who examined the temper of it attentively, and who tried the point on the tip of her finger.

"Well," said she, returning the knife to the young officer, "this is fine and good steel. You are a faithful friend, Felton."

Felton took back the weapon, and laid it upon the table, as he had agreed with the prisoner.

Milady followed him with her eyes, and made a gesture of satisfaction.

"Now," said she, "listen to me."

The request was needless. The young officer stood upright before her, awaiting her words as if to devour them.

"Felton," said Milady, with a solemnity full of melancholy, "imagine that your sister, the daughter of your father, speaks to you. While yet young, unfortunately handsome, I was dragged into a snare. I resisted. Ambushes and violences multiplied around me, but I resisted. The religion I serve, the God I adore, were blasphemed because I called upon that religion and that God, but still I resisted. Then outrages were heaped upon me, and as my soul was not subdued they wished to defile my body forever. Finally—"

Milady stopped and a bitter smile passed over her lips.

"Finally," said Felton—"finally, what did they do?"

"At length, one evening, my enemy resolved to paralyze the resistance he could not conquer. One evening he mixed a powerful narcotic with my water. Scarcely had I finished my repast, when I felt myself sink by degrees into a strange stupor. Although I was without mistrust, a vague fear seized me, and I tried to struggle against sleepiness. I arose. I wished to run to the window and call for help, but my legs refused their office. It appeared as if the ceiling sank upon my head and crushed me with its weight. I stretched out my arms. I tried to speak. I could only utter inarticulate sounds, and irresistible faintness came over me. I supported myself by a chair, feeling that I was about to fall, but this support was soon insufficient on account of my weak arms. I fell upon one knee, then upon both. I tried to pray, but my tongue was frozen. God doubtless neither heard nor saw me, and I sank upon the floor a prey to a slumber which resembled death.

"Of all that passed in that sleep, or the time which glided away while it lasted, I have no remembrance. The only thing I recollect is that I awoke in bed in a round chamber, the furniture of which was sumptuous, and into which light only penetrated by an opening in the ceiling. No door gave entrance to the room. It might be called a magnificent prison.

"It was a long time before I was able to make out what place I was in, or to take account of the details I describe. My mind appeared to strive in vain to shake off the heavy darkness of the sleep from which I could not rouse myself. I had vague perceptions of space traversed, of the rolling of a carriage, of a horrible dream in which my strength had become exhausted; but all this was so dark and so indistinct in my mind that these events seemed to belong to another life than mine, and yet mixed with mine in fantastic duality.

"At times the state into which I was fallen appeared so strange that I believed myself dreaming. I arose trembling. My clothes were near me on a chair; I neither remembered having undressed myself, nor going to bed. Then by degree the reality broke upon me, full of virginal terrors. I was no longer in the house where I had dwelt. As well as I could judge by the light of the sun, the day was already two-thirds gone. It was the evening before when I had fallen asleep; my sleep then must have lasted twenty-four hours! What had taken place during this long sleep?

"I dressed myself as quickly as possible; my slow and stiff motions all attested that the effects of the narcotic were not yet entirely dissipated. The chamber was evidently furnished for the reception of a woman; and the most finished coquette could not have formed a wish, but on casting her eyes about the apartment, she would have found that wish accomplished.

"Certainly I was not the first captive that had been shut up in this splendid prison; but you may easily comprehend, Felton, that the more superb the prison, the greater was my terror.

"Yes, it was a prison, for I tried in vain to get out of it. I sounded all the walls, in the hopes of discovering a door, but everywhere the walls returned a full and flat sound.

"I made the tour of the room at least twenty times, in search of an outlet of some kind; there was none. I sank exhausted with fatigue and terror into an armchair.

"Meantime, night came on rapidly, and with night my terrors increased. I did not know but I had better remain where I was seated. It appeared that I was surrounded with unknown dangers into which I was about to fall at every instant. Although I had eaten nothing since the evening before, my fears prevented my feeling hunger.

"No noise from without by which I could measure the time reached me; I only supposed it must be seven or eight o'clock in the evening, for it was in the month of October, and it was quite dark.

"All at once the noise of a door, turning on its hinges, made me start. A globe of fire appeared above the glazed opening of the ceiling, casting a strong light into my chamber; and I perceived with terror that a man was standing within a few paces of me.

"A table, with two covers, bearing a supper ready prepared, stood, as if by magic, in the middle of the apartment.

"That man was he who had pursued me during a whole year, who had vowed my dishonor, and who, by the first words that issued from his mouth, gave me to understand he had accomplished it the preceding night."

"Scoundrel!" murmured Felton.

"Yes, scoundrel!" cried Milady, seeing the interest which the young officer, whose soul seemed to hang on her lips, took in this strange recital. "Oh, yes, scoundrel! He believed, having triumphed over me in my sleep, that all was completed. He came, hoping that I would accept my shame, as my shame was consummated; he came to offer his fortune in exchange for my love.

"All that the heart of a woman could contain of haughty contempt and disdainful words, I poured out upon this man. Doubtless he was accustomed to such reproaches, for he listened to me calm and smiling, with his arms crossed over his breast. Then, when he thought I had said all, he advanced toward me; I sprang toward the table, I seized a knife, I placed it to my breast.

"'Take one step more,' said I, 'and in addition to my dishonor, you shall have my death to reproach yourself with.'

"There was, no doubt, in my look, my voice, my whole person, that sincerity of gesture, of attitude, of accent, which carries conviction to the most perverse minds, for he paused.

"'Your death?' said he; 'oh, no, you are too charming a mistress to allow me to consent to lose you thus, after I have had the happiness to possess you only a single time. Adieu, my charmer; I will wait to pay you my next visit till you are in a better humor.'

"At these words he blew a whistle; the globe of fire which lighted the room reascended and disappeared. I found myself again in complete darkness. The same noise of a door opening and shutting was repeated the instant afterward; the flaming globe descended afresh, and I was completely alone.

"This moment was frightful; if I had any doubts as to my misfortune, these doubts had vanished in an overwhelming reality. I was in the power of a man whom I not only detested, but despised—of a man capable of anything, and who had already given me a fatal proof of what he was able to do."

"But who, then, was this man?" asked Felton.

"I passed the night on a chair, starting at the least noise, for toward midnight the lamp went out, and I was again in darkness. But the night passed away without any fresh attempt on the part of my persecutor. Day came; the table had disappeared, only I had still the knife in my hand.

"This knife was my only hope.

"I was worn out with fatigue. Sleeplessness inflamed my eyes; I had not dared to sleep a single instant. The light of day reassured me; I went and threw myself on the bed, without parting with the emancipating knife, which I concealed under the pillow.

"When I awoke, a fresh meal was served.

"This time, in spite of my terrors, in spite of my agony, I began to feel a devouring hunger. It was forty-eight hours since I had taken any nourishment. I ate some bread and some fruit; then, remembering the narcotic mixed with the water I had drunk, I would not touch that which was placed on the table, but filled my glass at a marble fountain fixed in the wall over my dressing table.

"And yet, notwithstanding these precautions, I remained for some time in a terrible agitation of mind. But my fears were this time ill-founded; I passed the day without experiencing anything of the kind I dreaded.

"I took the precaution to half empty the *carafe*, in order that my suspicions might not be noticed.

"The evening came on, and with it darkness; but however profound was this darkness, my eyes began to accustom themselves to it. I saw, amid the shadows, the table sink through the floor; a quarter of an hour later it reappeared, bearing my supper. In an instant, thanks to the lamp, the chamber was once more lighted.

"I was determined to eat only such things as could not possibly have anything soporific introduced into them. Two eggs and some fruit composed my repast; then I drew another glass of water from my protecting fountain, and drank it.

"At the first swallow, it appeared to me not to have the same taste as in the morning. Suspicion instantly seized me. I paused, but I had already drunk half a glass.

"I threw the rest away with horror, and waited, with the dew of fear upon my brow.

"No doubt some invisible witness had seen me draw the water from that fountain, and had taken advantage of my confidence in it, the better to assure my ruin, so coolly resolved upon, so cruelly pursued.

"Half an hour had not passed when the same symptoms began to appear; but as I had drunk only half a glass of the water, I contended longer, and instead of falling entirely asleep, I sank into a state of drowsiness which left me a perception of what was passing around me, while depriving me of the strength either to defend myself or to fly.

"I dragged myself toward the bed, to seek the only defense I had left—my saving knife; but I could not reach the bolster. I sank on my knees, my hands clasped around one of the bedposts; then I felt that I was lost."

Felton became frightfully pale, and a convulsive tremor crept through his whole body.

"And what was most frightful," continued Milady, her voice altered, as if she still experienced the same agony as at that awful moment, "was that at this time I retained a consciousness of the danger that threatened me; as if my soul, if I may say so, waked in my sleeping body; as if I saw, and heard. It is true that it was all like a dream, but it was not the less frightful.

"I saw the lamp ascend, and leave me in darkness; and then I heard the well-known creaking of the door, although I had heard that door open but twice.

"I felt instinctively that someone approached me; it is said that the doomed wretch in the deserts of America thus feels the approach of the serpent.

"I wished to make an effort; I attempted to cry out. By an incredible effort of will I even raised myself up, but only to sink down again immediately, and to fall into the arms of my persecutor."

"Tell me who this man was!" cried the young officer.

Milady saw at a single glance all the painful feelings she inspired in Felton by dwelling on every detail of her recital; but she would not spare him a single pang. The more profoundly she wounded his heart, the more certain he would avenge her. She continued, then, as if she had not heard his exclamation, or as if she thought the moment was not yet come to reply to it.

"Only this time it was no longer an inert body, without feeling, that the villain had to deal with. I have told you that without being able to regain the complete exercise of my faculties, I retained the sense of my danger. I struggled, then, with all my strength, and doubtless opposed, weak as I was, a long resistance, for I heard him cry out, 'These miserable Puritans! I knew very well that they tired out their executioners, but I did not believe them so strong against their lovers!'

"Alas! this desperate resistance could not last long. I felt my strength fail, and this time it was not my sleep that enabled the coward to prevail, but my swoon."

Felton listened without uttering any word or sound, except an inward expression of agony. The sweat streamed down his marble forehead, and his hand, under his coat, tore his breast.

"My first impulse, on coming to myself, was to feel under my pillow for the knife I had not been able to reach; if it had not been useful for defense, it might at least serve for expiation.

"But on taking this knife, Felton, a terrible idea occurred to me. I have sworn to tell you all, and I will tell you all. I have promised you the truth; I will tell it, were it to destroy me."

"The idea came into your mind to avenge yourself on this man, did it not?" cried Felton.

"Yes," said Milady. "The idea was not that of a Christian, I knew; but without doubt, that eternal enemy of our souls, that lion roaring constantly around us, breathed it into my mind. In short, what shall I say to you, Felton?" continued Milady, in the tone of a woman accusing herself of a crime. "This idea occurred to me, and did not leave me; it is of this homicidal thought that I now bear the punishment."

"Continue, continue!" said Felton; "I am eager to see you attain your vengeance!"

"Oh, I resolved that it should take place as soon as possible. I had no doubt that he would return the following night. During the day I had nothing to fear.

"When the hour of breakfast came, therefore, I did not hesitate to eat and drink. I had determined to make believe to sup, but to eat nothing. I was forced, then, to combat the fast of the evening with the nourishment of the morning.

"Only I concealed a glass of water, which remained after my breakfast, thirst having been the chief of my sufferings when I remained forty-eight hours without eating or drinking.

"The day passed away without having any other influence on me than to strengthen the resolution I had formed; only I took care that my face should not betray the thoughts of my heart, for I had no doubt I was watched. Several times, even, I felt a smile on my lips. Felton, I dare not tell you at what idea I smiled; you would hold me in horror—"

"Go on! go on!" said Felton; "you see plainly that I listen, and that I am anxious to know the end."

"Evening came; the ordinary events took place. During the darkness, as before, my supper was brought. Then the lamp was lighted, and I sat down to supper. I only ate some fruit. I pretended to pour out water from the jug, but I only drank that which I had saved in my glass. The substitution was made so carefully that my spies, if I had any, could have no suspicion of it.

"After supper, I exhibited the same marks of languor as on the preceding evening; but this time, as if I yielded to fatigue, or as if I had become familiarized with danger, I dragged myself toward my bed, let my robe fall, and lay down.

"I found my knife where I had placed it, under my pillow, and while feigning sleep, my hand grasped the handle of it convulsively.

"Two hours passed away without anything fresh happening. Oh, my God! who could have said so the evening before? I began to fear that he would not come.

"At length I saw the lamp rise softly and disappear in the depths of the ceiling; my chamber was filled with darkness and obscurity, but I made a strong effort to penetrate this darkness and obscurity.

"Nearly ten minutes passed; I heard no other noise but the beating of my own heart. I implored Heaven that he might come.

"At length, I heard the well-known noise of the door, which opened and shut; I heard, notwithstanding the thickness of the carpet, a step which made the floor creak; I saw, notwithstanding the darkness, a shadow which approached my bed."

"Haste, haste!" said Felton; "do you not see that each of your words burns me like molten lead?"

"Then," continued Milady, "then I collected all my strength; I recalled to my mind that the moment of vengeance, or rather, of justice, had struck. I looked upon myself as another Judith; I gathered myself up, my knife in my hand, and when I saw him near me, stretching out his arms to find his victim, then, with the last cry of agony and despair, I struck him in the middle of his breast.

"The miserable villain! He had foreseen all. His breast was covered with a coat of mail; the knife was bent against it.

" 'So!' cried he, seizing my arm, and wresting from me the weapon that had so badly served me, 'you want to take my life, do you, my pretty Puritan? But that's more than dislike, that's ingratitude! Come, come, calm yourself, my sweet girl! I thought you had softened, and I am not one of those tyrants who detain women by force. Plainly you don't love me. With my usual fatuity I doubted it; now I am convinced. Tomorrow you shall be free.'

"I had but one wish; that was that he should kill me.

" 'Beware!' said I, 'for my liberty is your dishonor.'

" 'Explain yourself, my pretty sibyl!'

" 'Yes; for as soon as I leave this place I will tell everything. I will proclaim the violence you have used toward me. I will describe my captivity. I will denounce this palace of infamy. You are placed on high, my lord, but tremble! Above you there is the king; above the king there is God!'

"However perfect master he was over himself, my persecutor allowed a movement of anger to escape him. I could not see the expression of his countenance, but I felt the arm tremble upon which my hand was placed.

" 'Then you shall not leave this place,' said he.

" 'Very well,' cried I, 'then the place of my punishment will be that of my tomb. I will die here, and you will see if a phantom that accuses is not more terrible than a living being that threatens!'

" 'You shall have no weapon left in your power.'

" 'There is a weapon which despair has placed within the reach of every creature who has the courage to use it. I will allow myself to die with hunger.'

" 'Come,' said the wretch, 'is not peace much better than such a war as that? I will restore you to liberty this moment; I will proclaim you a piece of immaculate virtue; I will name you the Lucretia of England.'

" 'And I will say that you are the Sextus. I will denounce you before men, as I have denounced you before God; and if it be necessary that, like Lucretia, I should sign my accusation with my blood, I will sign it.'

" 'Ah!' said my enemy, in a jeering tone, 'that's quite another thing. My faith! everything considered, you are very well off here. You shall want for nothing, and if you let yourself die of hunger that will be your own fault.'

"At these words he retired. I heard the door open and shut, and I remained overwhelmed, less, I confess it, by my grief than by the mortification of not having avenged myself.

"He kept his word. All the day, all the next night passed away without my seeing him again. But I also kept my word with him, and I neither ate nor drank. I was, as I had told him, resolved to die of hunger.

"I passed the day and the night in prayer, for I hoped that God would pardon my suicide.

"The second night the door opened; I was lying on the floor, for my strength began to abandon me.

"At the noise I raised myself up on one hand.

" 'Well,' said a voice which vibrated in too terrible a manner in my ear not to be recognized—'well! Are we softened a little? Will we not pay for our liberty with a single promise of silence? Come, I am really a good sort of a prince,' added he, 'and although I like not Puritans I do them justice; and it is the same with Puritanesses, when they are pretty. Come, take a little oath for me on the cross; I won't ask anything more of you.'

" 'On the cross,' cried I, rising, for at that abhorred voice I had recovered all my strength—'on the cross I swear that no promise, no menace, no force, no torture, shall close my mouth! On the cross I swear to denounce you everywhere as a murderer, as a thief of honor, as a base coward! On the cross, I swear, if I ever leave this place, to call down vengeance upon you from the whole human race!'

" 'Beware!' said the voice, in a threatening accent that I had never yet heard. 'I have an extraordinary means which I will not employ but in the last extremity to close your mouth, or at least to prevent anyone from believing a word you may utter.'

"I mustered all my strength to reply to him with a burst of laughter.

"He saw that it was a merciless war between us—a war to the death.

" 'Listen!' said he. 'I give you the rest of tonight and all day tomorrow. Reflect: promise to be silent, and riches, consideration, even honor, shall surround you; threaten to speak, and I will condemn you to infamy.'

" 'You?' cried I. 'You?'

" 'To interminable, ineffaceable infamy!'

" 'You?' repeated I. Oh, I declare to you, Felton, I thought him mad!

" 'Yes, yes, I!' replied he.

" 'Oh, leave me!' said I. 'Begone, if you do not desire to see me dash my head against that wall before your eyes!'

" 'Very well, it is your own doing. Till tomorrow evening, then!'

" 'Till tomorrow evening, then!' replied I, allowing myself to fall, and biting the carpet with rage."

Felton leaned for support upon a piece of furniture; and Milady saw, with the joy of a demon, that his strength would fail him perhaps before the end of her recital.

Means for Classical Tragedy

After a moment of silence employed by Milady in observing the young man who listened to her, Milady continued her recital.

"It was nearly three days since I had eaten or drunk anything. I suffered frightful torments. At times there passed before me clouds which pressed my brow, which veiled my eyes; this was delirium.

"When the evening came I was so weak that every time I fainted I thanked God, for I thought I was about to die.

"In the midst of one of these swoons I heard the door open. Terror recalled me to myself.

"He entered the apartment followed by a man in a mask. He was masked likewise; but I knew his step, I knew his voice, I knew him by that imposing bearing which hell has bestowed upon his person for the curse of humanity.

" 'Well,' said he to me, 'have you made your mind up to take the oath I requested of you?'

" 'You have said Puritans have but one word. Mine you have heard, and that is to pursue you—on earth to the tribunal of men, in heaven to the tribunal of God.'

" 'You persist, then?'

" 'I swear it before the God who hears me. I will take the whole world as a witness of your crime, and that until I have found an avenger.'

" 'You are a prostitute,' said he, in a voice of thunder, 'and you shall undergo the punishment of prostitutes! Branded in the eyes of the world you invoke, try to prove to that world that you are neither guilty nor mad!'

"Then, addressing the man who accompanied him, 'Executioner,' said he, 'do your duty.'

"Oh, his name, his name!" cried Felton. "His name, tell it to me!"

"Then in spite of my cries, in spite of my resistance—for I began to comprehend that there was a question of something worse than death—the executioner seized me, threw me on the floor, fastened me with his bonds, and suffocated by sobs, almost without sense, invoking God, who did not listen to me, I uttered all at once a frightful cry of pain and shame. A burning fire, a red-hot iron, the iron of the executioner, was imprinted on my shoulder."

Felton uttered a groan.

"Here," said Milady, rising with the majesty of a queen—"here, Felton, behold now the martyrdom invented for a pure young girl, the victim of the brutality of a villain. Learn to know the heart of men, and henceforth make yourself less easily the instrument of their unjust vengeance."

Milady, with a rapid gesture, opened her robe, tore the cambric that covered her bosom, and, red with feigned anger and simulated shame, showed the young man the ineffaceable impression which dishonored that beautiful shoulder.

"But," cried Felton, "that is a *fleur-de-lis* which I see there."

"And therein consisted the infamy," replied Milady. "For you see: the brand of England—it would be necessary to prove what tribunal had imposed it on me, and I could have made a public appeal to all the tribunals of the kingdom; but the brand of France!—oh, by that, by *that* I was branded indeed!"

This was too much for Felton.

Pale, motionless, overwhelmed by this frightful revelation, dazzled by the superhuman beauty of this woman who unveiled herself before him with an immodesty which appeared to him sublime, he ended by falling on his knees before her as the early Christians did before those pure and holy martyrs whom the persecution of the em-

perors gave up in the circus to the sanguinary sensuality of the popu-
lace. The brand disappeared; the beauty alone remained.

"Pardon! pardon!" cried Felton; "oh, pardon!"

Milady read in his eyes *love! love!*

"Pardon for what?" asked she.

"Pardon me for having joined with your persecutors."

Milady held out her hand to him.

"So beautiful! so young!" cried Felton, covering that hand with
his kisses.

Milady let one of those looks fall upon him which make a slave of
a king.

Felton was a Puritan; he abandoned the hand of this woman to
kiss her feet.

He no longer loved her; he adored her.

When this crisis was past, when Milady appeared to have resumed
her self-possession, which she had never lost; when Felton had seen
her recover with the veil of chastity those treasures of love which
were only concealed from him to make him desire them the more
ardently, he said: "Ah, now! I have only one thing to ask of you;
that is, the name of your betrayer. The name of your executioner.
For to me there is but one; the other was an instrument, that was
all."

"What, Brother!" cried Milady, "must I name him again! Have
you not yet divined who he is?"

"What?" cried Felton, "he—again he—always he? What—the truly
guilty?"

"The truly guilty," said Milady, "is the ravager of England, the
persecutor of true believers, the base ravisher of the honor of so
many women—he who, to satisfy a caprice of his corrupt heart, is
about to make England shed so much blood, who protects the
Protestants today and will betray them tomorrow—"

"Buckingham! It is, then, Buckingham!" cried Felton, in a high
state of excitement.

Milady concealed her face in her hands, as if she could not endure
the shame which this name recalled to her.

"Buckingham, the executioner of this angelic creature!" cried Felton. "And thou has not hurled thy thunder at him, my God! And
thou hast left him noble, honored, powerful, for the ruin of us all!"

"God abandons him who abandons himself," said Milady.

"But he will draw down upon his head the punishment reserved for the damned!" said Felton, with increasing exultation. "He wills that human vengeance should precede celestial justice."

"Men fear him and spare him."

"I," said Felton—"I do not fear him, nor will I spare him."

The soul of Milady was bathed in an infernal joy.

"But how can Lord de Winter, my protector, my Father," asked Felton, "possibly be mixed up with all this?"

"Listen, Felton," resumed Milady, "for by the side of base and contemptible men there are often found great and generous natures. I had an affianced husband, a man whom I loved, and who loved me—a heart like yours, Felton, a man like you. I went to him and told him all; he knew me, that man did, and did not doubt an instant. He was a nobleman, a man equal to Buckingham in every respect. He said nothing; he only girded his sword, wrapped himself in his cloak, and went straight to Buckingham Palace."

"Yes, yes," said Felton; "I understand how he would act. But with such men it is not the sword that should be employed; it is the poniard."

"Buckingham had left England the day before, sent as ambassador to Spain, to demand the hand of the infanta for King Charles I, who was then only Prince of Wales. My affianced husband returned.

"'Hear me,' said he; 'this man is gone, and for the moment has consequently escaped my vengeance; but let us be united, as we were to have been, and then leave it to Lord de Winter to maintain his own honor and that of his wife.'"

"Lord de Winter!" cried Felton.

"Yes," said Milady, "Lord de Winter; and now you can understand it all, can you not? Buckingham remained nearly a year absent. A week before his return Lord de Winter died, leaving me his sole heir. Whence came the blow? God knows all, knows without doubt; but as for me, I accuse nobody."

"Oh, what an abyss; what an abyss!" cried Felton.

"Lord de Winter died without revealing anything to his brother. The terrible secret was to be concealed till it burst, like a clap of thunder, over the head of the guilty. Your protector had seen with pain this marriage of his elder brother with a portionless girl. I was sensible that I could look for no support from a man disappointed in his hopes of an inheritance. I went to France, with a determination to remain there for the rest of my life. But all my fortune is in England. Communication being closed by the war, I was in want of everything. I was then obliged to come back again. Six days ago, I landed at Portsmouth."

"Well?" said Felton.

"Well; Buckingham heard by some means, no doubt, of my return. He spoke of me to Lord de Winter, already prejudiced against me, and told him that his sister-in-law was a prostitute, a branded woman. The noble and pure voice of my husband was no longer here to defend me. Lord de Winter believed all that was told him with so much the more ease that it was his interest to believe it. He caused me to be arrested, and had me conducted hither, and placed me under your guard. You know the rest. The day after tomorrow he exiles me among the infamous. Oh, the train is well laid; the plot is clever. My honor will not survive it! You see, then, Felton, I can do nothing but die. Felton, give me that knife!"

And at these words, as if all her strength was exhausted, Milady sank, weak and languishing, into the arms of the young officer, who, intoxicated with love, anger, and voluptuous sensations hitherto unknown, received her with transport, pressed her against his heart, all trembling at the breath from that charming mouth, bewildered by the contact with that palpitating bosom.

"No, no," said he; "no, you shall live honored and pure; you shall live to triumph over your enemies."

Milady put him from her slowly with her hand, while drawing him nearer with her look; but Felton, in his turn, embraced her more closely, imploring her like a divinity.

"Oh, death, death!" said she, lowering her voice and her eyelids—"oh, death rather than shame! Felton, my Brother, my friend, I conjure you!"

"No," cried Felton, "no; you shall live, and you shall be avenged."

"Felton, I bring misfortune to all who surround me! Felton, abandon me! Felton, let me die!"

"Well, then, we will live and die together!" cried he, pressing his lips to those of the prisoner.

Several strokes resounded on the door; this time Milady really pushed him away from her.

"Hark," said she, "we have been overheard! Someone is coming! All is over! We are lost!"

"No," said Felton; "it is only the sentinel warning me that they are about to change guard."

"Then run to the door, and open it yourself."

Felton obeyed; this woman was now his whole thought, his whole soul.

He found himself face to face with a sergeant commanding a watch patrol.

"Well, what is the matter?" asked the young lieutenant.

"You told me to open the door if I heard anyone cry out," said the soldier; "but you forgot to leave me the key. I heard you cry out, without understanding what you said. I tried to open the door, but it was locked inside; then I called the sergeant."

"And here I am," said the sergeant.

Felton, quite bewildered, almost mad, stood speechless.

Milady plainly perceived that it was now her turn to take part in the scene. She ran to the table, and, seizing the knife which Felton had laid down, exclaimed: "And by what right will you prevent me from dying?"

"Great God!" exclaimed Felton, on seeing the knife glitter in her hand.

At that moment a burst of ironical laughter resounded through the corridor. The baron, attracted by the noise, in his chamber gown, his sword under his arm, stood in the doorway.

"Ah," said he, "here we are, at the last act of the tragedy. You see, Felton, the drama has gone through all the phases I named; but be easy; no blood will flow."

Milady perceived that all was lost unless she gave Felton an immediate and terrible proof of her courage.

"You are mistaken, my lord, blood will flow; and may that blood fall back on those who cause it to flow!"

Felton uttered a cry, and rushed toward her. He was too late; Milady had stabbed herself.

But the knife had fortunately, we ought to say skillfully, come in contact with the steel bust, which, at that period, like a cuirass, defended the chests of women. It had glided down it, tearing the robe, and had penetrated slantingly between the flesh and the ribs. Milady's robe was not the less stained with blood in a second.

Milady fell down, and seemed to be in a swoon.

Felton snatched away the knife.

"See, my lord," said he, in a deep, gloomy tone, "here is a woman who was under my guard, and who has killed herself!"

"Be at ease, Felton," said Lord de Winter. "She is not dead; demons do not die so easily. Be tranquil, and go wait for me in my chamber."

"But, my lord—"

"Go, sir, I command you!"

At this injunction from his superior, Felton obeyed; but in going out, he put the knife into his bosom.

As to Lord de Winter, he contented himself with calling the woman who waited on Milady, and when she was come, he recommended the prisoner, who was still fainting, to her care, and left them alone.

Meanwhile, all things considered and notwithstanding his suspicions, as the wound might be serious, he immediately sent off a mounted man to find a physician.

Escape

As Lord de Winter had thought, Milady's wound was not dangerous. As soon as she was left alone with the woman whom the baron had summoned to her assistance, she opened her eyes.

It was, however, necessary to affect weakness and pain—not a very difficult task for so finished an actress as Milady. Thus the poor woman was completely the dupe of the prisoner, whom, notwithstanding her hints, she persisted in watching all night.

But the presence of this woman did not prevent Milady from thinking.

There was no longer a doubt that Felton was convinced; Felton was hers. If an angel appeared to that young man as an accuser of Milady, he would take him, in the mental disposition in which he now found himself, for a messenger of the Devil.

Milady smiled at this thought, for Felton was now her only hope —her only means of safety.

Toward four o'clock in the morning the doctor arrived; but since the time Milady stabbed herself, however short, the wound had closed. The doctor could therefore measure neither the direction nor the depth of it; he only satisfied himself by Milady's pulse that the case was not serious.

In the morning, Milady, under the pretext that she had not slept well in the night and wanted rest, sent away the woman who attended her.

She had one hope, which was that Felton would appear at the breakfast hour; but Felton did not come.

Were her fears realized? Was Felton, suspected by the baron, about to fail her at the decisive moment? She had only one day left. Lord de Winter had announced her embarkation for the twenty-third, and it was now the morning of the twenty-second.

Nevertheless she still waited patiently till the hour for dinner.

Although she had eaten nothing in the morning, the dinner was brought in at its usual time. Milady then perceived, with terror, that the uniform of the soldiers who guarded her was changed.

Then she ventured to ask what had become of Felton.

She was told that he had left the castle an hour before on horseback. She inquired if the baron was still at the castle. The soldier replied that he was, and that he had given orders to be informed if the prisoner wished to speak to him.

Milady replied that she was too weak at present, and that her only desire was to be left alone.

The soldier went out, leaving the dinner served.

Felton was sent away. The marines were removed. Felton was then mistrusted.

This was the last blow to the prisoner.

Left alone, she arose. The bed, to which she had kept from prudence, and that they might believe her seriously wounded, burned her like a bed of fire. She cast a glance at the door; the baron had had a plank nailed over the grating. He no doubt feared that by this opening she might still by some diabolical means corrupt her guards.

Milady smiled with joy. She was now free to give way to her transports without being observed. She traversed her chamber with the excitement of a furious maniac, or of a tigress shut up in an iron cage. *Certes*, if the knife had been left in her power, she would now have thought, not of killing herself, but of killing the baron.

At six o'clock Lord de Winter came in. He was armed at all points. This man, in whom Milady till that time had only seen a very simple gentleman, had become an admirable jailer. He appeared to foresee all, to divine all, to anticipate all.

A single look at Milady apprised him of all that was passing in her mind.

"Ay!" said he, "I see; but you shall not kill me today. You have no longer a weapon; and besides, I am on my guard. You had begun to pervert my poor Felton. He was yielding to your infernal influence; but I will save him. He will never see you again; all is over. Get your clothes together. Tomorrow you will go. I had fixed the embarkation for the twenty-fourth; but I have reflected that the more promptly the affair takes place the more sure it will be. Tomorrow, by twelve o'clock, I shall have the order for your exile, signed, *Buckingham*. If you speak a single word to anyone before going aboard ship, my sergeant will blow your brains out. He has orders to do so. If when on the ship you speak a single word to anyone before the captain permits you, the captain will have you thrown into the sea. That is agreed upon.

"*Au revoir*, then; that is all I have to say today. Tomorrow I will see you again, to take my leave." With these words the baron went out. Milady had listened to all this menacing tirade with a smile of disdain on her lips, but rage was in her heart.

Supper was served. Milady felt that she stood in need of all her strength. She did not know what might take place during this night which approached so menacingly—for large masses of cloud rolled over the face of the sky, and distant lightning announced a storm.

The storm broke about ten o'clock. Milady felt a consolation in seeing nature partake of the disorder of her heart. The thunder growled in the air like the passion and anger in her thoughts. It appeared to her that the blast as it swept along disheveled her brow, just as it would bend the branches of the trees and bear away their leaves. She howled as the hurricane howled; and her voice was lost in the great voice of nature; which also seemed to groan with despair.

All at once she heard a tap at her window, and by the help of a flash of lightning she saw the face of a man appear behind the bars.

She ran to the window and opened it.

"Felton!" cried she. "I am saved."

"Yes," said Felton; "but silence, silence! I must have time to file through these bars. Only take care that I am not seen through the wicket."

"Oh, it is a proof that the Lord is on our side, Felton," replied Milady. "They have closed up the grating with a board."

"That is well; God has made them senseless," said Felton.

"But what must I do?" asked Milady.

"Nothing, nothing, only shut the window. Go to bed, or at least lie down in your clothes. As soon as I have done I will knock on one of the panes of glass. But will you be able to follow me?"

"Oh yes!"

"Your wound?"

"Gives me pain, but will not prevent my walking."

"Be ready, then, at the first signal."

Milady shut the window, extinguished the lamp, and went, as Felton had desired her, to lie down on the bed. Amid the moaning of the storm, she heard the grinding of the file upon the bars, and by the light of every flash she perceived the shadow of Felton through the panes.

She passed an hour without breathing, panting, with a cold sweat upon her brow, and her heart oppressed by frightful agony at every movement she heard in the corridor.

There are hours which last a year.

At the expiration of an hour, Felton tapped again.

Milady sprang out of bed and opened the window. Two bars removed formed an opening for a man to pass through.

"Are you ready?" asked Felton.

"Yes, must I take anything with me?"

"Money, if you have any."

"Yes; fortunately they have left me all I had."

"So much the better, for I have expended all mine in chartering a vessel."

"Here," said Milady, placing a bag full of louis in Felton's hands.

Felton took the bag and threw it to the foot of the wall.

"Now," said he, "will you come?"

"I am ready."

Milady mounted upon a chair and passed the upper part of her body through the window. She saw the young officer suspended over the abyss by a ladder of ropes. For the first time an emotion of terror reminded her that she was a woman. The dark space frightened her.

"I expected this," said Felton.

"It's nothing, it's nothing!" said Milady. "I will descend with my eyes shut."

"Have you confidence in me?" said Felton.

"You ask that?"

"Put your two hands together. Cross them; that's right!"

Felton tied her two wrists together with his handkerchief, and then with a cord over the handkerchief.

"What are you doing?" asked Milady, with surprise.

"Pass your arms around my neck, and fear nothing."

"But I shall make you lose your balance, and we shall both be dashed to pieces."

"Don't be afraid. I am a sailor."

Not a second was to be lost. Milady passed her two arms around Felton's neck, and let herself slip out of the window. Felton began to descend the ladder slowly, step by step. Despite the weight of two bodies, the blast of the hurricane shook them in the air.

All at once Felton stopped.

"What is the matter?" asked Milady.

"Silence!" said Felton, "I hear footsteps."

"We are discovered!"

There was a silence of several seconds.

"No," said Felton, "it is nothing."

"But what, then, is the noise?"

"That of the patrol going their rounds."

"Where is their road?"

"Just under us."

"They will discover us!"

"No, if it does not lighten."

"But they will run against the bottom of the ladder."

"Fortunately it is too short by six feet."

"Here they are! My God!"

"Silence!"

Both remained suspended, motionless and breathless, within twenty paces of the ground, while the patrol passed beneath them laughing and talking. This was a terrible moment for the fugitives.

The patrol passed. The noise of their retreating footsteps and the murmur of their voices soon died away.

"Now," said Felton, "we are safe."

Milady breathed a deep sigh and fainted.

Felton continued to descend. Near the bottom of the ladder, when he found no more support for his feet, he clung with his hands; at length, arrived at the last step, he let himself hang by the strength of his wrists, and touched the ground. He stooped down, picked up the bag of money, and placed it between his teeth. Then he took Milady in his arms, and set off briskly in the direction opposite to that which the patrol had taken. He soon left the pathway of the patrol, descended across the rocks, and, when arrived on the edge of the sea, whistled.

A similar signal replied to him; and five minutes after, a boat appeared, rowed by four men.

The boat approached as near as it could to the shore; but there was not depth enough of water for it to touch land. Felton waded into the sea up to his middle, being unwilling to trust his precious burden to anybody.

Fortunately, the storm began to subside, but still the sea was disturbed. The little boat bounded over the waves like a nutshell.

"To the sloop," said Felton, "and row quickly."

The four men bent to their oars, but the sea was too high to let them get much hold of it.

However, they left the castle behind; that was the principal thing. The night was extremely dark. It was almost impossible to see the shore from the boat; they would therefore be less likely to see the boat from the shore.

A black point floated on the sea. That was the sloop. While the boat was advancing with all the speed its four rowers could give it, Felton untied the cord and then the handkerchief which bound Milady's hands together. When her hands were loosed he took some sea water and sprinkled it over her face.

Milady breathed a sigh, and opened her eyes.

"Where am I?" said she.

"Saved!" replied the young officer.

"Oh, saved, saved!" cried she. "Yes, there is the sky; here is the sea! The air I breathe is the air of liberty! Ah, thanks, Felton, thanks!"

The young man pressed her to his heart.

"But what is the matter with my hands?" asked Milady; "it seems as if my wrists had been crushed in a vice."

Milady held out her arms; her wrists were bruised.

"Alas!" said Felton, looking at those beautiful hands, and shaking his head sorrowfully.

"Oh, it's nothing, nothing!" cried Milady. "I remember now."

Milady looked around her, as if in search of something.

"It is there," said Felton, touching the bag of money with his foot.

They drew near to the sloop. A sailor on watch hailed the boat; the boat replied.

"What vessel is that?" asked Milady.

"The one I have hired for you."

"Where will it take me?"

"Where you please, after you have put me on shore at Portsmouth."

"What are you going to do at Portsmouth?" asked Milady.

"Accomplish the orders of Lord de Winter," said Felton, with a gloomy smile.

"What orders?" asked Milady.

"You do not understand?" asked Felton.

"No; explain yourself, I beg."

"As he mistrusted me, he determined to guard you himself, and sent me in his place to get Buckingham to sign the order for your transportation."

"But if he mistrusted you, how could he confide such an order to you?"

"How could I be supposed to know what I was the bearer of?"

"That's true! And you are going to Portsmouth?"

"I have no time to lose. Tomorrow is the twenty-third, and Buckingham sets sail tomorrow with his fleet."

"He sets sail tomorrow! Where for?"

"For Rochelle."

"He need not sail!" cried Milady, forgetting her usual presence of mind.

"Be satisfied," replied Felton; "he will not sail."

Milady started with joy. She could read into the depths of the heart of this young man; the death of Buckingham was written there at full length.

"Felton," cried she, "you are as great as Judas Maccabeus! If you die, I will die with you; that is all I can say to you."

"Silence!" cried Felton; "we are here."

In fact, they touched the sloop.

Felton mounted the ladder first, and gave his hand to Milady, while the sailors supported her, for the sea was still much agitated.

An instant after they were on the deck.

"Captain," said Felton, "this is the person of whom I spoke to you, and whom you must convey safe and sound to France."

"For a thousand pistoles," said the captain.

"I have paid you five hundred of them."

"That's correct," said the captain.

"And here are the other five hundred," replied Milady, placing her hand upon the bag of gold.

"No," said the captain, "I make but one bargain; and I have agree with this young man that the other five hundred shall not be due to me till we arrive at Boulogne."

"And shall we arrive there?"

"Safe and sound," said the captain; "as true as my name's Jack Butler."

"Well," said Milady, "if you keep your word, instead of five hundred, I will give you a thousand pistoles."

"Hurrah for you, then, my beautiful lady," cried the captain; "and may God often send me such passengers as Your Ladyship!"

"Meanwhile," said Felton, "convey me to the little bay of—you know it was agreed you should put in there."

The captain replied by ordering the necessary maneuvers, and toward seven o'clock in the morning the little vessel cast anchor in the bay that had been named.

During this passage, Felton related everything to Milady—how, instead of going to London, he had chartered the little vessel; how he had returned; how he had scaled the wall by fastening cramps in the interstices of the stones as he ascended, to give him foothold; and how, when he had reached the bars, he fastened his ladder. Milady knew the rest.

On her side, Milady tried to encourage Felton in his project; but at the first words which issued from her mouth, she plainly saw that the young fanatic stood more in need of being moderated than urged.

It was agreed that Milady should wait for Felton till ten o'clock; if he did not return by ten o'clock she was to sail.

In that case, and supposing he was at liberty, he was to rejoin her in France, at the convent of the Carmelites at Bethune.

What Took Place at Portsmouth Aug. 23, 1628

Felton took leave of Milady as a brother about to go for a mere walk takes leave of his sister, kissing her hand.

His whole body appeared in its ordinary state of calmness, only an unusual fire beamed from his eyes, like the effects of a fever; his brow was more pale than it generally was; his teeth were clenched, and his speech had a short dry accent which indicated that something dark was at work within him.

As long as he remained in the boat which conveyed him to land, he kept his face toward Milady, who, standing on the deck, followed him with her eyes. Both were free from the fear of pursuit; nobody ever came into Milady's apartment before nine o'clock, and it would require three hours to go from the castle to London.

Felton jumped on shore, climbed the little ascent which led to the top of the cliff, saluted Milady a last time, and took his course toward the city.

At the end of a hundred paces, the ground began to decline, and he could see only the mast of the sloop.

He immediately ran in the direction of Portsmouth, which he saw at nearly half a league before him, standing out in the haze of the morning, with its houses and towers.

Beyond Portsmouth the sea was covered with vessels whose masts, like a forest of poplars despoiled by the winter, bent with each breath of the wind.

Felton, in his rapid walk, reviewed in his mind all the accusations against the favorite of James I and Charles I, furnished by two years of premature meditation and a long sojourn among the Puritans.

When he compared the public crimes of this minister—startling crimes, European crimes, if so we may say—with the private and unknown crimes with which Milady had charged him, Felton found that the more culpable of the two men which formed the character of Buckingham was the one of whom the public knew not the life. This was because his love, so strange, so new, and so ardent, made him view the infamous and imaginary accusations of Milady de Winter as, through a magnifying glass, one views as frightful monsters atoms in reality imperceptible by the side of an ant.

The rapidity of his walk heated his blood still more; the idea that he left behind him, exposed to a frightful vengeance, the woman he loved, or rather whom he adored as a saint, the emotion he had experienced, present fatigue—all together exalted his mind above human feeling.

He entered Portsmouth about eight o'clock in the morning. The whole population was on foot; drums were beating in the streets and in the port; the troops about to embark were marching toward the sea.

Felton arrived at the palace of the Admiralty, covered with dust, and streaming with perspiration. His countenance, usually so pale, was purple with heat and passion. The sentinel wanted to repulse him; but Felton called to the officer of the post, and drawing from his pocket the letter of which he was the bearer, he said: "A pressing message from Lord de Winter."

At the name of Lord de Winter, who was known to be one of His Grace's most intimate friends, the officer of the post gave orders to let Felton pass, who, besides, wore the uniform of a naval officer.

Felton darted into the palace.

At the moment he entered the vestibule, another man was entering likewise, dusty, out of breath, leaving at the gate a post horse, which, on reaching the place, tumbled on its foreknees.

Felton and he addressed Patrick, the duke's confidential lackey, at the same moment. Felton named Lord de Winter; the unknown would not name anybody, and pretended that it was to the duke alone he would make himself known. Each was anxious to gain admission before the other.

Patrick, who knew Lord de Winter was in affairs of the service, and in relations of friendship with the duke, gave the preference to the one who came in his name. The other was forced to wait, and it was easily to be seen how he cursed the delay.

The valet led Felton through a large hall in which waited the deputies from Rochelle, headed by the Prince de Soubise, and introduced him into a closet where Buckingham, just out of the bath, was finishing his toilet, upon which, at all times, he bestowed extraordinary attention.

"Lieutenant Felton, from Lord de Winter," said Patrick.

"From Lord de Winter!" repeated Buckingham; "let him come in."

Felton entered. At the moment Buckingham was throwing upon a couch a rich toilet robe, worked with gold, in order to put on a blue velvet doublet embroidered with pearls.

"Why didn't the baron come himself?" demanded Buckingham. "I expected him this morning."

"He desired me to tell Your Grace," replied Felton, "that he very much regretted not having that honor, but that he was prevented by the guard he is obliged to keep at the castle."

"Yes, I know that," said Buckingham; "he has a prisoner."

"It is of that prisoner I wish to speak to Your Grace," replied Felton.

"Well, then, speak!"

"That which I have to say of her can only be heard by yourself, my lord!"

"Leave us, Patrick," said Buckingham; "but remain within sound of the bell. I shall call you presently."

Patrick went out.

"We are alone, sir," said Buckingham; "speak!"

"My lord," said Felton, "the Baron de Winter wrote to you the other day to request you to sign an order of embarkation relative to a young woman named Charlotte Backson."

"Yes, sir; and I answered him, to bring or send me that order and I would sign it."

"Here it is, my lord."

"Give it to me," said the duke.

And taking it from Felton, he cast a rapid glance over the paper, and perceiving that it was the one that had been mentioned to him, he placed it on the table, took a pen, and prepared to sign it.

"Pardon, my lord," said Felton, stopping the duke; "but does Your Grace know that the name of Charlotte Backson is not the true name of this young woman?"

"Yes, sir, I know it," replied the duke, dipping the quill in the ink.

"Then Your Grace knows her real name?" asked Felton, in a sharp tone.

"I know it"; and the duke put the quill to the paper. Felton grew pale.

"And knowing that real name, my lord," replied Felton, "will you sign it all the same?"

"Doubtless," said Buckingham, "and rather twice than once."

"I cannot believe," continued Felton, in a voice that became more sharp and rough, "that Your Grace knows that it is to Milady de Winter this relates."

"I know it perfectly, although I am astonished that you know it."

"And will Your Grace sign that order without remorse?"

Buckingham looked at the young man haughtily.

"Do you know, sir, that you are asking me very strange questions, and that I am very foolish to answer them?"

"Reply to them, my lord," said Felton; "the circumstances are more serious than you perhaps believe."

Buckingham reflected that the young man, coming from Lord de Winter, undoubtedly spoke in his name, and softened.

"Without remorse," said he. "The baron knows, as well as myself, that Milady de Winter is a very guilty woman, and it is treating her very favorably to commute her punishment to transportation."

The duke put his pen to the paper.

"You will not sign that order, my lord!" said Felton, making a step towards the duke.

"I will not sign this order!" said Buckingham; "and why not?"

"Because you will look into yourself, and you will do justice to the lady."

"I should do her justice by sending her to Tyburn," said Buckingham. "This lady is infamous."

"My lord, Milady de Winter is an angel; you know that she is, and I demand her liberty of you."

"Bah! Are you mad, to talk to me thus?" said Buckingham.

"My lord, excuse me! I speak as I can; I restrain myself. But, my lord, think of what you are about to do, and beware of going too far!"

"What do you say? God pardon me!" cried Buckingham; "I really think he threatens me!"

"No, my lord, I still plead. And I say to you: one drop of water suffices to make the full vase overflow; one slight fault may draw down punishment upon the head spared, despite many crimes."

"Mr. Felton," said Buckingham, "you will withdraw, and place yourself at once under arrest."

"You will hear me to the end, my lord. You have seduced this young girl, you have outraged, defiled her. Repair your crimes toward her; let her go free, and I will exact nothing from you."

"You will exact!" said Buckingham, looking at Felton with astonishment, and dwelling upon each syllable of the three words as he pronounced them.

"My lord," continued Felton, becoming more excited as he spoke— "my lord, beware! All England is tired of your iniquities; my lord, you have abused the royal power, which you have almost usurped; my lord, you are held in horror by God and men. God will punish you hereafter, but I will punish you here!"

"Ah, this is too much!" cried Buckingham, making a step toward the door.

Felton barred his passage.

"I ask it humbly of you, my lord," said he; "sign the order for the liberation of Milady de Winter. Remember that she is a woman whom you have dishonored."

"Withdraw, sir," said Buckingham; "or I will call my attendant, and have you placed in irons."

"You shall not call," said Felton, throwing himself between the duke and the bell, placed on a stand incrusted with silver. "Beware, my lord, you are in the hands of God!"

"In the hands of the Devil, you mean!" cried Buckingham, raising his voice so as to attract the notice of his people, without absolutely shouting.

"Sign, my lord; sign the liberation of Milady de Winter," said Felton, holding out a paper to the duke.

"By force? You are joking. Halloa, Patrick!"

"Sign, my lord!"

"Never."

"Never?"

"Help!" shouted the duke; and at the same time he sprang toward his sword.

But Felton did not give him time to draw it. He held the knife with which Milady had stabbed herself, open in his bosom; at one bound he was upon the duke.

At that moment Patrick entered the room, crying: "A letter from France, my lord."

"From France!" cried Buckingham, forgetting everything in thinking from whom that letter came.

Felton took advantage of this moment, and plunged the knife into his side up to the handle.

"Ah, traitor," cried Buckingham, "you have killed me!"

"Murder!" screamed Patrick.

Felton cast his eyes around for means of escape, and seeing the door free, he rushed into the next chamber, in which, as we have said, the deputies from Rochelle were waiting, crossed it as quickly as possible, and rushed toward the staircase; but upon the first step he met Lord de Winter, who, seeing him pale, confused, livid, and stained with blood on both his hands and face, seized him by the throat, crying: "I knew it! I guessed it! but too late by a minute, unfortunate, unfortunate that I am."

Felton made no resistance. Lord de Winter placed him in the hands of the guards, who led him, while awaiting further orders, to a little terrace commanding the sea; and then the baron hastened to the duke's chamber.

At the cry uttered by the duke and the scream of Patrick, the man whom Felton had met in the antechamber rushed into the chamber.

He found the duke reclining upon a sofa, with his hand pressed upon the wound.

"Laporte," said the duke, in a dying voice—"Laporte, do you come from her?"

"Yes, monsiegneur," replied the faithful cloak-bearer of Anne of Austria, "but too late, perhaps."

"Silence, Laporte, you may be overheard. Patrick, let no one enter. Oh! I cannot tell what she says to me! My God, I am dying!"

And the duke swooned.

Meanwhile, Lord de Winter, the deputies, the leaders of the expedition, the officers of Buckingham's household, had all made their way into the chamber. Cries of despair resounded on all sides. The news, which filled the palace with tears and groans, soon became known, and spread itself throughout the city.

The report of a cannon announced that something new and unexpected had taken place.

Lord de Winter tore his hair.

"Too late by a minute!" cried he—"too late by a minute! Oh, my God, my God! what a misfortune!"

He had been informed at seven o'clock in the morning that a rope ladder floated from one of the windows of the castle; he had hastened to Milady's chamber, had found it empty, the window open, and the bars filed, had remembered the verbal caution D'Artagnan had transmitted to him by his messenger, had trembled for the duke, and, running to the stable without taking time to have a horse saddled, had jumped upon the first he found, had galloped off like the wind, had alighted below in the courtyard, had ascended the stairs precipitately, and, on the top step, as we have said, had encountered Felton.

The duke, however, was not dead. He recovered a little, reopened his eyes, and hope revived in all hearts.

"Gentlemen," said he, "leave me alone with Patrick and Laporte —ah, is that you, De Winter? You sent me a strange madman this morning! See the state in which he has put me."

"Oh, my lord!" cried the baron, "I shall never console myself."

"And you would be quite wrong, my dear De Winter," said Buckingham, holding out his hand to him. "I do not know the man who deserves being regretted during the whole life of another man; but leave us, I pray you."

The baron went out sobbing.

There only remained in the closet of the wounded duke Laporte and Patrick. A physician was sought for, but none was yet found.

"You will live, my lord, you will live!" repeated the faithful servant of Anne of Austria, on his knees before the duke's sofa.

"What has she written to me?" said Buckingham, feebly, streaming with blood, and suppressing his agony to speak of her he loved—"what has she written to me? Read me her letter."

"Oh, my lord!" said Laporte.

"Obey, Laporte; do you not see I have no time to lose?"

Laporte broke the seal, and placed the paper before the eyes of the duke; but Buckingham in vain tried to make out the writing.

"Read!" said he—"read! I cannot see. Read, then! for soon, perhaps, I shall not hear, and I shall die without knowing what she has written to me."

Laporte made no further objection, and read:

My Lord, By that which, since I have known you, I have suffered by you and for you, I conjure you, if you have any care for my repose, to countermand those great armaments which you are preparing against France, to put an end to a war of which it is publicly said religion is the ostensible cause, and of which, it is generally whispered, your love for me is the concealed cause. This war may not only bring great catastrophes upon England and France, but misfortunes upon you, My Lord, for which I should never console myself.

Be careful of your life, which is menaced, and which will be dear to me from the moment I am not obliged to see an enemy in you.

Your affectionate

ANNE.

Buckingham collected all his remaining strength to listen to the reading of the letter; then, when it was ended, as if he had met with a bitter disappointment, he asked: "Have you nothing else to say to me by the living voice, Laporte?"

"The queen charged me to tell you to watch over yourself, for she had advice that your assassination would be attempted."

"And is that all, is that all?" replied Buckingham, impatiently.

"She likewise charged me to tell you that she still loved you."

"Ah," said Buckingham, "God be praised! My death, then, will not be to her as the death of a stranger!"

Laporte burst into tears.

"Patrick," said the duke, "bring me the casket in which the diamond studs were kept."

Patrick brought the object desired, which Laporte recognized as having belonged to the queen.

"Now the scent bag of white satin, on which her cipher is embroidered in pearls."

Patrick again obeyed.

"Here, Laporte," said Buckingham, "these are the only tokens I ever received from her—this silver casket and these two letters. You will restore them to Her Majesty; and as a last memorial"—he looked around for some valuable object—"you will add—"

He still sought; but his eyes, darkened by death, encountered only the knife which had fallen from the hand of Felton, still smoking with the blood spread over its blade.

"And you will add to them this knife," said the duke, pressing the hand of Laporte. He had just strength enough to place the scent bag at the bottom of the silver casket, and to let the knife fall into it, making a sign to Laporte that he was no longer able to speak; then, in a last convulsion, which this time he had not the power to combat, he slipped from the sofa to the floor.

Patrick uttered a loud cry.

Buckingham tried to smile a last time; but death checked his thought, which remained engraven on his brow like a last kiss of love.

At this moment the duke's surgeon arrived, quite terrified; he was already on board the admiral's ship, where they had been obliged to seek him.

He approached the duke, took his hand, held it for an instant in his own, and letting it fall: "All is useless," said he, "he is dead."

"Dead, dead!" cried Patrick.

At this cry all the crowd re-entered the apartment, and throughout the palace and town there was nothing but consternation and tumult.

As soon as Lord de Winter saw Buckingham was dead, he ran to Felton, whom the soldiers still guarded on the terrace of the palace.

"Wretch!" said he to the young man, who since the death of Buckingham had regained that coolness and self-possession which never after abandoned him—"wretch! What have you done?"

"I have avenged myself!" said he.

"Avenged yourself," said the baron. "Rather say that you have served as an instrument to that accursed woman; but I swear to you that this crime shall be her last."

"I don't know what you mean," replied Felton, quietly, "and I am ignorant of whom you are speaking, my lord. I killed the Duke of Buckingham because he twice refused you yourself to appoint me captain; I have punished him for his injustice, that is all."

De Winter, stupefied, looked on while the soldiers bound Felton, and could not tell what to think of such insensibility.

One thing alone, however, threw a shade over the pallid brow of Felton. At every noise he heard, the simple Puritan fancied he recognized the step and voice of Milady coming to throw herself into his arms, to accuse herself, and to die with him.

All at once he started. His eyes became fixed upon a point of the sea, commanded by the terrace where he was. With the eagle glance of a sailor, he had recognized there, where another would have only seen a gull hovering over the waves, the sail of a sloop which was directed toward the coast of France.

He grew deadly pale, placed his hand upon his heart, which was breaking, and at once perceived all the treachery.

"One last favor, my lord!" said he to the baron.

"What?" asked his lordship.

"What o'clock is it?"

The baron drew out his watch. "It wants ten minutes to nine," said he.

Milady had hastened her departure by an hour and a half. As soon as she heard the cannon which announced the fatal event, she had ordered the anchor to be weighed. The vessel was making way under a blue sky, at a great distance from the coast.

"God has so willed it!" said he, with the resignation of a fanatic; but without, however, being able to take his eyes from that ship, on board of which he doubtless fancied he could distinguish the white outline of her to whom he had sacrificed his life.

De Winter followed his look, observed his feelings, and guessed all.

"Be punished *alone*, for the first, miserable man!" said Lord de Winter to Felton, who was being dragged away with his eyes turned toward the sea; "but I swear to you by the memory of my brother whom I loved so much that your accomplice is not saved."

Felton lowered his head without pronouncing a syllable.

As to Lord de Winter, he descended the stairs rapidly, and went straight to the port.

Chapter VI

THE FATE OF MONTE-CRISTO

THE publication of *The Three Musketeers* had made Dumas famous, yes, but this fame was still as nothing compared to the celebrity he was to acquire when *The Count of Monte-Cristo* would make its appearance. Then he would really become world-famous.

Impossible for us now to picture such fame. For a writer, I mean. No writer in our day and age enjoys anything approaching it. For today it is not the written word, but the picture that makes a person famous. And the candidates for celebrity today are therefore the motion-picture stars, the pin-ups, those with kissable lips (no matter how much the product of the make-up man) those with the touch-inviting flank, or else those who can render popular songs and twang a guitar. In short, people of a secondary order, people for whom material has to be created, people who are themselves incapable of creation, but are wonderful vehicles for the spread of that creation.

But in Dumas's time the primary creator could still be truly famous. In fact with the spread of the cheap penny paper, and its continued serially running stories, the writer of popular fiction stood on the topmost rung of the ladder of renown, along with statesmen and politicians, and enjoying often a longer stay in the sunlight of popular adulation.

This was because it was the word that still dominated in the field of communication. Not the picture. Engravings and woodcuts had to be patiently carved, line by line, or drawn and etched on stone for the process of lithography, in order to produce a picture on paper. I have no statistics at hand, but I feel safe in saying that today more pictures are put before the public in one single day, than reached all the people of the world in the whole of the nineteenth century.

Photography had indeed come into being early in that century (first Niepce camera in 1822, the first permanent photographs by the Daguerre process in 1839) but all the attendant inventions that have speeded the production of pictures to its present blizzard were still in the future: film instead of glass plates, rapid or almost instantaneous exposure, quick machine developing, plus the halftone process, color photography and color printing, all the many kinds of motion-picture cameras and projectors, culminating in the home television set that practically pours pictures into our lives like water from a faucet.

Who today would discover what the Chinese are supposed to have declared that "a picture is worth a thousand words?" Pictures are now rained down upon us with such abundance that few of them can be considered as worth anything more than a quick glance. The same is true of words also. For something to be precious it must also be rare. The pineapple was precious, and was proudly carved on the furniture of wealthy homes, until production got hold of it and canned it for the world. Peas were once so rare that they were reserved for the table of the king, while now they are handed to children as ammunition for their peashooters. Sugar itself was once an expensive drug, prescribed by physicians—and now is a drug on the market.

We live in the day of the surfeit, when the problem is not how to gain weight, but how to lose it. When the problem is not how to kill your enemy, but how to manage things so that you don't have to kill him—and he doesn't have to kill you. True, this is not the case in large areas of the world where people still suffer from malnutrition, but it is the case in some of the advanced countries, and all other nations of the world are screaming for the right to reach a similar state of glut, and they will succeed—if the world will only last that long.

How much more precious must have been the novels of Dumas in that world which was still not assailed by the millions of cheap books which are available today! (By the word "cheap," I am not referring to anything but the price.) I wrote the story of Dumas's bibliographer in my novel about the three Dumases, *King of Paris*, but I will tell it again here since it illustrates what the novels of Dumas must have meant to many a poor lad of years ago. F. W. Reed told the story himself, in several articles written for bibliographical magazines.

F. W. Reed was a poor boy in Whangarei, New Zealand, than

which nothing would seem more remote from Paris. He worked in a drugstore at tasks that were almost beyond his strength and that absorbed almost every minute of his waking hours from dawn until late at night. Even his Saturdays and Sundays were not free of labor.

Then one day there fell into the life of this hard-working boy, a tattered paper-bound book: *Monte-Cristo*. Short as his spare time was, he managed to push his way through the book, indeed nothing could have prevented him from reading it through and through for it had gripped him from the very first page. Curiosity, enthusiasm stole into a boy's life and transmuted its drabness into color and adventure.

Who could this man be, this Alexandre Dumas, whose name appeared on the title page of this wonderful book?

In little Whangarei in those days, there was neither bookstore nor library, and all the boy could discover was that Dumas was a Frenchman and that the *s* at the end of his name was generally not pronounced, and that he was dead.

The boy grew up. His long hours of work continued. But each week he managed to find a couple of hours that he could fill with Dumas. In time, from Auckland, then from London, and finally from Paris, he drew ever-new books from the inexhaustible works of Dumas.

Slowly, with infinite patience, he used the minutes of his spare time to master French and thus enabled himself to read the many works of Dumas that had still not been translated. And so despite a lifetime devoted to business, which gradually led him to a modest affluence, F. W. Reed became the world's authority on Dumas and the owner of the largest collection of his works.

For many years, until his death, it was to F. W. Reed that one might address oneself for answers to all the many questions that could arise concerning Dumas. No one knew better than he just how much of any Dumas book was really Dumas, and how much from the hand of a collaborator. It was F. W. Reed who could best deny such stories as that Dumas once copied out an article on snakes and sent it off as the day's installment for his serial. Dumas had never done such a thing, and Reed could assert that it was just another one of those exaggerations that the French people loved to tell about their favorite character. Like the story of the autumn leaf that once floated through the open window of Dumas's study and landed on his desk, where it was promptly signed and sent off to his printer as an original piece of work.

One may exaggerate in such tales about Dumas, but one cannot exaggerate the fame of Dumas in that story-parched world of long ago. Dumas was not merely the Hemingway of his times, he was also the Marilyn Monroe, the Grace Kelly. He was called "the uncrowned king of Paris," and it was said of him that "when Dumas snores, all Paris turns in her sleep."

He was thus naturally the intimate of the great people of his day. Sometimes, it is true, with condescension on their part. But he returned that. For even in the presence of kings, he remained himself: a vigorous personality, champion of democratic principles.

All this is in fact involved in the origin of the *Monte-Cristo* novel, which was named before it was written. In this way: Dumas happened to go to Florence in 1842, while his *Three Musketeers* was running as a serial in the Paris paper *Le Siècle*. Naturally he was at once a person of consequence in Florence, and as such invited to the villa Quadro by its owner, the Prince de Montfort. This prince was actually Jerome, the brother of Napoleon, who had risen to the throne of Westphalia with the rise of Napoleon, and fallen from that eminence when Napoleon fell. For when Napoleon was vanquished the Bonaparte dynasty collapsed with him.

Dumas came as guest of honor to the ex-king's Saturday dinners. And it was at one of those dinners that the prince said to Dumas: "When my son comes home I'd like you to take charge of him."

Dumas wondered what he could possibly do with this prince, whose name was Napoleon too, who was only eighteen years old and had been in service in one of the German duchies, but was now coming back to Florence, because there was danger of a general coalition being created to attack France, and Jerome didn't wish to compromise the Bonaparte dynasty by having a son take the field in a war against France.

"What you will do with him?" Jerome asked. "Travel with him. Teach him."

It seemed a good idea to take the young prince to see the island where his famous uncle had once been imprisoned: the island of Elba. So the two went off on this "historical pilgimage." And afterward they went to the neighboring island of Pianoza for some shooting. Rabbits and partridges abounded there, at the time, and perhaps still do.

About to return from this expedition, just as they were getting into their boat, Dumas was intrigued by a great mountain of rock that rose out of the sea some distance away. It had the shape of a great loaf of sugar, jutting a thousand feet or more out of the sea.

Their guide said: "If Your Excellencies should decide to go there, I can promise you some real hunting. The place is uninhabited, and overrun with wild goats."

"What is the name of that fortunate isle?" Dumas asked.

"That's the island of Monte-Cristo."

"Monte-Cristo. Monte-Cristo," Dumas repeated. He was suddenly enchanted with that name. It seemed to ring with the music of romance and mystery.

A trip was immediately decided upon. But when their rowboat was about to find a landing spot on the rocky coast, one of the rowers warned that the authorities had ruled that the place was infected and that anyone putting foot on it would have to be quarantined.

Instead of landing, Dumas and the young Napoleon merely had themselves rowed around the place.

How lofty and forbidding was that mass of rock, which giant clefts had split here and there, giving a foothold to stubborn vegetation where scrawny goats nibbled to still the pangs of semi-starvation.

Did Dumas already at that time imagine, hidden in that rock, some almost inaccessible cave piled high with a treasure greater than any known in the world?

Or did that notion come to him only later when he was back in Paris, where Eugene Sue, Dumas's friend, was making such a fantastic success with *The Mysteries of Paris* that he was rivaling Dumas for the position as top feuilletonist of France, and at the same time making the fortune of his publishers?

Béthune and Plon, a firm of publishers, had a contract with Dumas to do a series of eight volumes of travel impressions on Paris. And Dumas, who loved old Paris, was looking forward to writing essays on the history of the town, its old buildings, its bridges, and its famous people.

But Béthune and Plon, envious of the wealth that was pouring into the coffers of a rival firm due to Eugene Sue's success, insisted that Dumas should write for them a novel about Paris, instead of travel impressions. Dumas didn't put up any serious objections. He looked forward, in fact, to outdoing Sue.

He had found, sometime before, a series of books by Jacques

Peuchot, called: *Memoirs Drawn from the Archives of the Paris Police*. And in this series he had noticed in particular a chapter called "The Diamond and the Vengeance," which was in Volume 5.

This Peuchot had in fact been the keeper of records of the Paris police and as such his stories were probably fairly authentic. This one concerned a young shoemaker who had managed to fall in love with a beautiful girl who was also rich and in love with him. The marriage was about to be celebrated when his friends, jealous of such good fortune, and anxious for some amusing horseplay, concocted a denunciation that linked the shoemaker with the secret efforts of Louis XVIII to tumble Napoleon and attain the throne of France.

Result: the young shoemaker disappears into the prisons of Napoleon, so mysteriously and so permanently that his fiancée and her parents cannot find so much as a trace of him. Years pass. Napoleon falls. And one day, out of the prison of Fenestrelle, comes a man, so destroyed by long years in a dank cell that he could not possibly be recognized as the former shoemaker.

But in prison this shoemaker had learned from a dying priest the story of a great treasure hidden in Milan. He goes there and gets it. Then, back in Paris, rich, and living under another name, he looks up his past. He discovers that his bride had mourned him for a few years and then married one of his friends, precisely the one most responsible for his denunciation.

And thus Paris is startled by a series of deaths. One man is found with a dagger in him, and on the dagger these words: *Number One*. Then a man is found dead of poisoning. And on the cloth thrown over his coffin, a note pinned to it, where one can read: *Number Two*. Then the ringleader, the man who married his girl: *Number Three*. Then, instead of a *Number Four*, it is the shoemaker himself who is killed. The killer later, about to die, dictates a confession.

Here, in a crude and brief form, is the entire plot of *The Count of Monte-Cristo*. The marriage about to be performed. The groom mysteriously flung into prison. The dying priest bequeathing his treasure. And then the grand vengeance.

But that's the dream of every man! Every man to whom life has been unjust. And which of us has never felt that injustice? Which of us has never felt that there has been a secret conspiracy against us, so that born to wealth and fame, we have somehow lived in misery? Which of us has not felt robbed of a beautiful and rich bride?

And who has not dreamed of finding some great treasure? And then appearing among our false friends in an impenetrable disguise, rich as Croesus, to administer stern and well-deserved punishment upon his enemies?

Nor was it strange that Dumas should have recognized in this material a basic bit of folklore, with a secret appeal to everyman's unconscious. Had not his father, the General, suffered just such a mysterious imprisonment in the dungeons of Brindisi? Through the treachery of Napoleon? The material appealed to Dumas himself as much, if not more than it did to every person.

In his first draft of the novel, Dumas had not given any space to the prison episodes, which today are still the best and the most famous part of the book. He began his first version with the appearance of the rich Count of Monte-Cristo in Rome, seeking introductions to Parisians there, in order to discover his former friends, and wreak his revenge.

But he showed this early draft to Maquet and the latter immediately pointed out to him that he was omitting what might be the best part of it: the prison story. Whereupon Dumas agreed to take on Maquet as collaborator, and deciding to place the prison sequence in the Château d'If (which is stuck on an island in the harbor of Marseilles the way Alcatraz is in the bay of San Francisco), they both went to Marseilles to investigate the place.

Then both men retired to the then still completely unknown fishing village of Trouville, and in a matter of two weeks or so, had turned out half of the long novel, and immediately dispatched parts of it to the *Journal des Débats*, where it began to appear as a serial, while the final installments of *The Three Musketeers* were still coming out in *Le Siècle!*

If for a moment there may have been some doubt as to who was the king of the feuilletonists, there was henceforth no possible question in that matter. Dumas was following up his wonderful *Three Musketeers* with an even greater success: *The Count of Monte-Cristo*. Of course the contribution of Maquet must not be forgotten. Nor must it be exaggerated.

Whereas in the actual case as set down by Peuchot, the hero had been sent to the dungeons of Fenestrelle by the Bonapartist police, and released when Napoleon fell, Dumas set his story in the year 1815, just before the "Hundred Days" of Napoleon's return from Elba and his renewed bid for power.

Edmond Dantes, the hero, is mate on the merchant ship Pharaon, and is about to be appointed captain. Nothing could make him happier, unless it be the fact that he is about to wed the beautiful Mercedes. Then suddenly he finds himself arrested as a dangerous Bonapartist conspirator, carrying letters from the emperor, still in exile in Elba, to his supporters in France.

Such letters are in fact found in his cabin, but the examining magistrate knows that Dantes is not guilty. Nevertheless he condemns him to the dank dungeons of the Château d'If, for he wants him out of the way.

Dantes simply cannot understand how minutes before his wedding he has been struck down. He knows at this point nothing of the envy, the hatred, the self-interest of his friends that have united to get rid of him. He is convinced that it is some mistake, some stupidity, that should be cleared up soon. Thus he alternates between fury and confidence, with the result that on the register of the prison there appears eventually the following notation:

"Edmond Dantes. Violent Bonapartist. Took an active hand in Napoleon's return from Elba. Maximum security measures to be enforced at all times."

And the national inspector of prisons finds no reason to alter this notation, as we see in the following excerpt that also introduces to us the other main character of the prison sequence: Abbé Faria, the madman.

A year after Louis XVIII's restoration, a visit was made to the Château d'If by the inspector general of prisons. Dantes could hear from the recesses of his cell the noises caused by the frantic preparations for receiving him—sounds that at the depth where he lay would have been inaudible to any but the ear of a prisoner accustomed to hear in the silence of the night the spider weaving his web, and the periodic fall of a drop of water that formed every hour on the ceiling of his dungeon. He guessed something uncommon was passing among the living; he had so long ceased to have any intercourse with the world that he looked upon himself as dead.

The inspector visited one after the other the cells and dungeons of several of the prisoners whose good behavior or stupidity recommended them to the clemency of the government. The inspector inquired how they were fed, and if they had anything to demand. The universal response was that the fare was detestable, and that

they required their freedom. The inspector asked if they had anything else to demand. They shook their heads! What could they
desire beyond their liberty? The inspector turned smilingly to the
governor:

"I do not know what reason government can assign for these useless visits; when you see one prisoner, you have seen them all—
always the same thing, ill-fed and innocent. Are there any others?"

"Yes; the dangerous and mad prisoners are in the dungeons."

"Let us visit them," said the inspector, with an air of fatigue. "I
must fulfill my mission. Let us descend."

"Let us first send for two soldiers," said the governor. "The prisoner
somctimes, through mere uneasiness of life, and in order to be
sentenced to death, commits acts of useless violence, and you might
fall a victim."

"Take all needful precautions," replied the inspector.

Two soldiers were accordingly sent for, and the inspector descended a stair so foul, so humid, so dark that the mere descent
through such a place affected painfully the eye, the smell, and the
respiration.

"Oh!" cried the inspector, stopping midway, "what devil can
possibly be lodged here?"

"A most dangerous conspirator, a man we are ordered to keep the
most strict watch over, as he is daring and resolute."

"Is he alone?"

"Certainly."

"How long has he been here?"

"About a year."

"Was he placed here when he first arrived?"

"No, not until he attempted to kill the turnkey."

"To kill the turnkey?"

"Yes; the very one who is lighting us. Is it not true, Antoine?"
asked the governor.

"True enough; he wanted to kill me!" replied the turnkey.

"He must be insane," said the inspector.

"He is worse than that—he is a monster!" returned the turnkey.

"Shall I complain of him?" demanded the inspector.

"Oh no; it is useless. He is sufficiently punished already. Besides,
he is almost mad now, and in another year he will be quite so."

"So much the better for him—he will suffer less," said the inspector. He was, as this remark shows, a man full of philanthropy, and in every way fit for his office.

"You are right, monsieur," replied the governor; "and this remark proves that you have deeply considered this question. Now, we have in a dungeon about twenty feet distant, and to which you descend by another stair, an abbé, ancient leader of a party in Italy, who has been here since 1811, and in 1813 went mad, and who from that time has undergone an astonishing change. He used to weep; he now laughs. He grew thin, he now grows fat. You had better see him rather than the other, for his madness is amusing."

"I will see them both," returned the inspector; "I must conscientiously perform my duty." This was the inspector's first visit; he wished to display his authority: "Let us visit this one first."

"Willingly," replied the governor; and he signed to the turnkey to open the door. At the sound of the key turning in the lock, and the creaking of the hinges, Dantes, who was crouched in a corner of the dungeon, where he received with unspeakable happiness the slight ray of light that pierced through his grating, raised his head. At the sight of a stranger, lighted by two turnkeys, accompanied by two soldiers, and to whom the governor spoke bareheaded, Dantes, who guessed the truth, and that the moment to address himself to the superior authorities was come, sprang forward with clasped hands.

The soldiers presented their bayonets, for they thought he was about to attack the inspector, and the latter recoiled two or three steps. Dantes saw that he was represented as a dangerous prisoner. Then, uniting in the expression of his features all that the heart of man can contain of gentleness and humility, and speaking with a sort of pious eloquence that astonished the attendants, he tried to touch the soul of the inspector.

The inspector listened attentively; then turning to the governor, he observed: "He will turn religious; he is already more gentle. He is afraid, and retreated before the bayonets; madmen are not afraid of anything. I made some curious observations on this at Charenton." Then turning to the prisoner: "What do you demand?" said he.

"I demand a knowledge of my crime; I demand to be brought to trial; I demand, in short, that I may be shot if I am guilty, and may be set at liberty if innocent."

"Are you well fed?" the inspector asked.

"I believe so; I know not, but that matters little. What matters really, not only to me, an unhappy prisoner, but even more to the officers administering justice, and still more to the king who rules over us, is that an innocent man shall not be the victim of an infamous denunciation, and shall not die in prison cursing his executioners."

"You are very humble today," remarked the governor. "You are not so always; the other day, for instance, when you tried to kill the turnkey."

"It is true, sir, and I beg his pardon, for he has always been very good to me; but I was mad, I was furious."

"And you are not so any longer?"

"No; captivity has bent, broken, annihilated me. I have been here so long."

"So long? When were you arrested, then?" asked the inspector.

"The twenty-eighth of February, 1815, at half past two in the afternoon."

"Today is the thirtieth of June, 1816; why, it is but seventeen months."

"Only seventeen months!" replied Dantes. "Oh, you don't know what seventeen months are when spent in prison! Seventeen ages, rather, especially to a man who, like me, had arrived at the summit of his ambition; to a man who, like me, was on the point of marrying a woman he adored, who saw an honorable career open before him, and who loses everything in an instant—who from the enjoyment of the most beautiful day in his life falls abruptly into profoundest night; who sees his prospects destroyed, and is ignorant of the fate of his affianced wife, and whether his aged father is still living! Seventeen months' captivity to a man accustomed to the air of the sea, to the independence of a sailor's life, to space, to immensity, to infinity! Monsieur, seventeen months in prison is a greater punishment than is deserved by all the most odious crimes recognized in human speech. Have pity on me, then, and ask for me, not indulgence but a trial. Monsieur, I ask only for judges; they cannot refuse judgment to one who is accused."

"We shall see," said the inspector; then turning to the governor:

"On my word, the poor devil touches me. You must show me the register."

"Certainly; but you will find terrible notes against him."

"Monsieur," continued Dantes, "I know it is not in your power to release me, but you can plead for me, you can have me tried; and that is all I ask."

"Light me," said the inspector.

"Monsieur," cried Dantes, "I can tell by your voice you are touched with pity; tell me at least to hope."

"I cannot tell you that," replied the inspector; "I can only promise to look into your case."

"Oh, I am free then! I am saved!"

"Who arrested you?"

"Monsieur de Villefort. See him, and hear what he says."

"Monsieur de Villefort is no longer at Marseilles; he is now at Toulouse."

"I am no longer surprised at my detention," murmured Dantes, "since my only protector is removed."

"Had he any cause of personal dislike to you?"

"None; on the contrary, he was very kind to me."

"I can, then, rely on the notes he has left concerning you, or which he may give me?"

"Entirely."

"That is well. Wait patiently, then."

Dantes fell on his knees, and murmured a prayer in which he commended to God that man who had descended to his prison, like the Savior going to deliver the souls in hell. The door closed; but now a new inmate was left with Dantes: hope.

"Will you see the register at once," asked the governor, "or proceed to the other cell?"

"Let us visit them all," said the inspector. "If I once mounted the stairs, I should never have the courage to descend."

"Ah, this one is not like the other; and his madness is less affecting than the reason of his neighbor."

"What is his folly?"

"He fancies that he possesses an immense treasure. The first year he offered government a million livres for his release; the second, two; the third, three; and so on progressively. He is now in his fifth year of captivity; he will ask to speak to you in private, and offer you five million."

"Ah, that is indeed quite interesting. And what is the name of this millionaire?"

"The Abbé Faria."

"Number twenty-seven," said the inspector.

"It is here; unlock the door, Antoine."

The turnkey obeyed, and the inspector gazed curiously into the chamber of "the mad abbé." In the center of the cell, in a circle traced upon the floor with a fragment of plaster detached from the wall, sat a man whose tattered garments scarcely covered him. He was drawing in this circle geometrical lines, and seemed as much absorbed in his problem as Archimedes when the soldier of Marcellus slew him. He did not move at the sound of the door, and continued his problem until the flash of the torches lighted up with an unwonted glare the somber walls of his cell; then, raising his head, he perceived with astonishment the number of persons in his cell. He hastily seized the coverlid of his bed, and wrapped it around him.

"What do you demand?" said the inspector.

"I, monsieur?" replied the abbé, with an air of surprise, "I demand nothing."

"You do not understand," continued the inspector; "I am sent here by the government to visit the prisons, and hear the requests of the prisoners."

"Oh, that is different," cried the abbé; "and we shall understand each other, I hope."

"There, now," whispered the governor, "he begins just as I told you he would."

"Monsieur," continued the prisoner, "I am the Abbé Faria, born at Rome. I was for twenty years Cardinal Spada's secretary; I was arrested—why I know not—in 1811; since then I have demanded my liberty from the Italian and French governments."

"Why from the French Government?"

"Because I was arrested at Piombino; and I presume that, like Milan and Florence, Piombino has become the capital of some French department."

The inspector and the governor looked at each other with a smile.

"The devil! My good fellow," said the inspector, "your news from Italy is not fresh!"

"It dates from the day on which I was arrested," returned the Abbé Faria; "and as the emperor had created the kingdom of Rome for his infant son, I presume that he has realized the dream of Machiavel and Caesar Borgia, which was to make Italy one solid kingdom."

"Monsieur," returned the inspector, "Providence has changed this gigantic plan which you advocate so warmly."

"It is the only means of rendering Italy happy and independent."

"Very possibly; but I have not come to take with you a course in ultramontane politics; I have come to ask you if you have any complaints to make in regard to food and lodging."

"The food is the same as in other prisons—that is, very bad; the lodging is very unwholesome, but on the whole passable for a dungeon. No matter about that; what I would speak of is a secret which I have to reveal of the greatest importance."

"We are coming to the point," whispered the governor.

"It is for that reason I am delighted to see you," continued the abbé, "although you have disturbed me in a most important calculation, which if it succeeded would possibly change Newton's system. Could you allow me a few words in private?"

"What did I tell you?" said the governor.

"You obviously know him well," returned the inspector.

"What you ask is impossible, monsieur," continued he, addressing Faria.

"But," said the abbé, "I would speak to you of a large sum, amounting to five million."

"The very sum you named," whispered, in his turn, the inspector.

"However," continued Faria, perceiving the inspector was about to depart, "it is not absolutely necessary we should be alone; Monsieur the Governor can be present."

"Unfortunately," said the governor, "I know beforehand what you are about to say; it concerns your treasures, does it not?"

Faria fixed his eyes on him with an expression that would have convinced anyone else of his sanity. "Doubtless," said he; "of what else should I speak?"

"Monsieur the Inspector," continued the governor, "I can tell you the story myself, for it has been dinned in my ears for the last four or five years."

"That proves," returned the abbé, "that you are like those of whom the Bible speaks, who have eyes and see not, who have ears and hear not."

"The government does not want your treasures," replied the inspector; "keep them until you are liberated."

The abbé's eyes glistened; he seized the inspector's hand. "But if I am not liberated," cried he, "if, contrary to all justice, I am kept in this dungeon, if I die here without having disclosed to anyone my secret, that treasure will be lost! Would it not be better that the government should get some profit from it, and myself also? I will go as far as six million, monsieur; yes, I will relinquish six million, and content myself with what remains, if I may gain my liberty."

"On my word," said the inspector, in a low tone, "had I not been told beforehand this man was mad, I should believe what he says."

"I am not mad!" replied Faria, who, with that acuteness of hearing peculiar to prisoners, had not lost one of the inspector's words. "The treasure I speak of really exists; and I offer to sign a treaty with you in which I promise to lead you to the spot where you shall dig, and if I deceive you, bring me here again—I ask no more."

The governor laughed. "Is the spot far from here?"

"A hundred leagues."

"It is not a bad idea," said the governor. "If every prisoner took it into his head to travel a hundred leagues, and their guardians consented to accompany them, they would have a capital chance of escaping."

"The scheme is well known," said the inspector; "and Monsieur the Abbé has not even the merit of its invention." Then turning to Faria: "I inquired if you are well fed?" said he.

"Swear to me," replied Faria, "to free me, if what I tell you prove true, and I will stay here while you go to the spot."

"Are you well fed?" repeated the inspector.

"Monsieur, you run no risk, for, as I told you, I will stay here; so there is no chance of my escaping."

"You do not reply to my question," replied the inspector, impatiently.

"Nor you to mine," cried the abbé. "A curse upon you, then! as upon the other dolts who have refused to believe me. You will not accept my gold; I will keep it for myself. You refuse me my liberty; God will give it to me. Go! I have nothing more to say." And the abbé, casting away his coverlid, resumed his place, and continued his calculations.

"What is he doing there?" said the inspector.

"Counting his treasures," replied the governor.

Faria replied to this sarcasm by a glance of profound contempt. They went out, and the turnkey closed the door behind them.

"He has been wealthy once, no doubt," said the inspector.

"Or dreamed he was, and awoke mad."

"After all," said the inspector, with the naïveté of corruption, "if he had been rich, he would not have been here."

Thus ended this adventure for the Abbé Faria. He remained in his cell, and this visit only increased the belief in his insanity.

Caligula or Nero, those great treasure seekers, those desirers of the impossible, would have accorded to the poor wretch in exchange for his wealth the liberty and the air he so earnestly prayed for. But the kings of modern ages, retained within the limits of probability, have no longer the courage of their desires. They fear the ear that hears their orders and the eye that scrutinizes their actions. Formerly kings believed in themselves; they called themselves sons of Jupiter, and retained in some degree the manners of the god their father. What takes place beyond the clouds is not readily controlled; but the kings of today hold themselves answerable to all persons.

It has always been against the policy of despotic governments to suffer the victims of their policy to reappear. As the Inquisition rarely suffered its victims to be seen with their limbs distorted and their flesh lacerated by torture, so madness is always concealed in its cell, or, should it depart, it is conveyed to some gloomy hospital, where the doctor recognizes neither man nor mind in the deformed remnant of a human being which the jailer delivers to him. The very madness of the Abbé Faria, gone mad in prison, condemned him to perpetual captivity.

How prisoner Number 34 and prisoner Number 27 manage to meet in the dungeons of the Château d'If is told in this next segment:

Nevertheless, the visit of the inspector had instilled new life in Edmond Dantes. For one thing: he now knew the date again, something he had lost track of during his first ordeal. In order not to forget it again, he had immediately written it down with a bit of plaster: July 30, 1816. And thereafter he made a mark for each passing day, so that he would not lose his reckoning again.

Nevertheless, in time he lost track again.

This was because he had figured on a fortnight—and then freedom! But days passed, and then weeks, and finally months. And still nothing. He had calculated that the inspector would not busy himself with his case until he got back to Paris, and that this would take a little time, since there was a whole circuit of prisons to be examined. How long would it take then? Three months? Six months? Dantes was willing to wait even a year. But when ten months had passed and there was not a word of any kind, Dantes was shaken to his depths. Had it all been a dream, this visit by an inspector? Nothing but an illusion? An aberration of his brain?

A year passed and nothing happened except that the governor left. He had obtained something better: the superintendance of the prison of Ham. He took with him several of his subordinates, and amongst them Dantes's jailer. A new governor was installed. He found it too tedious to memorize all the names of the prisoners: he decided to refer to them by the number of their cell.

There were fifty stinking holes in the dungeons of the Château d'If, and in each one lived not a man, but a number. In the cell of Edmond Dantes there now lived something called "34."

This number, however, continued to experience all those sufferings that prisoners go through when they think themselves forgotten by the world. Pride had been his first emotion, the natural consequence of his sense of innocence and his belief in justice. But as hope died, he lost his pride, and even lost his sense of innocence. First he had appealed to Heaven. Then he appealed to his jailers.

Another cell—anything to bring some change into his life where the endless seconds ticked away so silently and so slowly. Or the chance to walk—in a straight line—instead of turning around and around like an animal in a cage. Or a book. Just one book! Or a tool, a toy, an instrument of some kind.

Not a thing was granted him. He pleaded just the same. What else could he do? There must be someone to whom one can appeal. His new jailer was if anything even more close-mouthed than the first one. Still he was a man, wasn't he? Something to talk to that was not plaster and stone.

Dantes spoke to himself. Spoke, perhaps just to hear the sound of his own voice again. When alone he couldn't speak. The sound of his voice, talking to no one, terrified him.

Before his captivity Dantes had sometimes glimpsed assemblages of prisoners, of thieves, vagabonds, murderers. They revolted him. But now he would have given anything for their company. Just to see another face, in addition to that of his jailer. He wished that he had been condemned to the galleys, in spite of their infamous costume, in spite of the chain they had to endure, in spite of the brand burned into the skin of their shoulder. At least galley slaves saw the sky. They breathed fresh air. They looked into each other's faces! They were undoubtedly extremely happy, those galley slaves!

If he couldn't be a galley slave, then let him at least have some sort of company. Even if it were to be only the mad abbé, of whose existence in the dungeon he had heard.

The jailer, though rude and hardened by daily contact with suffering, was still a man. Often, in the bottom of his heart, he felt a pang of pity for the unhappy young man who was rotting in cell 34. And he took Dantes's request to the governor. But the latter was too smart for such tricks. What else could a prisoner want company for except to plot some conspiracy, hatch some plan for escape. "Request denied," he wrote on the paper submitted by the jailer.

Fate had failed, and then man. What was left? There was always God, and Dantes turned to Him.

The prayers his mother had taught him came back to his mind. All the pious ideas of his early instruction returned to him. And he discovered new meaning in them. For in days of happiness these things are mere words, strung together without much meaning. Not until the day of misfortune do these words take on a sublimity of meaning and purpose. Not until then do we understand their passionate invocation of God's pity.

And so suddenly Dantes began to pray. To pray aloud, filling his cell with his voice, which no longer terrified him. He was taken by some kind of ecstasy. He bared all the secrets of his heart before God, ordered certain penances for himself on account of minor infractions committed long ago. And again and again he voiced those lines of prayer that are repeated more often than any other to the Almighty: "Forgive us our trespasses as we forgive those who have trespassed against us."

The religious ecstasy passed. Dantes was still nothing but a number.

Now a gloomy feeling took hold of him. He sensed his lack of education. He realized dimly the resources that he lacked. The knowledge that might have permitted him, in the narrowness of his confines, to build there the ancient empires that have passed, the cities that have risen and fallen, the tragedy of Babylon as it is pictured in Martin's wonderful engraving.

This resource was beyond him. His life had been so short that he had brought nothing with him into this prison. Nineteen years, spent in light and happiness, with little thought. Spirit he had had, but what good was it to him here in this cage, where he was like an eagle in a net. He could cling only to the one great calamity of his life: his happiness suddenly destroyed by an incredible fatality. And over and over again he would reconsider this idea, chewing it, devouring it, poisoning himself with it, much like Ugolino devours the skull of the Archbishop Roger in Dante's *Inferno*.

And thus he worked himself into a new stage: fury! But against whom? Against God! The God that would permit such things. Now the imprecations, the blasphemies, cried out by Dantes in a wild voice, shocked even the jailer, who, listening, could then hear the prisoner ramming himself against the walls, attacking everything, cursing and hammering his impotent fists against whatever happened to annoy him: a grain of sand, a bit of straw, even the air.

Then he turned against mankind. Exculpating Heaven. Picturing his unknown persecutors and imagining the horrible tortures he would submit them to, if ever he laid his hands on them. Tortures that would fall short of death, for death would release these miscreants from the unending pain that he wished on them.

But as his mind kept dwelling on these tortures constantly refined, tortures that were to bring pain without unconsciousness and without death, he began to understand that this was precisely what he himself craved: the end.

Death. Suicide. *There* was his escape. And now he began to be reconciled to his fate. The angel of death came and spread his great black wings soothingly over the poor tortured prisoner. Calm came once again to cell number 34. Death was inevitable, and therefore everything could be endured. Dantes recovered his composure, and looked forward with equanimity to death: man's ultimate refuge.

From that moment on Dantes grew quiet. He busied himself arranging his cell more to his comfort. He ate sparingly, slept little, found his existence almost supportable, since at any time that he wished, he could throw it off, like a garment that was worn-out.

How would he accomplish it? Well, there was first of all the iron stanchions of his window. His kerchief, knotted around his neck, and then to one of those bars, and death was simple. Slower, but just as sure, however, would be starvation. For Dantes had always entertained the greatest repugnance to those pirates who in the port of Marseilles were hanged to a yardarm. That seemed to him a dishonorable death, and he wanted none of it.

How long all these various stages of his imprisonment lasted, Dantes did not know. At some point in his different emotional seizures, he had stopped marking the date, and had gradually lost all sense of time. Actually four years had passed, two years since he had marked down the last day, when the time came that Dantes said to himself: I want to die. And immediately took an oath to eat nothing more.

He said nothing to his jailer. He simply decided: "When food is brought to me, both morning and evening, I will just throw it out of my window, and let the jailer go on thinking that I have eaten it."

He kept his word: twice each day he would fling his food out through the bars of his window. At first he did it gaily. Then he began to do it deliberately. And finally with regret. So that nothing but his determination not to break his oath lent him the strength to adhere to his decision. His food was miserable. It stank. And yet his craving grew so powerfully that he had to fight himself to throw out a morsel of bad meat, of tainted fish, of mouldy bread, and there were times when it took an hour of struggle with himself before he could cast it out.

It was the life-force still battling in him, still unvanquished. His youth, for after all he was only twenty-four or twenty-five and there were fifty years still left in him that wanted to be lived. Lived, yes, even in this dungeon, even without hope, for there is nothing so insistent as life able somehow to cast a glow over this cell, able somehow to evoke images of prison doors flung open for him.

But he clung to his oath and at last no longer had the force to throw his supper out of the barred aperture. And the following day he was too weak to rise from his cot. He could scarcely see or hear. The jailer feared he was dying, and Edmond hoped so.

A kind of stupor slowly took increasing hold of him, traveling up his body. The gnawing pain in his stomach began to diminish, along with his craving for water. Beneath the lids of his closed eyes danced myriads of lights, like the will-o'-the-wisps that play over marshes. He did not know it, but this was the twilight zone of that mysterious country known as Death.

Lying against the wall, slowly expiring, Dantes was roused by a hollow sound. It was unlike the usual sound of this noxious abode, where rats and mice and ugly insects abounded. Or perhaps abstinence had sharpened his senses, for a noise that would have otherwise been disregarded now caused him to raise his head and listen.

It was a continual scratching. As if some huge claw, or powerful tooth, or some iron tool, were attacking the stones.

Weak though he was, Edmond's brain was illuminated by a flash that said: liberty! No prisoner, no matter how near death, could have denied that dream that haunts every man locked in a cell. Had Heaven at last taken pity on him? Was it one of his friends from the outside, finally coming to rescue him?

He shook off such insane notions. No! He was dying, and his weakened brain was being deceived.

But for all that the sound continued. It went on for three hours, and then stopped as something heavy could be heard tumbling down. Then silence.

Several hours later the noise resumed. The same scratching, but nearer, more distinct. Edmond was completely absorbed in listening to the sound when he heard the jailer opening his cell door.

For a week he had been resolved to die. For four days he had denied himself every bit of food. Not since his oath had he addressed a word to his jailer, or given so much as a sign when he was asked bv the jailer what was the matter with him. But now suddenly he felt that he had to do something to prevent the jailer from hearing this noise and thus frustrate what now seemed the last ray of hope come to a dying man.

The jailer was just bringing him his breakfast. Dantes, in spite of his weakness, raised himself up and began to talk about this and that, complaining about the bad quality of the food, the coldness and dampness of his dungeon, grumbling in an ever-louder voice, and finally annoying the jailer who felt himself ill-used, since he had this morning managed to get some good broth and some fine white bread for the sick man.

The jailer nevertheless attributed this outburst to his prisoner's delirium, and setting the food down on the rickety table, he withdrew.

Edmond listened. The sound continued, and in fact, with each passing minute seemed to be becoming more distinct.

Suddenly an idea took possession of his mind. Misfortune had beaten down his hopes so often that now he was unable to continue in the belief that the noise was caused by an attempt to free him. It was on the contrary caused by the governor who had ordered the walls of the neighboring dungeon repaired and strengthened.

He said to himself: "I must put this matter to a test that will not compromise anyone. Suppose I knock. What then? If it is a workman, he may stop, wondering what the knock may mean. But since his conscience is easy, since his occupation is sanctioned by the governor, he will soon resume it."

Once again Edmond got up from his cot, but this time his legs did not tremble, his eyes were free from sparks and mist. He went to a corner of his dungeon where there was a loose stone, and picked it up to knock against the wall from which the noise was coming.

He struck three times.

At the first blow, as if by magic, the sound stopped.

Edmond listened intently. An hour passed. Still no sound. Two hours. The whole day. Silence.

"It's another prisoner," Edmond exulted within himself.

The whole night passed in perfect silence. While Edmond did not close his eyes, not even once.

Three days passed—seventy-two hours long. Each one more tedious than the previous one.

Then, one evening, just as the jailer was visiting him for the last time that night, Dantes fancied he heard an almost inaudible movement among the stones.

He recoiled from the wall, walked up and down his cell in order to collect his thoughts, and then, when alone, he quickly placed his ear against the wall.

What had happened? Why the change in sound? Was it not because the prisoner perceived that his scratching had called attention to his work, and that now he had left off working with his chisel, and was using a lever instead?

Encouraged by this discovery, Edmond decided to assist the unknown but indefatigable worker. He moved his bed aside and examined the stones of the wall. What tool could he use to penetrate that cement, and displace those stones?

He had neither knife nor sharp instrument of any kind. In his cell there was only the grating of bars at his tiny window that was made of iron. And how solid he knew that was! As for his furniture it consisted of nothing but a bed, a chair, a table, a pail, and a jug. The bed was sustained with angle irons, it is true, but these were screwed to the wood, and he had no screw driver with which he could have extracted them. The table and the chair offered nothing whatsoever. As for his pail, that had once had a handle, but it had been lost or removed.

There was the jug, to be sure. Why not break it? And then use the best fragment to attack the wall. He picked up the jug and let it drop. It broke into many pieces.

Dantes concealed two or three of the sharpest fragments inside his bed, and left the rest on the floor. The whole business showed every sign of being nothing but an accident, and no one could suspect that a couple of pieces were missing. He wanted to work in the darkness, but felt that he was working against stone instead of cement and only blunting his piece of pottery. So he put the matter off until daybreak.

In the morning he saw that he had indeed been attacking stone and laboring uselessly, when he should have been working at the plaster that bound the stones together.

Dampness had made some inroads on the consistency of the cement, so that with some pressure, bits of it would break loose, and after half an hour's work he already had a handful. At that rate it could take only a year or two to carve out a tunnel twenty feet long and wide enough to accommodate his body, lying on his belly.

In the years he had been in prison, working steadily, he might have carved his way out of the thickest walls!

But as it was, it took him three days to loosen enough cement to expose one stone. He was able to guess now that the wall was made up of rough stones, held within double walls of hewn stones, and the whole of it gripped in strong hard plaster.

It was against such a wall of hewn stones that he had been working. But now to pull out that stone from its socket. Dantes tried to do so with his fingernails, but only broke and shredded them. The stone would not budge. Even the pottery fragments could not move it. They only broke.

After an hour's useless work, Dantes paused. Suddenly an idea occurred to him, so that he smiled while the sweat dried on his forehead.

The jailer always brought Dantes's soup in an iron saucepan. Dantes had often noticed that this saucepan was either quite full, or else half-full. In either case he, Dantes, got a half a saucepan as his share. It was obvious, therefore, that he shared this pan of soup with some other prisoner who was either served first or later.

The handle of this saucepan was made of iron, and Dantes felt that he was ready to give up ten years of his life to get possession of that bit of iron.

But how was it to be done? The jailer each day poured out the soup into Dantes's plate, who spooned it out with a wooden spoon, washed his plate, and was ready for the next day's meal. But what if something happened to the plate?

Dantes placed it that evening near the door, so that when the jailer opened it the next morning he stepped on it and smashed it.

"I'll eat from the saucepan," said Dantes. "Just leave it."

And the jailer did. Because it saved him from going upstairs for another dish, coming down with it, and then going up again.

Dantes was beside himself with joy. He pulled aside his bed, took the handle of the saucepan, inserted the point at the edge of the stone, and soon saw that he had levered it loose. An hour later the stone had been gradually rocked out, leaving a cavity a foot and a half in diameter.

Carefully Dantes collected all the loose plaster and carried it into a corner of his cell where he buried it in the earth. Then, wishing to make the most of the time in which the saucepan was in his possession, he worked through the rest of the night at the inner stones and cement.

Toward dawn he replaced the stone, pushed back his bed, and lay down on it, pretending sleep.

The jailer entered with breakfast, consisting of nothing more than a piece of bread. He put it on the table and left.

Dantes clasped his hands beneath the blanket of his bed, and prayed to God in thanks.

Never had he felt such gratitude to our Creator as now when he had come into possession of this piece of iron. Only one thing troubled him: the prisoner on the other side had ceased to labor.

All day he toiled untiringly. And by evening he saw that he had managed to extract some ten handfuls of plaster and of rough stones. With only one misfortune: he had bent the handle of his saucepan. But when the evening visit of his jailer was due, he straightened it as best he could and left the saucepan where he would normally keep his plate.

Everything worked well, and the saucepan remained his for another day. And once again Dantes toiled all night. With only one thing troubling him: why did his neighbor remain silent still: three days now?

Dantes heaved a sigh at the thought that he was distrusted by his fellow prisoner. But he refused to be discouraged. He worked on, until he came to an annoying obstruction. Something hard and ungiving, against which the iron seemed helpless: it was a beam of tough wood. A beam blocking the hole made by Dantes.

It would be impossible to dig a hole a foot and a half wide through that wood. It would be necessary therefore to dig around it—either going over it, or under it.

"Oh my God, my God!" Dantes cried out. "How earnestly I have prayed to you! You denied me liberty. Then you denied me death. And now that you have shown me this way out, are you going to deny me again? What must I do? Die of despair? Oh, God have pity on me!"

"Who talks of God and despair in the same breath?" a voice said, seeming to come from beneath the earth, and sounding hollow and sepulchral to the young man.

Edmond's hair stood on end, and he rose to his knees: "Do I hear a human voice?" It had been years since he had heard anything but his own and that of his jailer. And a jailer is not really human: he is just another plank of oak added to the oaken door. He is an additional obstruction, bars of living flesh and blood.

"In the name of Heaven, speak to me again!" Dantes cried out. "Speak, speak! Even though your voice terrifies me."

"Who are you?" said the voice.

"An unhappy prisoner," Dantes replied at once.

"Of what country?"

"A Frenchman."

"Your name?"

"Edmond Dantes."

"Your profession?"

"A sailor."

"How long have you been here?"

"Since the twenty-eighth of February, 1815."

"Your crime?"

"I am innocent."

"But of what are you accused?"

"Of having conspired to aid the return of Napoleon."

"The return of Napoleon? You mean the emperor is no longer on his throne?"

"He abdicated at Fontainebleau in 1814, and was sent to the island of Elba. But how long have you been here that you did not know things that everyone knows?"

"Since 1811."

Dantes shuddered. This man had been here four years longer than himself. There was then no limit to how long one might be kept here?

"Do not dig any more," the voice said. "But tell me: how high up is your excavation?"

"On a level with the floor."

"Is it well concealed?"

"Yes. It begins behind my bed."

"Has your bed been moved since you have been a prisoner?"

"Never."

"And your cell, on what does it open?"

"On a corridor."

"And the corridor?"

"Gives onto a court."

"Alas," the voice sighed.

"What's the matter?"

"My plans were imperfect. And the slightest error in a line threw my tunnel fifteen feet off. I was expecting to mine through to the sea. Instead I shall reach your cell."

"You mean you intended to reach the sea?"

"That was my plan and my hope."

"But suppose you had?"

"I would have thrown myself into the water, swum to one of the islands near here—the Isle of Daume or the Isle of Tiboulen, and then I'd be safe."

"You could have swum as far as that?"

"Heaven would have given me strength—but now that is all in the past—mere speculation."

"You have no more hope?"

"Listen to me: carefully stop up your opening. Do not work any more. Wait until you hear from me."

"Tell me at least who you are?"

"I am—I am number twenty-seven."

"In other words—you refuse to trust me."

Edmond fancied that he heard a bitter laugh coming from the unknown prisoner below. And guessing that he meant to abandon him, Dantes cried out:

"You do not trust a Christian? One who will gladly swear to you by Him who died on the cross for us, that nothing could ever possibly induce me to breathe one syllable of what you tell me to the authorities. Oh I beg you, I conjure you, do not abandon me. If you do there will be nothing left for me to do but to dash out my brains here, against the wall, and you will have the privilege of being able to reproach yourself for my death!"

"How old are you? You sound to me—by your voice—like a young man."

"I do not know my age. Twice already I have lost track of the time. All I know is that I was just nineteen when I was arrested on the twenty-eighth of February, 1815."

"Not quite twenty-six!" the voice murmured from below, with obvious feeling of commiseration. "At such an age how can one be a traitor?"

"No, no! I swear to you I would sooner let myself be hacked to pieces, than betray you."

"You were right to appeal to me. For I was about to conceive a new plan, and leave you out of it. But your age and your plea have given me reassurance. I will not forget you. Depend on it."

"When will I hear from you?"

"When the time is right. I will give you a signal."

Thus begins the friendship between the two prisoners. Abbé Faria, first imprisoned at Fenestrelles in 1807, and brought to the Château d'If in 1811, was a man of over sixty . . . "of small stature, with hair blanched more by suffering than by age, but with a black beard almost reaching down over his chest. His eyes were deep-set, retreating behind bushy gray eyebrows. His garments hung about him in such rags that it would have been impossible to guess what color or what shape they had originally been."

For years this man had been burrowing through the hardest kind of rock and stone—and in order to conceal the debris from his gigantic efforts he had had to break through, under a staircase, to find a hollow into which he could throw this waste material. Over fifty feet long was his tunnel, but a miscalculation of the architecture of the great dungeon had brought him into Dantes's cell, instead of to the sea.

Merely to make the tools he had needed for this great enterprise had consumed four years! He had in addition written a treatise "which, when printed will make a large quarto volume, on 'The Practicability of Forming Italy into one General Monarchy.'"

"And on what have you written this?" Edmond wondered, since paper and ink as well as books were denied the prisoners.

"On two of my shirts. I invented a preparation that makes linen as smooth and as easy to write on as parchment."

"Then you must be a chemist?"

"To some degree. I knew Lavoisier in person. And I was an intimate friend of Cabanis."

"But for such a work did you not need other books? Reference works?"

"Before my arrest I possessed nearly five thousand volumes in my library at Rome. But after reading them over many times, I found out that with one hundred and fifty well-chosen books a man may be said to have the best of human knowledge, or at any rate, all that will be most useful to him. I set aside those one hundred and fifty books and devoted the next three years of my life to grounding myself thoroughly in them, until it may be said that I practically know them by heart. So that since I have been in prison it has cost me no more than a slight effort of my memory to bring those books before my mind's eye, so clearly that I could almost turn the pages. Right now I could recite to you the whole of Thucydides. Or all of Xenophon. Plutarch, Titus Livius, Tacitus, Strado, Jordanes, Dante, Montaigne, Shakespeare, Spinoza, Machiavelli, and Bossuet. And others too, of somewhat lesser importance."

"But then you must know many languages," Dantes exclaimed. "Or you had translations."

"Latin and Greek of the ancient tongues. And five of the modern ones: German, French, Italian, English, and Spanish. With the aid of ancient Greek I have managed to teach myself modern Greek, although I don't speak it nearly as well as I should like to, but I am making efforts now to improve myself."

"Improve yourself?" Dantes repeated. "How can you possibly improve yourself in modern Greek?"

"Why I made myself a vocabulary of the thousand words that I knew. These I manipulated, combining and arranging them in such a way that I found myself able to express all my thoughts in modern Greek, despite the smallness of my store of words. I know of course that a good dictionary contains upwards of a hundred thousand words, and so I can never hope to be very fluent, but I know too that I should have no difficulty in explaining all my wants and wishes to a Greek of today, and that is about all I should ever need."

One sees already how Abbé Faria will undertake the education of Dantes, and turn him into the man he will eventually be: the Count of Monte-Cristo. And of course the Count of Monte-Cristo is Dumas himself in one of his transparent disguises. Is this not how Dumas educated himself? And the way Abbé Faria learned modern Greek, is that not the way Dumas learned how to write a play?

Abbé Faria tells Dantes how he acquired pen and ink, manufacturing the one from fishbones and the other from patiently gathered soot and wine.

"What an enormous degree of intelligence and ability," Dantes exclaims, "you must have employed to reach the high perfection to which you have now attained. Good God! If you have thus managed to surpass all mankind while locked in prison, what could you not have accomplished if free?"

"Probably nothing at all," Abbé Faria replied. "I would have doubtlessly evaporated the excess of my energy and my intelligence in a thousand follies. It needs hardship and misfortune and danger to bring out the jewels that are hidden deep in the human mind and character. Think of gunpowder. It burns harmlessly unless under pressure, when it will explode and show its power. It was captivity that brought into focus all the scattered rays of my mind. It was prison that wedged all this into a narrow space and made it powerful. Lightning that flashes through the darkness of the night is produced by the collision of clouds. Pressure, yes, pressure, that is what we need in order to flash."

Abbé Faria's keenness of mind under the pressure of prison is so penetrating that he is able to do for Dantes what Dantes had not been able to do for himself: discover the reason for his being in prison, discover who were the false friends who forged the documents that implicated Dantes in an antigovernment plot.

Faria does more: he becomes the tutor of Dantes. And still more: he constitutes him as his heir, so that if Dantes should ever get free he will be able to go to the island of Monte-Cristo and get the treasure.

And finally Faria achieves the supreme sacrifice for Dantes: he gives his life so that Dantes may go free. Though the act is not a completely voluntary one. As we see in this excerpt which begins when Dantes, going through the secret tunnel, visits Abbé Faria's cell and sees him there, dead, already wrapped in his burial sheet.

On the bed, at full length, and faintly lighted by the pale ray that penetrated the window, was visible a sack of coarse cloth, under the large folds of which was stretched a long and stiffened form; it was Faria's last windingsheet—that windingsheet which, as the turnkey said, costs so little. All, then, was completed. A material separation had taken place between Dantes and his old friend; he could no longer see those eyes which had remained open as if to look even beyond death; he could no longer clasp that hand of industry which had lifted for him the veil that had concealed hidden and obscure things. Faria, the useful and the good companion with whom he was accustomed to live so intimately, no longer breathed. He seated himself on the edge of that terrible bed, and fell into a melancholy and gloomy revery.

Alone! he was alone again!—fallen back into silence! He found himself once again in the presence of nothingness! Alone—no longer to see, no longer to hear the voice of the only human being who attached him to life! Was it not better, like Faria, to go and ask of God the meaning of life's enigma at the risk of passing through the mournful gate of suffering?

The idea of suicide, driven away by his friend and forgotten in his presence while living, arose like a phantom before him in presence of his dead body. "If I could die," he said, "I should go where he goes, and should assuredly find him again. But how to die? It is very easy," he continued with a smile of bitterness; "I will remain here; I will rush on the first person who opens the door; I will strangle him, and then they will guillotine me."

But as it happens that in excessive griefs, as in great tempests, the abyss is found between the tops of the loftiest waves, Dantes recoiled from the idea of this infamous death and passed suddenly from despair to an ardent desire for life and liberty.

"Die! oh no!" he exclaimed; "not die now, after having lived so long, and suffered so much! It might have been good to die when I formed the purpose to do so, years ago; but now it would be indeed to give way to my bitter destiny. No, I will live; I will struggle to the very last; I will reconquer the happiness of which I have been deprived. Before I die I must not forget that I have my executioners to punish, and perhaps too, who knows, some friends to reward. But here I am forgotten; and I shall go out from my dungeon only as Faria goes."

As he said this he remained motionless, his eyes fixed like a man struck with a sudden idea, but whom the idea fills with amazement. Suddenly he rose, lifted his hand to his brow as if his brain were giddy, paced twice or thrice around the chamber, and then paused abruptly at the bed. "Ah! ah!" he muttered, "who inspires me with this thought? Is it thou, gracious God? Since none but the dead pass freely from this dungeon, let me assume the place of the dead!"

Without giving himself time to reconsider his decision, and indeed that he might allow his thoughts to be distracted from his desperate resolution, he bent over the appalling sack, opened it with the knife which Faria had made, drew the corpse from the sack, and carried it to his cell, laid it on his couch, passed around its head the strip of cloth he wore at night around his own, covered it with his counterpane, once again kissed the ice-cold brow, and tried vainly to close the resisting eyes, which remained open, turned the head toward the wall, so that the jailer might, when he brought his evening meal, believe that he was asleep, as was his frequent custom, returned along the gallery, drew the bed against the wall, returned to the other cell, took from the hiding place his needle and thread, flung off his rags, that they might feel nothing but naked flesh beneath the coarse sackcloth, and getting inside the sack, placed himself in the posture in which the dead body had been laid, and sewed up the mouth of the sack on the inside.

The beating of his heart might have been heard if by any mischance the jailers had entered at that moment. He might have waited until the evening visit was over, but he was afraid the governor might change his resolution and order the dead body to be removed earlier; in that case his last hope would have been destroyed. Now his project was settled under any circumstances, and he hoped thus to carry it into effect.

If on the way out the gravediggers should discover that they were conveying a live instead of a dead body, Dantes did not intend to give them time to recognize him, but with a sudden cut of the knife he meant to open the sack from top to bottom, and, profiting by their alarm, escape. If they tried to catch him, he would use his knife. If they conducted him to the cemetery and laid him in the grave, he would allow himself to be covered with earth. And then, as it was night, the gravediggers would scarcely have turned their backs ere he would work his way through the soft soil and escape. He hoped that the weight would not be too heavy for him to support. If he was deceived in this, and the earth proved too heavy, he would be stifled, and then so much the better; all would be over. Dantes had not eaten since the previous evening, but he had not thought of hunger or thirst, nor did he now think of it. His position was too precarious to allow him time to think of anything else.

The first risk that Dantes ran was that the jailer, when he brought his supper at seven o'clock, might perceive the substitution he had effected; fortunately, twenty times at least, from misanthropy or fatigue, Dantes had received his jailer in bed; and then the man placed his bread and soup on the table, and went away without saying a word. This time the jailer might not be silent as usual, but speak to Dantes, and, seeing that he received no reply, go to the bed and thus discover all.

When seven o'clock came, Dantes's agony really commenced. His hand placed upon his heart was unable to repress its throbbings, while with the other he wiped the perspiration from his temples. From time to time shudderings ran through his whole frame and oppressed his heart as if it were seized in an icy grasp. Then he thought he was going to die. Yet the hours passed on without any stir in the château, and Dantes perceived that he had escaped this first danger: it was a good augury. At length, about the hour the governor had appointed, footsteps were heard on the stairs. Edmond understood that the moment had arrived, and, summoning up all his courage, held his breath. He would have been glad to repress at the same time the rapid pulsations of his arteries.

The footsteps paused at the door; there were steps of two persons, and Dantes guessed it was the two gravediggers who came to seek him. This idea was soon converted into certainty when he heard the noise they made in putting down the hand-bier. The door opened, and a dim light reached Dantes's eyes through the coarse sack that covered him. He saw two shadows approach his bed, a third remaining at the door with a torch in his hand. Each of these two men, approaching the ends of the bed, took the sack by its extremities.

"He's heavy, though, for an old and thin man," said one, as he raised the head.

"They say every year adds half a pound to the weight of the bones," said another, lifting the feet.

"Have you tied the knot?" inquired the first speaker.

"What would be the use of carrying so much more weight," was the reply; "I can do that when we get there."

"Yes, you're right," replied the companion.

"What's the knot for?" Dantes wondered.

They deposited the supposed corpse on the bier. Edmond stiffened himself in order to play his part of a dead man, and then the party, lighted by the man with the torch, who went first, ascended the stairs. Suddenly Dantes felt the fresh and sharp night air, and he recognized the *mistral*. It was a sudden sensation, at the same time replete with delight and agony. The bearers advanced twenty paces, then stopped, putting their bier down on the ground. One of them went away, and Dantes heard his shoes on the pavement.

"Where am I, then?" he asked himself.

"Really, he is by no means a light load!" said the other bearer, sitting on the edge of the handbarrow. Dantes's first impulse was to escape, but fortunately he did not attempt it.

"Light me, stupid," said the other bearer, "or I shall not find what I am looking for." The man with the torch complied, although not asked in the most polite terms.

"What can he be looking for?" thought Edmond. "The spade, perhaps?"

An exclamation of satisfaction indicated that the gravedigger had found the object of his search. "Here it is at last," he said, "not without some trouble, though."

"Yes," was the answer; "but it has lost nothing by waiting."

As he said this, the man came toward Edmond, who heard a heavy and sounding substance laid down beside him, and at the same moment a cord was fastened around his feet with sudden and painful violence.

"Well, have you tied the knot?" inquired the gravedigger who was looking on.

"Yes, and pretty tight too, I can tell you," was the answer.

"Move on, then." And the bier was lifted once more, and they proceeded. They advanced fifty paces farther, and then stopped to open a door, then went forward again. The noise of the waves dashing against the rocks on which the château is built, reached Dantes's ear distinctly as they proceeded.

"Bad weather!" observed one of the bearers; "not a pleasant night for a dip in the sea."

"Why, yes, the abbé runs a chance of being wet," said the other; and then there was a burst of laughter. Dantes did not comprehend the jest, but his hair stood erect on his head.

"Well, here we are at last," said one of them.

"A little farther! a little farther!" said the other. "You know very well that the last was stopped on his way, dashed on the rocks, and the governor told us next day that we were careless fellows."

They ascended five or six more steps, and then Dantes felt that they took him, one by the head and the other by the heels, and swung him to and fro. "One!" said the gravediggers, "two! three, and away!" And at the same instant Dantes felt himself flung into the vast void, passing through the air like a wounded bird—falling, falling with a rapidity that made his blood curdle. Although drawn downward by some heavy weight which hastened his rapid descent, it seemed to him that the fall continued through a hundred years. At last, with a terrific dash he entered the ice-cold water; and as he did so he uttered a shrill cry, stifled in a moment by his immersion beneath the waves.

Dantes had been flung into the sea, into whose depths he was dragged by a thirty-six pound shot tied to his feet. The sea is the cemetery of the Château d'If!

Dantes, though giddy from his flight through space, and suffocated by water, had yet sufficient presence of mind to hold his breath, while his right hand, prepared with the knife, used it to slit the sack open; he extricated his arm and even his body, but his feet could not shake off that ball of iron that kept dragging him deeper and deeper into the sea.

His lungs were ready to burst while he worked at the heavy cord with his knife, and finally he felt the iron and the sack suddenly dropping away, while he himself immediately began to rise, and with several vigorous strokes he rose to the surface, leaving behind the cloth that had almost become his shroud.

It was only in order to gulp air that Dantes rose to the surface, and immediately dived down again in order to make sure that he should not be seen.

He swam underwater, so that when he surfaced again he was some fifty paces from where he had first sunk. Overhead he glimpsed a black and tempest-threatening sky, where a strong wind drove gray vapors that only now and then permitted a twinkling star to appear. All about him was a vast expanse of waters, somber and forbidding, whose waves rose and fell, roaring and foaming as if before the approach of a storm.

Behind him, blacker than the sea, blacker than the sky, rose like a phantom the giant of granite, whose projecting crags seemed like arms stretched out to seize their prey, while above rose a pinnacle carrying a lighted torch. It seemed as if the prison had become his pursuer, and was searching the sea to bring back the escaped man. Had the gravediggers heard his cry of dismay when they had flung him into the water?

Dantes dived again and remained as long as he could under the water. This trick was not unknown to him. Years before he had used to attract spectators in the bay before the lighthouse of Marseilles when he would swim there, and when everyone agreed that he was the best swimmer of the port.

When he finally came up for breath, the light on the prison tower had disappeared.

It was nevertheless necessary that he should strike out to the open sea. The islands nearest to that of the Château d'If are Ratonneau and Pomegue. But those two islands, as well as the tiny islet of Daume are inhabited. Not so Tiboulen and Lemaire. But both of those are at least a league, that is to say a good two and a half miles from the Château d'If. And worse than the distance was the blackness of the night.

But suddenly he was aware of the lighthouse of Planier, shining ahead of him like a brilliant star.

He knew that if he kept this light on his right, he would find Tiboulen a little to his left. But there were nearly three miles to go. And that into pitch darkness.

Fear clutched at his throat, cut off his breath, paralyzed his muscles. His ears ached from trying to hear above the sound of his own strokes. His eyes pained from trying to pierce the darkness where at every moment he was certain that his jailers would surround him. This constant twisting about, this constant prying into every corner of the horizon, weakened him just at this time when he was exerting himself to his utmost.

Thus he swam on and on, until the Château d'If was not to be seen, and yet it still remained with him: he could feel its presence. But diminishing, and the sense of freedom gradually coming to dominate, as he continued to push himself through the waves.

"Now let's see," he cogitated. "I have swum at least an hour or more. I ought to be close to Tiboulen. Unless the wind has retarded me more than I imagine. Or unless I have forgotten where Tiboulen is. What if I am mistaken?"

A shudder passed through him. He tried to rest while treading water. But so violent was the sea that he realized that he could not find any repose that way.

"I must swim on," he said. "I must swim until worn out. Or until I get a cramp. Then I will have been drowned in spite of my escape." Despair lent some strength to his tired body.

Suddenly the sky grew solidly dark. It was as if a compact cloud had enveloped him. At the same moment he felt himself struck in the knee so violently that he was certain he had been hit by a bullet. In a moment he would hear the report of the musket. But he heard nothing. Instead, when he put out his hand he felt something hard. His foot hit bottom.

He had struck land. And the cloud was nothing but a mass of rock looming over him, rock so strangely formed that it seemed like nothing but fire frozen into a black mass at the height of its conflagration. That could only be the isle of Tiboulen.

Dantes rose, advanced a few steps to dry rock, and breathing a prayer of gratitude to God, he stretched himself out on the granite, which at the moment seemed to him softer than down. In spite of wind and spats of rain, he fell into that deep sweet sleep that comes only to those who are worn out with fatigue.

But scarcely an hour later he was roused by a violent clap of thunder. The heavens seemed as if rent apart, dropping rain in cataracts, while chains of lightning played across the sky like serpents of fire, illuminating a great chaos of mountainous black clouds.

Weather had no terrors for the sailor Dantes. He was even grateful to see by the lightning that he had indeed reached Tiboulen, and he cogitated that the morning would bring a calm sea enabling him to swim to nearby Lemaire, which if equally arid was nevertheless a larger island and consequently better adapted for concealment.

An overhanging rock offered him temporary shelter, and just in time, for the storm was rising to even greater fury, so that it seemed to Dantes that the very rocks shuddered and made him feel giddy. Then he recollected that he must indeed be weak, since it was twenty-four hours since he had eaten or drunk. He found rain water accumulated in the hollow of a rock and cupped it up greedily with his hands.

Suddenly a particularly violent display of lightning seemed to rip the sky apart from the earth to the dazzling throne of God, and by its light Dantes saw what at first glance seemed the ghost of a ship fleeing before the wind and the waves, and heading straight for perdition on the rocks between Lemaire and Cape Croiselle.

Dantes screamed a warning to the fishing smack. But already it was too late. Another flash of lightning showed the crew of four or five clinging to shattered mast and rigging, and one man frantically holding on to the broken rudder. Then, in the churning sea amidst the cliffs, the broken vessel was ground to pieces. Dantes saw despairing faces amidst the fragments, gaunt arms stretched toward the sky. And over the noise of the storm it seemed to him that he heard voices begging for mercy.

Then all was dark and as if the whole terrible spectacle had never really taken place.

Dantes ran down the rocks at the risk of being himself dashed to pieces. He listened. He looked. He could see nothing. He could hear nothing. Nothing but the tempest that continued to rage until gradually it exhausted itself, the wind abated, the great masses of gray clouds rolled toward the west, and the blue firmament appeared, studded with bright stars.

Then a strange flaming streak became visible on the horizon, as if some great conflagration had burst into existence. The waves of the ocean whitened, and their crests even reflected the fire. Dantes was startled, until he realized that this was only the dawn, a phenomenon that millions witnessed every day, but which he, locked up for so many years, had almost forgotten.

By the light of the day he could see the fortress from which he had escaped, and he could imagine how, in two or three hours, his turnkey would enter his cell and there discover not Dantes, but the body of Abbé Faria. He would discover too the secret tunnel, and the men who had cast Dantes's body into the sea would be questioned, and doubtless they would recollect that last shrill cry that Dantes, feeling himself plunging into ice-cold water, had not been able to stifle.

Then a massive attempt would be launched to recapture the fugitive. Armed men would fill boat after boat to sweep the sea in every direction. A cannon would be fired from the tower to warn all the neighborhood of an escape and that the law would punish anyone who dared to shelter or feed the prisoner. On land it would be the police of Marseilles, on sea it would be the governor of the fortress that would make every effort to lay hands on the fugitive and bring him back either dead or alive.

"Oh God!" Dantes cried out in an involuntary prayer forced from his lips by exhaustion and delirium. "Oh God, have I not suffered enough? I am frozen with cold, dropping with hunger. I have even lost the knife that saved me. Have pity on me now, and do for me what I can no longer do for myself!"

At this moment, looking out to sea, Dantes saw a kind of ship that he knew and understood from his boyhood: a Genoese tartan. She had obviously just recently left the harbor of Marseilles and was standing out to sea with her prow cleaving the waves sharply. "In a half hour," Dantes thought, "I could join her. Yes, but what story could I invent so that they would accept me? For they are smugglers, without a doubt, and the reward for returning me to the Château d'If would easily overcome any pity they might have for me."

While these thoughts were passing through his head, Dantes noticed a red woolen cap hung on a point of rock surrounded by the debris of the fishing smack that had piled up there in the storm of a few hours ago. In an instant Dantes's plan was formed. He swam out to the cap, placed it on his head, seized one of the fragments of the keel, and struck out so as to cross the line the vessel was taking.

"I am saved," he murmured. And this conviction restored his strength.

But the vessel was tacking so as to pass between the islands of Jaros and Calasseraigne, as do most ships bound from Marseilles to Italy, and so swimmer and vessel would come closer only to part again. At their nearest, Dantes would rise on his floating bit of wood, reaching up and waving his hand. But it was as if no one saw him. He would have cried out, but he knew that the waves would drown his voice. And in all his actions he had to reflect that he must not attract the attention of anyone on shore, or in the fortress.

But finally during one of the vessel's tacks, he realized that he had been seen. There was activity on board. A boat was lowered. And Dantes, in his eagerness, abandoned the beam which he felt only delayed his rescue and swam out vigorously to meet the rowing sailors.

What a mistake! Almost at once his strength left him. His arms grew stiff, his legs cramped up into knots. He could scarcely breathe from pain.

He screamed, and it seemed to him as if he heard one of the sailors shout back: "Courage!" in Italian. Then the water covered him. He struggled with superhuman efforts against drowning, but his mind was already wandering, and he felt himself back in the burial sack again, with the heavy cannon ball tied to his feet and dragging him down into the darkness. One more violent effort was all he could make, but it was enough to bring him to the surface. He felt his hair being grabbed and then he saw and heard nothing.

He had fainted.

When he opened his eyes again Dantes found himself on the deck of the tartan. Instinctively his eyes sought to divine the direction the vessel was going. He realized that they were rapidly leaving the Château d'If behind, and a cry of joy escaped him, but fortunately sounded more like a sign of pain, so exhausted was his frame.

But now he was clear about his situation. He was lying on the deck. A sailor was rubbing his cold limbs with a woolen cloth. Another, whom he recognized now as the one who had cried "courage!" was holding a gourd of rum to his mouth, whilst a third, an old sailor, who was both captain and pilot, looked on with that egotistical pity men feel for a misfortune that they have escaped so far, but which may run them down tomorrow.

A few drops of rum brought the blood flowing back through Dantes's limbs, while the friction of the cloth gave them back their elasticity.

"Who are you?" said the pilot, in bad French.

In bad Italian, Dantes replied: "I'm a Maltese sailor. We were coming from Syracuse with a load of grain. Last night's storm caught us at Cape Morigon and wrecked us on these rocks."

"Where do you come from?"

"From these rocks that I had the good luck to cling to whilst our captain and the rest of the crew were all lost. I saw your ship, and afraid that you might not see me and that I would be left to perish on that desolate island, I swam off on a fragment of the ship. You have saved my life. I thank you. I would have died if one of your sailors had not caught me by the hair."

"That was me," said one of the sailors, a fellow of fine manly appearance. "High time too, for you were sinking."

"Indeed," said Dantes, and held out his hand. "I thank you again."

"I had some hesitation," the sailor confessed. "With that beard of yours, you looked more like a cutthroat than an honest man. Six inches of beard and hair a foot long . . ."

Dantes realized that ever since he had been imprisoned no scissors had ever touched his hair or his beard. "That's because of a vow I made," he explained quickly. "A vow to our Lady of the Grotto, not to cut my hair or beard for ten years if in a moment of danger I should be saved. Now my prayer has been granted, and my vow expires."

"But now that you're saved," said the captain, "what are we to do with you?"

"Alas! anything you please. My captain is dead. I have escaped, but with nothing of my own. But I can be of assistance: I'm a good sailor. Leave me off at the first port you make: I'll have no trouble finding a berth."

"Do you know the Mediterranean?"

"I have sailed every cranny of it since childhood."

"And the harbors?"

"I could get in and out of any one of them with my eyes bandaged."

"I say, Captain," said the sailor who had cried "courage." "Why not let him stay with us? That is if what he says is true."

"Yes, if what he says is true," said the captain doubtfully. "In his present condition he will promise us the world—but will he keep his word?"

"I will do more than I have promised," said Dantes.

"We shall see," returned the other, smiling.

"Where are you bound for?" Dantes asked.

"To Leghorn."

"Then why do you keep tacking? Why don't you sail closer to the wind?"

"There's the island of Rion. We mustn't pile up on that."

"You'll pass it by a good twenty fathoms."

"Take the helm. Let's see what you know."

The young man took the helm, ascertained by a slight pressure if the vessel answered the rudder, and seeing that it responded all right, and that, though it was no first-rate sailor, it was still tolerably obedient:

"To the braces!" he cried.

The four seamen who composed the crew obeyed, whilst the pilot looked on.

"Haul taut!"

They obeyed.

"Belay!"

The order was carried out promptly, and the vessel glided twenty fathoms to the right of Rion.

"Bravo!" cried the captain.

"Bravo!" the sailors repeated.

And they looked with some admiration and astonishment at this man whom they had just pulled out of the sea, almost naked, and with his hair and beard growing wild like that of a hermit.

"You see," said Dantes, leaving the helm, "I shall manage to be of some slight value to you during this voyage. And if at Leghorn you feel that you have no use for me, than just let me off, and I will arrange to pay you out of my first wages for any food or clothes you give me."

"Ah," said the captain, "we can agree I'm sure, provided you are willing to be reasonable."

"I want nothing more than you give your other men," Dantes replied.

"That's not fair," said the one who had drawn Dantes from the sea. "Because you obviously know a lot more than we do."

"You keep out of this, Jacopo!" said the captain. "A man is free to ask for his own terms."

"Yes, of course," said Jacopo, "I was just making a remark."

"Instead of making remarks," said the captain, "why don't you let him have a jacket and a pair of trousers?"

"I haven't got an extra jacket," said Jacopo. "But I have a shirt and another pair of trousers."

"That's all I need," said Dantes.

Jacopo dived into the hold and came back in a moment with the clothing.

"Anything else you want," said the captain.

"A piece of bread," said Dantes. "And some of that good rum. For I haven't had a morsel of food for a long time."

It had been in fact forty hours since he had eaten.

A piece of bread was brought, and Jacopo offered him the gourd.

"Larboard your helm!" cried the captain to the steersman.

Dantes glanced to that side while he lifted the gourd to his mouth. He froze midway.

"Look!" cried the captain. "Something wrong at the Château d'If!"

In fact a little white cloud could be seen rising from the bastion of the prison. And at the same moment came the faint report of a gun. The sailors looked at one another.

"What's going on?" the captain wondered.

"It's the alarm cannon," said Dantes. "It is always fired when a prisoner has escaped."

The captain looked at him, but Dantes had calmly raised the gourd to his lips and was drinking rum with such composure that no one could possibly have suspected him of being that escaped prisoner.

Under the pretense of being fatigued for more laborious duty, Dantes asked to be allowed to take the helm, and the steersman, enchanted to turn over that responsibility to him, looked at the captain who signaled his approval. Dantes too was pleased. For now he could keep an eye on Marseilles in case of any danger.

"What's the date?" he asked Jacopo, who took a seat beside the helm.

"February twenty-eighth," Jacopo said.

"Of what year?"

"Of what year? You mean you don't know what year it is?"

"That's exactly what I mean," said Dantes.

"What is it? You've forgotten?"

Dantes smiled. "I got such a fright last night, that it's been driven out of my mind. So I ask you again: what year is it?"

"This is 1829," Jacopo replied.

1829! Fourteen years to a day since he had been arrested.

Nineteen he had been when they had thrown him into his cell at the Chateau d'If. At thirty-three he had escaped.

Chapter VII

FAME, HUMOR, AND HUMILITY

W E HAVE already given some illustrations of the success that *The Count of Monte-Cristo* had, but the following excerpt from Dumas's *Travel Impression* called *On Board the Emma*, will illustrate not only that fact, but also the man himself. The expansiveness of him.

Dumas had chartered a kind of sailing vessel which was known as a *speronare* in 1835, and written three travel books as a result of his voyages in the Mediterranean. The first was called *The Speronara*, the second *Captain Arena* (who was the master of the boat) and the third, from which I have already quoted a short passage, was *The Corricolo*.

These volumes, when published some five or six years later, created a furore for traveling to the various islands and ports of the Mediterranean, as a result of which people said that Dumas had discovered this inland sea.

Years later, in 1860, Dumas wanted to complete his tour of the Mediterranean, and for that reason bought a Liverpool-built schooner called the *Emma*. And the book he wrote about his journeys on this vessel, translated into English under the title *On Board the Emma* (but known in French as *Les Garibaldiens: Révolution de Sicile et Naples*, because in the main the volume deals with Dumas's devotion to the Garibaldian cause of a united Italy), contains the selection which follows.

Incidentally there are critics who claim that it is this book that initiated the modern war correspondent as a distinct kind of writer. And it is worth noting that Dumas, whose interest would have seemed to be in the past, was nevertheless as up-to-date as one can be.

Before we quote the passage that refers to his *Count of Monte-Cristo*, it might be well if we were to give here a little excerpt that shows Dumas in action as a war correspondent:

I arrived in Turin on January 4, 1860, and immediately asked for Garibaldi. He was staying at the Hotel Trombella. I took a carriage and had myself driven there.

As always Garibaldi's door was open to all. There was not so much as an orderly in the antechamber, nor a valet to announce his visitors. I walked right in. He was on his feet, a South American poncho flung over himself. Colonel Turr, my friend for over a dozen years, and Colonel Carrasso were seated. As I stepped over the threshold I turned my eyes toward the clock.

"General," I asked, "what time is it?"

"Eleven o'clock," said Garibaldi, not without some show of astonishment that an unknown should enter his room and ask him the time.

"What is the day of the month?" I went on.

"Wednesday, the fourth of January," he answered, his astonishment growing.

"Well, General, listen carefully to what I now predict for you, on this fourth of January, at eleven o'clock in the morning. Within one year you will be the victor. Now let me embrace you."

"You are Alexandre Dumas," he said, stretching out his arms to me.

The result was that Garibaldi gave him a personal pass to all his troops and all the towns that had declared for him, and that he promised Dumas to dictate to him his memoirs. But Dumas went further: he began to buy guns for Garibaldi, and use his schooner to run them. And when Garibaldi was finally victorious, Dumas was made "Director of Excavations and Museums" at Pompeii! And in addition began to publish a Garibaldian newspaper—in Italian! (Also partly in French.)

Naturally that wasn't all he did. He continued to write novels, plays, works of history, etc.

But to return to the excerpt dealing with *The Count of Monte-Cristo*. Here it is:

When I visited Marseilles for the first time, in 1834, I asked to see the house of Milo and the bust over its door; the clock tower of Accouls, which was all that remained of the church of Our Lady of Accoas; the old abbey of St. Victor, built at the very spot where Cassius,

arriving from the deserts of Thebais, found the relics of the Saint
from which it takes its name, and where is worshiped the Black
Virgin—the most adored of all the Madonnas of Marseilles, for the
reason that it was at her intercession that rain fell in the great
droughts; the tower of St. Paul, from the top of which the cannon
had replied to the cannon of the Constable of Bourbon; the Hotel
de Ville, where stands the statue of Libertat, the liberator of Marseilles, who killed Casaulx; finally, the Château d'If, where Mirabeau
was in prison and where one can find the remains of Kléber's coffin.

Today the stranger visiting Marseilles asks to be shown only three
things—the house of Morrel in the allées de Meillan, the house of
Mercedes at the Catalans, and the dungeons of Dantes and the Abbé
Faria.

It goes without saying that although the house of Morrel in the
allées de Meillan, although the house of Mercedes at the Catalans,
although the dungeons of Dantes and Faria at the Château d'If have
never existed, except as scenery at the *Théâtre Historique*, the obliging guides, not to disappoint strangers, show them all they wish to
see.

Three *concierges*, during the space of fifteen years, have successively retired with a competence which they owe to the persistency of
travelers—English ones above all—in visiting the dungeons of Dantes
and Faria.

Today, it is not the coffin of Kléber or the prison in which
Mirabeau composed his famous *Erotica Biblion* that is asked about
—Dantes and Faria have monopolized everything.

It is the privilege of romancers to create characters who kill off
those of the historians; the reason is that, for the most part, the
historians are content to invoke phantoms, while the romancers create
people made of flesh and blood.

And so, when I visited Marseilles two years ago, I desired, in my
turn, to see the dungeons of Dantes and Faria. That I was within
my rights, no one, I hope, will dispute. I had known for some time
that Marseilles believed in my romance.

When, in 1848, I was producing the drama of "Monte-Cristo" at
the *Théâtre Historique*, I wrote to Marseilles for a sketch of the
Château d'If. I received a very fine one, signed by Crapelet, with these
two lines written beneath it:

"The Château d'If, taken from the spot where Dantès was precipitated."

I could not ask for anything better. I could not even have hoped for anything so good.

Those who had witnessed my drama, therefore, saw the Château d'If from the point from which the artist had sketched it—that is to say, from the place where Dantès had been precipitated.

The revolution of 1848 broke out, interrupting the performances in the midst of their career, and many people went to gaze at the Tuileries from the spot where Charles X and Louis Philippe had been precipitated, and so the Château d'If and the dungeons of Dantès and Faria were, for the moment, forgotten.

But the real misfortunes of the Bourbons, whether of the elder branch or the younger, presently lost interest; and the fabulous adventures of the abbé and the sailor again held sway.

The pilgrimages to Goritz and to Claremont diminished in number; those to the Château d'If increased.

In 1857 I was, as I have said, myself among the visitors.

On stepping into the little boat, casually selected to take me to the château, I had my first surprise.

A boatman with a boat next mine called out:

"I will buy your passengers."

"For how much?"

"Ten francs," said the first.

"Done," replied the second.

And the boatman who had valued us at the exorbitant price of ten francs stepped from his boat into ours.

I looked on the matter as one of pure speculation, and did not concern myself with the reasons that lay beneath it.

We reached the Château d'If.

The *concierge* was an old Catalan who had obtained the coveted post on the plea that she was a country woman of Mercédès.

The Franco-Spanish *patois* spoken by her proved that on that point, at least, she had told the exact truth.

She did not even ask me my wishes.

"You have come to see the dungeons of Dantès and the abbé Faria?" said she, as she took up her keys. "You shall see them."

"Thanks, my good woman," I replied, "but first I would like to see the remains of the coffin of Kléber and the prison of Mirabeau."

She gave me an astonished look, and made me repeat what I had said.

I repeated it.

"I know nothing about them," said she.

My triumph was complete. Not only had I created what did not exist, but I had annihilated what did exist!

"Ah, well," said I, "forward then for the dungeons of Dantes and Faria."

She gave me another look, and with a shrug of her shoulders, as much as to say, "You shall see then," she led the way.

I would state, in praise of whosoever invented the idea of exhibiting the dungeons, that very clever alterations have been carried out by him to give the legend every appearance of truth. A subterranean passage is shown filled with stones, which, it is true, were added later on, and which prevent any communication with the neighboring dungeon; but on visiting the latter, one sees the other end of the same passage.

In the early days this passage was accessible, and through it one could get from one dungeon to the other. All visitors of the masculine gender made use of their hands and knees to struggle through it. Some women, English women in particular, followed their example, taking such risks as there were; but when crinolines came into fashion, a female encased in a gigantic cage became wedged in a part too narrow for her, and was obliged to stay where she was, being unable either to advance or retreat.

Her husband, assisted by the *concierge*, pulled her so lustily that he ended by extracting her from the mousetrap, but she was very much bruised.

Then it was that the municipal authorities interfered, and ordered the passage to be filled up so as to prevent the occurrence of a like catastrophe.

The office for the dearer tickets lost thereby, for there were two scales of charges: one for those who were satisfied to see only the dungeons, and another for those who wished to get access to Faria's by means of his passage.

As may be supposed, I eclipsed everyone in the multiplicity of questions put to the female guide. I may say that my unconcealed pleasure in hearing her answers encouraged her not to keep anything from me.

She declared that in her young days she had known Mercedes, of whom, indeed, she was a distant family connection. As regards Fernand, she only remembered him vaguely, seeing that he had not reappeared since his departure from the Catalans.

But concerning Mercedes, it was quite another story—she had been there on two or three occasions. In her pilgrimages she was invariably dressed in black, and maintained the strictest incognito; nevertheless, my informant had immediately recognized her, and could assure me that my heroine was either still living, or had died but recently.

Seeing her to be so well informed, I asked her if she could give me any tidings of Dantes, or rather of the Count of Monte-Cristo.

For a moment she seemed embarrassed and hesitating, and while she paused I believed that she was going to help me write the sequel to my romance for which all the world asks me, but which, in all probability, I shall never put on paper.

But, contrary to my expectation, she was very much more circumspect about Monte-Cristo than about Mercedes.

"The Count of Monte-Cristo," said she; "about him only one man can give you definite information."

"And who may that man be," I asked her.

"Monsieur Alexandre Dumas, who was his intimate friend, and with whom he still remains in communication."

This time, I admit, I was beaten, and not hoping to get a better reply, I ceased questioning her.

As I was leaving the Château d'If, I gave five francs to the good woman, who begged me to sign the visitors' book. I should have asked to do so if she had not made the request.

I was not content with signing my name. I set it at the foot of a formal certificate which declared that the time-honored customary recital of the concierge concerning Dantes and Faria and Mercedes was the exact truth.

I can only hope that my declaration will not be prejudicial to her interests.

On stepping again on the Cannebière, I turned toward my boatman.

"Now," said I, "my good friend, I want to settle with you."

"To settle with me," said he; "that will not be difficult, I am pleased to say."

"Well, then, first I owe you that purchase money—the ten francs, you remember, and also for the two journeys—to the château and back."

"You owe me nothing whatever."

"What! nothing whatever?"

"No! nothing whatever."

"You are joking."

"Evidently you think I have not recognized you."

"What! you have recognized me?"

"Yes. Just say that you are not Monsieur Alexandre Dumas."

"But I have not the slightest intention of denying it, my good friend."

"Very well, then," said he, with a movement of the shoulder impossible to describe.

"But—but—the fact that I am Monsieur Alexandre Dumas is not a reason for rowing me to the Château d'If for nothing."

"Not only ought I to row you to the Château d'If for nothing, and all the other boatmen to do the like, but we ought to join together and give you a pension; you are the father of us all; you it is who put the bread into our mouths by writing the romance of 'Monte-Cristo'; so you are the cause of our making three journeys instead of one. Everyone wants to go to the Château d'If, and in all weathers. Why, when there is a sea on, and we pretend we do not want to go, the English give us anything up to two louis d'or to row them there. You pay me? Never! And whenever you are at Marseilles, the boat and its owner will be at your disposal, but on this condition, mind: that you never talk of giving me a sou. Otherwise I am upset. My name is Paulet; my boat is called the *Ville de Paris*. We understand each other—you always have me, and no one else; and never, any money, or I shall think that you look down on me."

All this was said so earnestly that it admitted of no doubt as to the sincerity of the speaker.

"Well, well, so be it, Paulet. Tomorrow at nine o'clock I shall want you."

"Good, at nine o'clock I will await you with the boat."

"Shake hands, my good Paulet."

"Oh, as to that, with pleasure."

We exchanged a hearty grasp of the hand, and separated.

I wrote at once to Paris for the edition of my works published by Dufour and Mulat—the finest edition, the illustrated one.

The next morning at nine o'clock I was on the Cannebière. Paulet was waiting there. I stepped into the *Ville de Paris*, saying:

"To the Réserve."

"The Réserve! That is all we have left, the Château d'If with the legend of Dantes excepted. The Catalans have gone, the Réserve is going. In a year's time the Château d'If will be the sole survivor. It is true that it is a prison, and that prisons live long."

The Réserve was, two years ago, and still is today, the restaurant where one enjoys the best *bouillabaisse* in all Marseilles.

I ordered a monstrous one.

When it appeared I invited Paulet to share it with me. He made some difficulty, but yielded to my threat of "no dinner, no boat."

Four days later Paulet received at his address, 25 Cours Liotard, an almost complete edition of my works.

I say "almost complete," for I really do not know of a complete one.

I do not wish to be unfair to Paulet's fellow boatmen, but I may be permitted nevertheless to recommend Paulet to visitors to the Château d'If, and particularly to English people who wish to see it in spite of rough weather, and who pay two louis d'or to accomplish their caprice.

When Dumas said "an almost complete edition of my works, for I do not know of a complete one," he was not stretching things. F. W. Reed's *Bibliography of Alexandre Dumas* lists over 1000 titles. Some of these titles, but not many, are mere poems. Some of them are works in which he had only a small part. But the great bulk of them are plays or novels or books of history or travel. A. Craig Bell lists nearly 300 works, of which none are poems, but some are shorter pieces. But mingled with those shorter pieces are solid works that are not easily printed in one volume. The Michel Levy edition runs to 301 volumes.

And within that size there is not just wordage: there is an encyclopedic range. Not part of the Michel Levy edition, for example, is Dumas's huge cookbook. It has been published in at least one edition that runs to nearly a thousand pages. I own a recent reprint that is some 740 extra-large pages. Given to me by an enthusiastic Dumas fan, Barnett Shaw of San Antonio.

Turn to the letter E, and read the entry under Elephant. Here it is, freshly translated:

ELEPHANT. Don't let that word frighten you. I have no intention of forcing my reader to consume all by himself one of those monstrous beasts, but we would like to induce him, if ever an elephant's trunk, or feet, should fall into his hands, to prepare it in the following way, seasoning it according to my suggestions, and let us know what you think of it.

Perhaps only in Cochin-China today, is the elephant really generally eaten, and there it is considered a very tasty dish. So much so that when the king has one slaughtered for his table, he sends various cuts to his favorite courtiers, this being taken as a mark of graciousness. But among the cuts, none is held in greater esteem than the trunk and the feet.

Levaillant (a famous French explorer) says that it is an exquisite meat. "The feet, roasted, are fit for royalty. It would never have occurred to me that such a ponderous animal, something so bulky and seemingly coarse, could turn into such a delicate dish. I devoured the feet of my elephant without bread."

We shall therefore give to those of our readers who may be tempted to follow Levaillant, the following recipe for elephant's feet, which we owe to M. Duglerez of the Rothschild firm.

Take one or more feet of young elephants, skin and bone them after first softening them in lukewarm water for four hours. Cut them lengthwise in four slices, and each slice into halves, and parboil them for a quarter of an hour, wash them off in cold water, and let them drain on a napkin.

You should have a stewpan with space in the lid to hold live coals, and that lid should seal your pan hermetically, and put at the bottom two slices of Bayonne ham, strew your pieces of elephant foot over them, then add four onions, a knob of garlic, some curry powder, half a bottle of Madeira, and three spoons of heavy stock.

Cover well, and let simmer with as low a heat as possible, for ten hours. Cool, remove all fat, and add a glass of port, plus some fifty little pimentoes, which you will have first skinned in plenty of boiling water in order to retain their green color.

It is important that the sauce shall be quite spicy and tasty. Though it must be said that the natives don't make any such fuss over the cooking of elephant's feet. Perhaps because they are less well versed in the mysteries of *haute cuisine*. At any rate they simply wrap them in leaves, bind together with strips of rattan, and cook them in hot ashes.

And then what a feast!

In short this is no ordinary cookbook. Look up, for example, under B, the word burns. It's there. Brûlure. And beginning with the line: "Burns are the most frequent accident that can happen to a conscientious cook who really devotes himself to his art." And going on to give the simplest remedy of all: "immediate application of cold water or ice to the burnt area. Afterward a little application of an alum solution, and nothing else except a bandage to protect it."

It is in short one of those cookbooks now so popular, where the book itself is devoured rather than the food described in it. Pages are given to the subject of Spanish cuisine. Other pages to the subject of wines. His recipes for eggs is a little book in itself. There was no food that Dumas was more fond of.

And the whole of it is infused with that heart-warming charm that Dumas so generally and generously displayed, the right mixture of pride and humility that permits a man to accept both success and failure with a smile.

Witness this little bit from a source that right now escapes me. And I have no intention of looking the matter up in all those one thousand titles and those three hundred volumes of his.

One day when I was riding about Paris in one of those old-style cabriolets still in vogue, where passengers and coachman sit abreast, I had occasion—for what reason I can no longer recall—to mention to my companion that I was originally from the Department of the Aisne.

At which the driver spoke up: "Ah, so you come from the Aisne, do you?"

"I do," I said, "and is there something in that to which you object?"

"Not at all, not at all," he said. "Quite the contrary!"

The man's original question and subsequent reply to my question were both equally obscure. Why should he have spoken up at all upon hearing that I came from that particular department? And what the devil could that "quite the contrary" mean? What else but that he somehow *preferred* my coming from there than from one of the eighty-five others into which all France is divided.

Had I been alone in the carriage I should certainly have questioned him until I had got to the bottom of it, but at the time I was deep in conversation with my friend; I put off my curiosity of the moment, intending to come back to it, but in fact never returning.

But a week later chance would have it that I should step into the same cab. And immediately from the driver:

"Ah ha! It's the gentleman from the Aisne."

"Right you are," I said. "And you are the coachman who drove me a week ago."

"Myself and no one else, sir. Now where to today?"

"To the Observatoire."

"Sh!" he cautioned. "Not so loud, please."

"But why?"

"My horse," he said. "The Observatoire is so far away. If he heard you—you understand. Giddap, Bijou! My horse—there's a fellow if he ever struck it rich, would never buy himself a carriage."

I looked with some interest on my driver.

"Tell me, why did you ask me if I came from the Department of the Aisne?"

"Because if monsieur had been alone, and willing to chat, we could have made conversation about that department."

"You know it well then?"

"Know it well? I should think so. A noble department! The department that gave France her General Foy, her Monsieur Méchin, her Monsieur Lherbette, as well as her Camille Demoustier, the author of the *Letters to Emilia on Mythology*."

I must admit, dear reader, that I felt rather left out in this enumeration of the famous men of our department. And I will admit to taking a sudden dislike to my gossipy friend.

"Do you know the geography of the Aisne just as well as you know its famous people?"

"There's not a spot I don't know."

"For example."

"What example? I know every place there."

"Well, do you know Laon?" I asked, pronouncing the place as we locally pronounce it, namely like the word *long* before you get to the *g*.

He corrected me: "You mean Laon, don't you?" he asked, pronouncing it with two distinct syllables.

"La-on or Lon," I said. "It's all the same. Laon is the way it's spelled, but Lon is the way it's pronounced."

"As for me," he said, "I like to say a word the way I see it written."

"A disciple of Monsieur Marle, eh? Phonetic spelling, I mean."

"I know nothing about your Monsieur Marle and his phonetic spelling. But Laon I know well. It's the *Bibrax* of the Romans, and the *Laudanum* of the Middle Ages. Why do you look at me that way?"

"Look?" I said. "I'm not looking. I'm admiring. I'm marveling."

"Poke fun if you like, but that can't stop me from knowing Laon and the whole Department of the Aisne. For example, there's the tower built there by Louis d'Outremer, and there's a vast trade in artichokes."

"I won't argue that with you. You speak God's own truth, my good man. Now what about Soissons? You know Soissons, of course?"

"Do I know *Noviodunum*—that's Soissons, you understand. Well, I should think I do know *Noviodunum*.

"My congratulations. For myself, though I know Soissons pretty well, I'm utterly ignorant of *Noviodunum*."

"But it's the same thing, sir. Six of one and half a dozen of the other. That's where the cathedral is, the one to the watery saint, Saint Médard, you know. If it rains on Saint Médard's Day, why it will rain for forty days on end. That Saint Médard should be the patron saint of us cabdrivers, I think. Do I know Soissons? Well, well, well—you ask me if I know Soissons. The birthplace of Louis d'Héricourt, of Callot d'Herbois, of Quinette. It's where Charles Clovis defeated Siagrus, and Charles Martel vanquished Chilperic, where King Robert died. It's the main city of the department.

Divided into six counties, to wit: Braisne-sur-Vesle, Oulchy-le-château, Soissons, Vailly-sur-Aisne, Vic-sur-Aisne, Villers-Cotterêts—"

At the mention of my own birthplace, which I knew as well as I know the back of my hand, I thought to trip him up. "Ah, Villers-Cotterêts, you know that place too?"

"*Villerii ad Cotiam retiae*," he said at once. "Villers-Cotterêts, or Coste de Retz. Yes, indeed. Quite a respectable village."

"Really a small town," I protested.

"A big village," he insisted. "Just a big village."

I gave in. What could I do? People tend to exaggerate the places of their birth and youth. They loom so much bigger in childish eyes.

"Big village, so be it," I said, surrendering.

"It's not a matter of so be it," he replied. "A fact is a fact. I know this Villers-Cotterêts. I know its forest covering 25,000 acres. Its population, 2,692 souls. Principal places of interest: old castle of the time of François I, now used as a poorhouse. Birthplace of Charles Albert Demoustier, author of *Letters to Emilia on Mythology* . . ."

"And birthplace of Alexandre Dumas," I added, affecting diffidence.

"You mean Alexandre Dumas, the author of *Monte-Cristo* and *The Three Musketeers?*"

"The same," I said.

He shook his head. "No," he declared with decision.

"What do you mean, *no?*"

"I mean, *no!*"

"Are you saying that Alexandre Dumas was not born at Villers-Cotterêts?"

"That's exactly what I'm saying. He wasn't born there."

"Come, come now, that's going a bit far."

"Well you can say what you please. But I tell you Alexandre Dumas does not come from Villers-Cotterêts. After all he's a Negro."

I confess that I was dumfounded. The man was so well informed about the Department of the Aisne, that I was shaken in my own belief. His absolute certainty was such that I was almost ready to imagine myself some blackamoor from Senegal or the Congo.

"From what part of the Aisne are you?" I asked him.

"Me? I'm not from there at all. I'm from Nanterre."

"But you've lived there. Where?"

"Never set foot in the place."

"Never set foot in the Aisne?"

"Never once."

"Then how in the devil do you come to know so much about that department?"

"Very simple. Look here." And he offered me a tattered volume.

"What's this?"

"My library."

"Your library?"

"That's it. From cellar to garret, that's the only book I own."

"And you've read this through?"

"Through? I've read nothing else for the past twenty years."

"Yes. I can see from the appearance of this book, that you've read it often."

"What else is there to do when you have to wait for a customer? With times so hard, you spend half your day at the stand."

I opened the volume, curious to know what those worn covers contained that was so precious, so enjoyable, that it could fascinate a man for twenty years, to the exclusion of all other reading material.

Inside, on the title page, I read: *Statistical Compendium of the Department of the Aisne.*

Chapter VIII

THE QUEEN AND THE PHYSICIAN

Perhaps the novel nearest to achieving the popularity of *The Three Musketeers* and *Monte-Cristo* was Dumas's *Memoirs of a Physician*, with the subtitle: *Joseph Balsamo*. It is a novel laid in the period between 1770 and 1774, between the arrival in France of Marie Antoinette, who was to marry the Dauphin, and the year when she became queen of France upon the death of her father-in-law Louis XV.

Joseph Balsamo became, like *The Three Musketeers*, a series of novels. *The Three Musketeers* was followed by *Twenty Years After*, and then by the *Viscount of Bragelonne*. While the *Memoirs of a Physician* was followed by *The Queen's Necklace*, and then by *Ange Pitou* and *The Countess of Charny*. Another one in the same series is *The Chevalier de Maison Rouge*, which really closes the series, although it was written first. All of them deal with France before and during the Revolution, *The Chevalier de Maison Rouge* being the story of the attempted rescue of Marie Antoinette from the menace of the guillotine.

Maquet was in general the collaborator in all these works. Which earned huge sums not only as feuilleton, but again as published books, and finally as hit plays. Impossible, of course, within the limits imposed on this anthology, to give all the excerpts that one would like. But two, both from *Balsamo*, ought to find a place here.

The first will give the reader a delightful picture of Madame Dubarry and show the sparkling corruption of the era. The second is more somber, and ends with one of the most startling bits of name-dropping ever used in historical fiction. Suddenly we are face to face with the Terror, which is like the *mene, mene, tekel upharsin*, of the fall of Babylon.

In this first extract we are at the levee of the Countess Dubarry.

"Good morning, my dear enemy!" said the countess, without looking around, but seeing the chief of police in the mirror before her.

"Your enemy, madame?"

"Yes; my world is divided into two classes—friends and enemies. I admit no neutrals. I class them as enemies."

"And you are right, madame; but tell me how I, notwithstanding my well-known devotion to your interests, deserve to be classed as neutral or hostile."

"By allowing to be printed, distributed, sold, and sent to the king an ocean of pamphlets, libels, verses—all against me. It is ill-natured, it is odious, it is stupid!"

"But, madame, I am not responsible—"

"Yes, monsieur, you are; for you know the wretch who wrote them."

"Madame, if they were all written by one author, we should have no trouble in sending him to the Bastille. But as it is, Hercules himself would be crushed under such labor!"

"Upon my word, you are highly complimentary to me!"

"If I were your enemy, madame, I should not speak the truth thus."

"Well, I believe you! We understand each other now. But one thing still gives me some uneasiness."

"What is that, madame?"

"You are on good terms with the Choiseuls."

"Madame, Monsieur de Choiseul is prime minister; he issues his orders, and I must obey them."

"So if Monsieur de Choiseul orders that I am to be vexed, tortured, worried to death, you will allow me to be vexed, tortured, worried! Thank you!"

"Let us discuss matters a little," said Sartines, sitting down, without being asked to do so, but without eliciting any sign of displeasure on the part of the favorite—for much must be pardoned to the man who knew better than any other all that was doing in France. "Let us discuss this a little. What have I done for you in these last three days?"

"You informed me that a courier had been sent from Chanteloup to hasten the arrival of the dauphiness."

"Was that done like an enemy?"

"But about my presentation to her, on which you know my heart is set—what have you been doing for me?"

"All that I possibly could."

"Monsieur de Sartines, you are not candid!"

"Ah, madame, I assure you, you are unjust! Did I not find and bring you Vicomte Jean from the back room of a tavern in less than two hours, when you wanted him in order to send him I don't know where—or rather, I do know where."

"I had much rather you had allowed my brother-in-law to stay there," said Madame Dubarry, laughing. "A man allied to the royal family of France!"

"Well, but was that not a service to be added to my many other services?"

"Oh, very well! So much for three days ago, and so much for day before yesterday; now tell me what you did for me yesterday."

"Yesterday, madame!"

"Oh! you may well endeavor to recollect; that was your day for obliging others."

"I don't understand you, madame."

"Well, I understand myself. Answer, monsieur, what were you doing yesterday?"

"Yesterday morning I was occupied as usual, dictating to my secretary."

"Till what hour?"

"Till ten."

"What did you do then?"

"I had a chat with a friend of mine from Lyons, who had made a wager that he would come to Paris without my knowledge, but for whom one of my lackeys was waiting as he entered the capital."

"Well, after dinner?"

"I sent to the Austrian lieutenant of police information concerning the haunt of a famous robber whom he was unable to discover."

"And who was where?"

"At Vienna."

"So you do police duty, not only for Paris, but for foreign courts as well?"

"Only in my leisure moments, madame."

"Well, I shall take a note of that. Then, after having dispatched the courier to Vienna?"

"I went to the opera."

"To see the little Guimard? Poor Soubise!"

"No—to arrest a famous pickpocket. But seeing him occupied exclusively with farmers-general, I did nothing until he had the audacity to rob two or three noblemen."

"You should say 'the indiscretion.' Well, after the opera?"

"After the opera?"

"Yes. That is a rather puzzling question, is it not?"

"No. After the opera? Let me think—"

"Ah! it seems that now your memory fails."

"Oh! after the opera—yes, I remember."

"Well?"

"I went to the house of a certain lady who keeps a gaming table, and I myself conducted her to For-l'Evêque."

"In her carriage?"

"No, in a fiacre."

"Well?"

"Well, that is all."

"No, it is not all! No, no, no!"

"I got into my fiacre again."

"And whom did you find in it?"

Monsieur de Sartines changed color.

"Oh!" cried the countess, clapping her little hands, "I have really had the honor of making a minister of police blush!"

"Madame—" stammered Sartines.

"Well, I will tell you who was in the fiacre; it was the Duchess de Grammont!"

"The Duchess de Grammont?"

"Yes, the Duchess de Grammont—who came to ask you to contrive to get her admitted to the king's private apartments."

"Faith, madame!" said the minister, moving uneasily in his chair, "I ought to give up my portfolio to you. It is you who manage the police of Paris, not I."

"To tell the truth, monsieur, I have a police of my own. So beware! Oh, the Duchess de Grammont in a fiacre with the minister of police at midnight! It was capital! Do you know what I did?"

"No; but I am afraid it was something dreadful! Fortunately, the hour was very late."

"Yes; but that doesn't help you. Night is the time for vengeance!"

"Well, what, then, did you do?"

"Just as I keep a police of my own, so I keep a body of writers, also—shocking, ragged, hungry scribblers!"

"Hungry? You must feed them badly."

"I don't feed them at all. If they became fat, they would be as stupid as the Prince de Soubise. Fat, we are told, absorbs the gall."

"Go on; you make me shudder!"

"I recollected all the disagreeable things you have allowed the Choiseuls to do against me, and determined to be revenged. I gave my legion of famishing Apollos the following program: First, Monsieur de Sartines, disguised as a lawyer, visiting an innocent young girl who lives in a garret, and giving her on the thirtieth of every month a wretched pittance of a hundred crowns."

"Madame, that is a purely benevolent action which you are endeavoring to misconstrue."

"It is only benevolent actions that *can* be misconstrued. Second, Monsieur de Sartines, disguised as a reverend missionary, introducing himself into the convent of the Carmelites of the Rue St.-Antoine."

"I was bringing those good nuns some news from the Indies."

"East or West? Third, Monsieur de Sartines, disguised as lieutenant of the police, driving through the streets at midnight in a fiacre with the Duchess de Grammont."

"No, madame!" exclaimed he. "No—you would not bring such ridicule on my administration!"

"Why not? What do you do to protect me from ridicule?" said the countess, laughing. "But wait! I set my rogues to work, and they began, like boys at college, with exordium, narration, and amplification; and I have received this morning an epigram, a song, and a ballad, of which you are the subject."

"Ah, my God!"

"Frightful, all three of them! I amused the king with them this morning, and also with the new *Pater noster* which you have allowed to circulate. You know what it is: 'Our Father who art at Versailles, dishonored be thy name, as it deserves to be. Thy kingdom is in disorder; thy will is not done on earth any more than it is in heaven.

Give us our daily bread, which thy favorites have taken from us. Forgive thy parliaments, which uphold thine interests, as we forgive thy ministers who have sold them. Yield not to the seductions of the Dubarry, and deliver us from thy devil of a chancellor. Amen.'"

"Where in the world did you find that?" asked M. de Sartines, clenching his hands.

"Oh! I had no need to find it; someone has the politeness to send me every day the best things in that line as they come out. I have even supposed that it is you who have done me that honor."

"Oh! madame!"

"And so, by way of reciprocity, tomorrow you will receive the epigram, the song, and the ballad I have mentioned."

"Why not today?"

"I must have some time first to distribute them. Is not that the way? Besides, the police ought always to hear last about any new affair. I assure you, you will be very much amused! I laughed three quarters of an hour at them this morning, and the king was made ill with laughing; it is that which makes him so late."

"I am ruined!" cried Sartines, beating his head with his hands.

"Ruined? Nonsense! You are only celebrated in song. Am I ruined by all the verses made on me? No; I only get in a passion at them, and then for revenge I determine to put somebody else in a passion too. Ah, what delightful verses! I was so pleased with them that I ordered some white wine for my literary scorpions, and I suppose that by this time they are dead drunk."

"Ah, Countess, Countess!"

"But, *pardieu*, you must hear the epigram:

> "'O France! how wretched is thy fate,
>   When women hold the helm of state!'

"No, no—I am wrong; that is what you have allowed to be circulated against me. But there are so many, I get confused. Listen, listen! here it is:

> "'A perfumer once sought of a painter a sign.
>   His skill than his genius was duller;
>   For in a huge bottle, with knavish design,
>   He makes Boynes, Maupeou, and Terray to shine,

> *Displayed in their own proper color.*
> *But for Sartines still room in the vessel he leaves,*
> *And he labels the mixture "The Essence of Thieves.'"*

"Cruel woman, you will drive me mad!" cried Sartines.

"Now we must look at the song. You must know it is Madame de Grammont who speaks:

> "'*Dear minister, you know my skin*
> *Is to the purest snow akin;*
> *Then grant to me this single thing—*
> *Oh, say so, say so, to the king!'*"

"Madame, madame!" cried Sartines, more furious than ever.

"Oh, don't be disturbed," said the countess; "I have had only ten thousand copies printed. But you ought to hear the ballad."

"You have a press, then?"

"Certainly. Has not the Duke de Choiseul one?"

"Let your printer take care!"

"Oh, it is kept in my own name! I am the printer."

"Shocking, shocking! And the king laughs at these infamies!"

"Laughs? He sometimes gives me rhymes himself, when my spiders give out."

"You know how I serve you, and you treat me thus!"

"I know you are betraying me. The Duchess de Grammont is a Choiseul; she wishes to ruin me."

"Madame, I declare to you she took me by surprise!"

"You confess, then, that I was informed correctly?"

"I am forced to confess it."

"Why did you not tell me?"

"I came now for that purpose."

"I don't believe you."

"Upon my honor!"

"I bet two to one against it."

"Behold me at your feet!" and he fell on his knees. "I beg forgiveness!"

"You do well."

"Let us make peace, countess, in Heaven's name!"

"So you are afraid of a few bad verses—you, a man, a minister!"

"Ah! if I had only that to fear!"

"And you never reflect how many wretched hours such things make me spend—me, a woman!"

"You are a queen."

"A queen? And not presented at court?"

"I swear to you I have never done anything hurtful to your interests!"

"No; but you have allowed others to do so. The matter, however, is now not the doing nothing against them, but the doing all in your power to forward them. Are you on my side—yes, or no?"

"Certainly, on your side."

"Will your devotion go so far as to help me with my presentation?" asked the countess.

"You yourself shall fix its limits."

"Remember, my press is in order; it works night and day. In twenty-four hours my scribblers will be hungry; and when they are hungry they bite."

"I will be good. What do you wish?"

"That nothing which I undertake shall be opposed."

"For myself, I promise everything."

"No," said the countess, stamping with her foot. "I will not accept that; there is a loophole in it for you to crawl out. You will be supposed to do nothing against me yourself, but the Duke de Choiseul will do all. All or nothing. Give me up to the Choiseuls, bound hand and foot, and I will destroy you, annihilate you! Take care! Verses are not my only weapons!"

"Do not threaten me, madame," said Sartines, thoughtfully; "there are difficulties about this presentation which you cannot understand."

"Obstacles have purposely been thrown in the way of it. You can remove them."

"I am only one person; we need a hundred."

"You shall have a million!"

"The king will not give his consent."

"He will give it!"

"And when you have got it, you will need a lady to present you."

"I am seeking for one now."

"It is useless; there is a league against you."

"At Versailles?"

"Yes. All the ladies have refused, in order to pay their court to the Duke de Choiseul, the Duchess de Grammont, the dauphiness —the party of prudes, in short."

"Do not fear; I have nearly obtained what I want."

"Ha! it was for that you sent your sister to Verdun!"

"So you know that, do you?" said she, angrily.

"Oh, I have also my police, you know!" said Sartines, laughing.

"And your spies?"

"And my spies."

"In my apartments?"

"In your apartments."

"In my stable, or in my kitchen?"

"In your antechamber, in your salon, in your bedroom, under your pillow."

"Now, as the first pledge of our peace," said the countess, "give me the names of those spies."

"No, Countess; I should not wish to embroil you with your friends."

"But name only the last who told you a secret."

"What would you do?"

"I would turn him out."

"If you begin in that way, you will soon have to live in an empty house."

"This is frightful!"

"Yet perfectly true. Oh, you know we could not govern without spies! So excellent a politician as you must have discovered that long ago."

Madame Dubarry leaned her elbow on a table, and seemed to reflect for some minutes; then she said: "You are right. Let us say no more on the subject. What are to be the conditions of our treaty?"

"Make them yourself. You are the conqueror."

"I am as magnanimous as Semiramis. Let me hear what you wish."

"Well, then, you are never to speak to the king about petitions on the subject of wheat; for, traitress! you have promised your support to those petitions."

"Very well. Take away all the petitions with you; they are in a box there."

"Take in exchange this document, drawn up by the peers of the kingdom, respecting presentations and the right of sitting in the royal presence."

"A document which you were charged to give His Majesty?"

"Yes."

"But what will you say to them?"

"That I have given it. You will thus gain time; and you are too clever in your tactics not to take advantage of it."

At this moment the folding doors were thrown open, and an usher announced: "The king!"

The two allies hastened to hide their mutual pledges of peace and good understanding, and turned to salute His Majesty, Louis XV.

The king entered with head erect, with a firm step, his eye full of life, and a smile on his lips. As the doors were opened, a double file of bowing heads was seen, belonging to the courtiers, who had been waiting in the antechamber, and who were now more desirous of admittance than ever, since they could thus pay their court to two powers at once; but the doors closed on them, for the king made a sign that no one should follow him. He found himself alone, therefore, with the countess and the minister of police; for we need make no account of the waiting maid or a little Negro who was in attendance.

"Good morning, Countess!" said the king, kissing Madame Dubarry's hand. "Ha! fresh as a rose, I see! Good morning, Sartines! Is this your cabinet, where you write your dispatches? Heavens, what heaps of papers! Hide them, hide them! Ha! what a beautiful fountain, Countess!" And with the versatile curiosity of one always in search of something to amuse him, he fixed his eyes on a large china ornament, which had been brought in the evening before, and placed in a corner of the countess's bedroom.

"Sire," replied the countess, "it is a Chinese fountain. On turning this cock, the water comes out and makes these birds sing and these fishes swim; then the doors of the pagoda open, and there comes out a procession of mandarins."

"Very pretty, very pretty indeed!"

At this moment the little Negro walked across the room, dressed in the fantastic fashion in which, at this period, they dressed their

Osmans and Othellos. He wore a little turban, ornamented with a lofty plume of feathers, on one side of his head, a vest embroidered with gold, breeches of white brocaded satin; around his waist was a scarf of various bright colors, which connected the breeches with a richly embroidered jacket; and a dagger, ornamented with precious stones, was stuck in the scarf bound around his waist.

"*Peste!*" cried the king, "how splendid Zamore is today!"

The Negro stopped to admire himself before a mirror.

"Sire, he has a favor to ask of Your Majesty."

"Madame," replied the king, with a courtly smile, "I am afraid Zamore is very ambitious."

"How so, Sire?"

"Because he has already been granted the greatest favor he can desire."

"What is that?"

"The same that has been granted me," the king said.

"I do not understand you, Sire."

"You have made him your slave."

The minister of police bowed, smiling, and bit his lip at the same time.

"Oh, how charming you are, Sire!" cried the countess. Then, leaning toward the king, she said, in a low tone: "France, I adore thee!"

The king smiled in his turn. "Well," he asked, "what do you want for Zamore?"

"The reward of his long and numerous services."

"How so? He is twelve years old."

"His long and numerous future services."

"Oh, very well!"

"Yes, indeed, Sire. Past services have been rewarded long enough; it is now time to begin rewarding those of the future. There would not then be so much ingratitude."

"Ha! not a bad idea," said the king. "What do you think of it, Sartines?"

"That it would benefit all devoted servants of Your Majesty, Sire; therefore I support it."

"Well, Countess, come, what do you ask for Zamore?"

"Sire, you know my little country seat of Luciennes?"

"I have heard it spoken of only."

"That's your own fault; I have invited you to it a hundred times."

"You know the etiquette, dear Countess; unless on a journey of national importance, the king can sleep only in a royal château."

"Exactly; this is the favor which I have to ask. We will make Luciennes a royal château, and we will appoint Zamore to be its governor."

"But, Countess, that would be a burlesque."

"I love burlesques, Sire."

"The governors of the other royal castles would all cry out—and this time with reason."

"So much the better; they have so often cried out without reason. Kneel down, Zamore, and thank His Majesty."

"What's this for?" asked Louis XV.

The Negro knelt.

"For the reward you are going to give him for bearing my train, and putting all the prudes of the court in a rage," said the countess.

"He is really a hideous creature," said the king, bursting into a fit of laughter.

"Rise, Zamore," said the countess; "you are appointed governor of Luciennes."

"But indeed, madame—"

"I shall send Zamore all the writings necessary for his governorship. And now, Sire, you may come to Luciennes; you have one more royal château from this day."

"Is there any way of refusing her anything, Sartines?"

"There may be a way, Sire," replied Sartines; "but it has not yet been discovered."

"And if it should be found out, Sire, there is one thing certain; it is Monsieur de Sartines who will be the discoverer."

"How can you think so, madame?" asked Sartines, trembling.

"Sire, only imagine that I have requested a favor of Monsieur de Sartines for three months past, and it is not yet granted."

"And what is it?" asked the king.

"Oh, he knows very well!"

"I! I swear to you, madame—"

"Does it fall within the duties of his office?"

"Yes; within either his or those of his successor."

"Madame," cried Sartines, "you really make me uneasy."

"What is the request?" again inquired the king.

"To find me a sorcerer."

Sartines breathed more freely.

"For burning?" asked the king. "Isn't it rather hot for that, Countess? Why not wait till the winter?"

"No, Sire; I wish to present him with a golden wand."

"Then this sorcerer has foretold some misfortune which has not befallen you."

"On the contrary, Sire, he predicted a piece of good fortune which has come to pass."

"Let us hear it then, Countess," said the king, throwing himself back in an armchair like one who is not quite sure whether he is to be amused or bored, but takes his chances.

"With all my heart; but if I tell the tale, you must contribute one half of the sorcerer's reward."

"The whole, if you like!"

"Royally said. Now listen."

"I am all attention."

"There was once—"

"It begins like a fairy tale."

"It is one, Sire."

"Delightful; I adore enchanters!"

"There once was a poor young girl, who at the time my story begins had neither page, nor carriage, nor Negro, nor parrot, nor monkey—"

"Nor king," added Louis.

"Oh, Sire!"

"And what did the poor girl do?"

"She trotted about through the streets of Paris like any other common mortal, only she always went very quickly; for it is said she was very pretty, and she was afraid of meeting some rude man."

"The young girl was a Lucretia, eh?"

"Oh! Your Majesty knows there have been no Lucretias since the year—I don't know what—of the foundation of Rome."

"Oh, heavens! Countess, are you going to become learned?"

"No; if I were learned, I should have given you a wrong date, but I have given you none."

"True," said the king; "go on."

"The young girl one day was trotting along, as usual, when all at once, while crossing the Tuileries, she discovered that a man was following her."

"Oh, the deuce! Then she stopped, I presume."

"Ah, Sire, what a bad opinion you have of women! It is easily seen that you have associated with only marchionesses and duchesses."

"And princesses?"

"I am too polite to contradict Your Majesty. But what frightened the young girl was that a fog came on, which became every moment denser."

"Sartines, do you know what causes fogs?"

The minister, thus taken unawares, started.

"Faith! no, Sire."

"Nor I. Well, go on, dear Countess."

"She ran as fast as she could, passed through the gate, and found herself in the square which bears Your Majesty's name, when she met the unknown, from whom she thought she had escaped, face to face. She uttered a cry—"

"Was he so very ugly, then?"

"No, Sire; he was a handsome young man, of twenty-six to twenty-eight years of age, of a dark complexion, with large, speaking eyes, and a pleasing voice."

"And the heroine was afraid? *Peste!* how easily she was frightened."

"She was not quite so much so when she looked at him; still, it was not a pleasant situation in that dense fog. So, clasping her hands, she said: 'I implore you, monsieur, not to do me any harm.' The unknown shook his head, smiled, and replied: 'Heaven is my witness, I have no such intention.' 'What, then, do you want?' she asked. 'To obtain a promise from you.' 'What can I promise you, monsieur?' 'Promise to grant me the first favor I shall ask when—' 'When?' repeated the young girl with curiosity. 'When you are queen.'"

"And what did the young girl do?" said the king.

"Sire, she thought it would be engaging herself to nothing; she promised."

"And what became of the sorcerer?"

"He disappeared."

"And Sartines refuses to find him? He is wrong."

"Sire, I do not refuse; but I cannot find him."

"Oh, monsieur," said the countess, "that word *cannot* should never be in the dictionary of the police."

"Madame, we are on his track."

"Yes—that's what you always say when you are baffled."

"It is the truth; but consider what trivial directions you have given."

"What?—trivial?—young, handsome, dark complexion, black hair, splendid eyes, a sonorous voice."

"Oh, the devil! how you speak of him, Countess! Sartines, I forbid you to find that young man," said the king.

"You are wrong, Sire; for I only wish to ask one simple question."

"Is it about yourself?"

"Yes."

"Well, what is it? Hasn't his prediction been accomplished."

"Do you think so?"

"Yes; you are queen."

"Very nearly. But not quite."

"This sorcerer, then, is to tell more?"

"He has to tell me when the queen will be presented. It is not enough to reign at night, Sire; it is necessary to reign a little also by day."

And here is the second excerpt from *Joseph Balsamo*, the somber counterpoint to the scene between the king and his mistress. This is the place which I said ended with the dropping in of a startling name.

Marat preceded Balsamo in the narrow alley leading to the lecture room, which was situated at the extremity of the rue Hautefeuille. Balsamo followed him unhesitatingly until they reached a long narrow room, where two corpses, a male and a female, lay stretched upon a marble table.

The woman had died young; the man was old and bald. A soiled sheet was thrown over their bodies, leaving their faces half-uncovered. They were lying side by side upon this cold bed—they who had perhaps never met before in the world, and whose souls, now voyaging in eternity, must, could they have looked down on earth, have been struck with astonishment at the proximity of their mortal remains.

Marat with a single movement raised and threw aside the coarse linen which covered the two bodies, whom death had thus made equal before the anatomist's scalpel.

"Is not the sight of the dead repugnant to your feelings?" asked Marat, in his usual boasting manner.

"It makes me sad," replied Balsamo.

"Want of custom," said Marat. "I, who see this sight daily, feel neither sadness nor disgust. We practitioners live with the dead, and do not interrupt any of the functions of our existence on their account."

"It is the sad privilege of your profession, monsieur."

"Besides," added Marat, "why should I be sad, or feel disgust? In the first case, reflection forbids it; in the second, custom."

"Explain your ideas," said Balsamo; "I do not understand you clearly. Reflection first."

"Well, why should I be afraid? Why should I fear an inert mass—a statue of flesh instead of stone, marble, or granite?"

"In short, you think there is nothing in a corpse?"

"Nothing—absolutely nothing."

"Do you believe that?"

"I am sure of it."

"But in the living body."

"There is motion," said Marat proudly.

"And the soul—you do not speak of it, monsieur."

"I have never found it in the bodies which I have dissected."

"Because you have dissected only corpses."

"Oh, no, monsieur! I have frequently operated upon living bodies."

"And you have found nothing more in them than in the corpses?"

"Yes, I have found pain. Do you call pain the soul?"

"Then you do not believe in it?"

"In what?"

"In the soul."

"I believe in it, because I am at liberty to call it motion, if I wish."

"That is well. You believe in the soul; that is all I asked. I am glad you believe in it."

"One moment, Master. Let us understand each other, and above all, let us not exaggerate," said Marat, with his serpent smile. "We practitioners are rather disposed to materialism."

"These bodies are very cold," said Balsamo, dreamily, "and this woman was very beautiful."

"Why, yes."

"A lovely soul would have been suitable in this lovely body."

"Ah! There was the mistake of him who created her. A beautiful scabbard, but a vile sword. This corpse, Master, is that of a wretched woman who had just left Saint Lazare when she died of cerebral inflammation in the Hôtel Dieu. Her history is long, and tolerably scandalous. If you call the motive power which impelled this creature 'soul,' you wrong our souls, which must be of the same essence, since they are derived from the same source."

"Her soul should have been cured," said Balsamo; "it was lost for want of the only physician who is indispensable—a physician of the soul."

"Alas, Master, that is another of your theories! There are only physicians for the body," replied Marat, with a bitter smile. "Now you have a word on your lips which Molière has often employed in his comedies; and it is this word which makes you smile."

"No," said Balsamo, "you make a mistake; you cannot know why I smile. What we concluded just now was that these corpses are void, was it not?"

"And insensible," added Marat, raising the young woman's head and letting it fall noisily upon the marble, while the body neither moved nor shuddered.

"Very well," said Balsamo; "let us now go to the hospital."

"Wait one moment, Master, I entreat you, until I have separated from the trunk this head, which I am most anxious to have, as it was the seat of a very strange disease. Will you allow me?"

"Do you ask?" said Balsamo.

Marat opened his case, took from it a bistoury, and picked up in a corner a large wooden mallet stained with blood. Then with a practiced hand he made a circular incision, which separated all the flesh and the muscles of the neck; and having thus reached the bone, he slipped his bistoury between two joints of the vertebral column, and struck a sharp blow upon it with the mallet.

The head rolled upon the table, and from the table upon the floor. Marat was obliged to seize it with his damp hands. Balsamo turned away, not to give too much joy to the triumphant operator.

"One day," said Marat, who thought he had hit the master in a weak point—"one day some philanthropist will occupy himself with the details of death as others do with those of life, and will invent a machine which shall sever a head at a single blow, and cause instantaneous annihilation, which no other instrument of death does. The use of the wheel, quartering with horses, hanging, these are punishments suitable for savages, but not for civilized people. An enlightened nation like France should punish, but not revenge. Those who condemn a criminal to the wheel, or to hang or be quartered, revenge themselves upon the criminal by inflicting pain before punishing him by death; and that, in my opinion, is too much by half."

"And in mine also, monsieur. But what kind of an instrument do you mean?"

"I can fancy a machine cold and impassive as the law itself. The man who is charged with fulfilling the last office is moved at the sight of his fellow man and sometimes strikes badly, as in the case of the Duke of Monmouth and that of Chalais. This could not happen with a machine having, for instance, two arms of oak wielding a cutlass."

"And do you believe, monsieur, that because the knife would pass with the rapidity of lightning between the base of the occiput and the trapezoid muscles, death would be instantaneous and the pain momentary?"

"Certainly; death would be instantaneous, for the iron would sever at a blow the nerves which cause motion. The pain would be momentary, for the blade would separate the brain, which is the seat of feeling, from the heart, which is the center of life."

"Monsieur," said Balsamo, "the punishment of decapitation exists in Germany."

"Yes, but by the sword; and, as I said before, a man's hand may tremble."

"Such a machine exists in Italy; an arm of oak wields it. It is called the *mannaja*."

"Well?"

"Well, monsieur, I have seen criminals decapitated by the executioner raise their headless bodies from the bench on which they were seated, and stagger off, to fall ten steps from there. I have picked up heads which had rolled to the foot of the *mannaja*, —as that head you are holding by the hair has just rolled from the marble table—and on pronouncing in their ears the name by which those persons had been called, I have seen the eyes open again and turn in their orbits, seeking to discover who from the earth had called to them in that passage from time to eternity."

"A nervous movement—nothing else."

"Are the nerves not the organs of sensibility?"

"What do you conclude from that, monsieur?"

"I conclude that it would be better, instead of inventing a machine which kills in order to punish, that man should seek a means of punishing without killing. The society which will invent this means will assuredly be the best and the most enlightened of societies."

"Utopia again—always Utopia!" said Marat.

"Perhaps you are right," said Balsamo; "time will show. But did you not speak of the hospital? Let us go!"

"Come then," said Marat; and he tied the woman's head in his pocket handkerchief, carefully knotting the four corners. "Now I am sure, at least," said he, as he left the hall, "that my comrades will have only my leavings."

They took the way to the Hôtel Dieu—the dreamer and the practitioner side by side.

"You have cut off this head very coolly and very skillfully, monsieur," said Balsamo. "Do you feel less emotion when you operate upon the living than the dead? Does the sight of suffering affect you more than that of immobility? Have you more pity for living bodies than for corpses?"

"No; that would be as great a fault as for the executioner to be moved. You may kill a man by cutting this thigh unskillfully, just as well as by severing the head from the body. A good surgeon operates with his hand, not with his heart; though he knows well at the same time, in his heart, that for one moment of suffering he gives years of life and health. That is the fair side of our profession, Master."

"Yes, monsieur; but in the living bodies you meet with the soul, I hope."

"Yes, if you will agree with me that the soul is motion, or sensibility. Yes, certainly, I meet with it; and it is very troublesome too, for it kills far more patients than any scalpel."

They had by this time arrived at the threshold of the Hôtel Dieu, and now entered the hospital. Guided by Marat, who still carried his funereal burden, Balsamo penetrated to the hall where the operations were performed, in which the head-surgeon and the students in surgery were assembled. The attendant had just brought in a young man who had been run over the preceding week by a heavy carriage, the wheel of which had crushed his foot. A hasty operation performed upon the limb when benumbed by pain had not been sufficient; the inflammation had rapidly extended, and the amputation of the leg had now become an urgent necessity.

The unfortunate man, stretched upon his bed of anguish, looked, with a horror which would have melted tigers, at the band of eager students who were watching for the moment of his martyrdom, perhaps of his death, that they might study the science of life—that marvelous phenomenon behind which lies the gloomy phenomenon of death.

He seemed to implore a pitying look, a smile, or a word of encouragement from each of the students and attendants; but the beatings of his heart were responded to only by indifference, his beseeching looks encountered only steel. A remnant of courage and of pride kept him silent. He reserved all his strength for the cries which pain would soon wring from him. But when he felt the heavy hand of the attendant upon his shoulder, when the arms of the assistants twined around him like the serpents of Laocoön, when he heard the operator's voice cry, "Courage!" the unfortunate man ventured to break the silence, and asked in a plaintive voice, "Shall I suffer much?"

"Oh, no! make your mind easy," replied Marat, with a hypocritical smile, which to the patient seemed kind, but to Balsamo ironical.

Marat saw that Balsamo had understood him; he approached and whispered; "It is a dreadful operation. The bone is full of cracks and fearfully sensitive. He will die, not of the wound, but of the pain. That is what the soul does for this poor man."

"Then why do you operate? Why do you not let him die in peace?"

"Because it is the surgeon's duty to attempt a cure, even when the cure seems impossible."

"And you say he will suffer?"

"Fearfully."

"And that his soul is the cause?"

"His soul, which has too much sympathy with the body."

"Then why not operate upon the soul? Perhaps the tranquillity of the one would cause the cure of the other."

"I have done so," said Marat, while the attendants continued to bind the patient.

"You have prepared his soul?"

"Yes."

"How so?"

"As one always does—by words. I spoke to his soul, his intelligence, his sensibility—to that organ which caused the Greek philosopher to exclaim, 'Pain, thou art no evil,'—the language suitable for it. I said to him: 'You will not suffer.' That is the only remedy hitherto known, as regards the soul—falsehood! Why is this she-devil of a soul connected with the body? When I cut off this head just now, the body said nothing, yet the operation was a serious one. But motion had ceased, sensibility was extinguished, the soul had fled, as you spiritualists say. This is the reason why the head I severed said nothing, why the body which I mutilated allowed me to do so; while this body which is yet inhabited by a soul—for a short time indeed, but still inhabited—will cry out fearfully. Stop your ears well, Master, you who are moved by this union of body and soul, which will always defeat your theory until you succeed in isolating the body from the soul."

"And you believe we shall never arrive at this isolation?"

"Try," said Marat; "this is an excellent opportunity."

"Well, yes, you are right," said Balsamo; "the opportunity is a good one, and I will make the attempt."

"You will make the attempt?"

"I will."

"How will you do it?"

"This young man interests me; he shall not suffer."

"You are an illustrious chief," said Marat, "but you are neither God the Father, nor God the Son, and you cannot prevent this man from suffering."

"If he were not to feel the pain, do you think he would recover?"

"His recovery would be more probable, but not certain."

Balsamo cast an inexpressible look of triumph upon Marat, and placed himself before the young patient, whose frightened eyes, already dilated with the anguish of terror, met his.

"Sleep," said Balsamo, not alone with his lips, but with his look, with his will, with all the heat of his blood, all the vital energy of his body.

The head-surgeon was just beginning to feel the injured leg, and to point out the aggravated nature of the case to his students; but at Balsamo's command the young man, who had raised himself upon his seat, oscillated for a moment in the arms of his attendants, his head drooped, and his eyes closed.

"He is ill," said Marat.

"No, monsieur."

"But do you not see that he loses consciousness?"

"He is sleeping."

"What, he sleeps?"

"Yes."

Everyone turned to look at the strange physician, whom they took for a madman. An incredulous smile hovered on Marat's lips.

"Is it usual for people to talk while in a swoon?" asked Balsamo.

"No."

"Well, question him—you will see—he will reply."

"Eh! young man!" cried Marat.

"You need not speak so loud," said Balsamo; "speak in your usual tone."

"Tell us what is the matter with you."

"I was ordered to sleep, and I sleep," replied the patient.

His voice was perfectly calm, and contrasted strangely with that they had heard a few moments before. All the attendants looked at each other.

"Now," said Balsamo, "release him."

"That is impossible," said the head-surgeon; "the slightest movement will spoil the operation."

"He will not stir."

"Who can assure me of that?"

"I, and he also—ask him."

"Can you be left untied, my friend?"

"Yes."

"And will you promise not to move?"

"I will promise it, if you command me."

"I command it."

"Faith! monsieur, you speak so positively that I am tempted to make the trial."

"Do so, monsieur; and fear nothing."

"Untie him."

The assistants obeyed. Balsamo advanced to the bedside. "From this moment," said he, "do not stir until I order you."

A statue upon a tombstone could not have been more motionless than the patient, upon this injunction.

"Now operate, monsieur," said Balsamo; "the patient is quite ready."

The surgeon took his bistoury; but when upon the point of using it, he hesitated.

"Cut, monsieur! cut, I tell you!" said Balsamo, with the air of an inspired prophet.

And the surgeon, yielding—like Marat, like the patient, like every one present—to the irresistible influence of Balsamo's words, made ready to begin. The sound of the knife passing through the flesh was heard, but the patient did not stir, nor even sigh.

"From what country do you come, my friend?" asked Balsamo.

"I am a Breton, monsieur," replied the patient, smiling.

"And you love your country?"

"Oh, monsieur, it is so beautiful!"

In the meantime the surgeon was making the circular incisions in the flesh, by means of which, in amputations, the bone is laid bare.

"You left it when young?" asked Balsamo.

"At ten years of age, monsieur."

The incisions were made; the surgeon placed the saw on the bone.

"My friend," said Balsamo, "sing me that song which the salt-makers of Batz chant as they return to their homes after the day's work is over. I can remember only the first line—

"My salt covered o'er with its mantle of foam."

The surgeon was now severing the bone; but at Balsamo's command the patient smiled, and began to sing in a low, melodious, ecstatic voice, like a lover or like a poet, the following verses:

"My salt covered o'er with its mantle of foam,
The lake of pure azure that mirrors my home,
My stove where the peats ever cheerfully burn,
And the honeyed wheatcake which awaits my return;

"The wife of my bosom, my silver-haired sire,
My urchins who sport round the clear evening fire;
And there, where the wild flowers, in brightest of bloom,
Their fragrance diffuse round my loved mother's tomb,

"Blest, blest be ye all! Now the day's task is o'er,
And I stand once again at my own cottage door;
And richly will love my brief absence repay,
And the calm joys of eve the rude toils of the day."

The leg fell upon the bed while the patient was still singing.

Everyone looked with astonishment at the patient—with admiration at the physician. Some said that both were mad. Marat communicated this opinion to Balsamo in a whisper. "Terror has made the poor devil lose his senses," said he; "that is why he feels no pain."

"I think not," replied Balsamo; "and far from having lost his senses, I am sure that if I asked him, he could tell us the day of his death if he is to die, or the period of his convalescence if he is to recover."

Marat was almost inclined to adopt the general opinion—that Balsamo was as mad as his patient. In the meantime, however, the surgeon was tying up the arteries, from which spouted streams of blood.

Balsamo drew a small phial from his pocket, poured a few drops of the liquid it contained upon a little ball of lint, and begged the chief surgeon to apply the lint to the arteries. The latter obeyed, with a certain feeling of curiosity. He was one of the most celebrated practitioners of that period—a man truly enamored of his profession, who repudiated none of its mysteries, and for whom chance was but the makeshift of ignorance.

He applied the lint to the artery, which quivered, bubbled, and then allowed the blood to escape only drop by drop. He could now tie up the artery with the greatest ease.

This time Balsamo obtained an undoubted triumph, and all present asked him where he had studied, and of what school he was.

"I am a German physician of the school of Goettingen," he replied, "and I have made this discovery you have just witnessed. However, gentlemen and fellow practitioners, I wish this discovery to remain a secret for the present, as I have a wholesome terror of the stake, and the parliament of Paris might perhaps resume their functions once more, for the pleasure of condemning a sorcerer to be burned."

The head-surgeon was still plunged in a revery. Marat also seemed thoughtful, but he was the first to break the silence. "You said just now," said he, "that if you were to question this man about the result of this operation, he would reply truly, though the result is still veiled in futurity."

"I assert it again," replied Balsamo.

"Well, let us have the proof."

"What is this poor fellow's name?"

"Havard," replied Marat.

Balsamo turned to the patient, whose lips were yet murmuring the last words of the plaintive air.

"Well, my friend," asked he, "what do you augur from the state of this poor Havard?"

"What do I augur from his state?" replied the patient. "Stay! I must return from Brittany, where I was, to the Hôtel Dieu, where he is."

"Just so. Enter, look at him, and tell me the truth respecting him."

"Oh! he is very ill, his leg has been cut off."

"Indeed!" said Balsamo. "And has the operation been successful?"

"Exceedingly so; but—"

The patient's face darkened.

"But what?" asked Balsamo.

"But," resumed the patient, "he has a terrible trial to pass through. The fever—"

"When will it come on?"

"At seven o'clock this evening."

All the spectators looked at each other.

"And this fever?" asked Balsamo.

"Oh! it will make him very ill, but he will recover from the first attack."

"Are you sure?"

"Oh yes!"

"Then, after this first attack, will he be saved?"

"Alas, no," said the wounded man, sighing.

"Will the fever return, then?"

"Oh yes! and more severely than before. Poor Havard! poor Havard!" he continued, "he has a wife and several children," and his eyes filled with tears.

"Must his wife be a widow, then, and his children orphans?" asked Balsamo.

"Wait, wait!"

He clasped his hands.

"No, no," he exclaimed, his features lighting up with an expression of sublime faith; "no, his wife and children have prayed so much that they have obtained God's mercy for him."

"Then he will recover?"

"Yes."

"You hear, gentlemen," said Balsamo; "he will recover."

"Ask him in how many days," said Marat.

"In how many days, do you say?"

"Yes; you said he could indicate the phases, and the duration of his convalescence."

"I ask nothing better than to question him on the subject."

"Well, then, question him now."

"And when do you think Havard will recover?" said Balsamo.

"Oh! his cure will take a long time—a month, six weeks, two months. He entered this hospital five days ago, and he will leave it two months and two weeks after having entered."

"And he will leave it cured?"

"Yes."

"But," said Marat, "unable to work, and consequently unable to maintain his wife and children."

Havard again clasped his hands. "Oh! God is good; God will provide for him!"

"And how will God provide for him?" asked Marat. "As I am in the way of learning today, I should much like to learn that."

"God has sent to his bedside a charitable man, who has taken pity upon him, and who has said to himself, 'poor Havard shall not want.'"

The spectators were amazed; Balsamo smiled.

"This is in truth a strange scene," said the head-surgeon, at the same time taking the patient's hand, and feeling his chest and forehead; "this man is dreaming."

"Do you think so?" said Balsamo.

Then darting upon the sick man a look of authority and energy: "Awake, Havard!" said he.

The young man opened his eyes with some difficulty, and gazed with profound surprise upon all these spectators, who had so soon laid aside their threatening attitude, and assumed an inoffensive manner toward him.

"Well," said he, sadly, "have you not operated yet? Are you still going to make me suffer?"

Balsamo was quick to make the reply, for he feared the invalid's emotion. But there was no need for such haste; the surprise of all the spectators was so great that none would have anticipated him.

"My friend," said he, "be calm. The head-surgeon has operated upon your leg in such a manner as to satisfy all the requirements of your condition. It seems, my poor fellow, that you are not very strong-minded, for you fainted at the first incision."

"Oh! so much the better," said the Breton, smilingly; "I felt nothing, and my sleep was even sweet and refreshing. What happiness—my leg will not be cut off!"

But just at that moment the poor man looked down, and saw the bed full of blood, and his amputated leg lying near him. He uttered a scream, and this time fainted in reality.

"Now question him," said Balsamo, coldly, to Marat; "you will see if he replies."

Then, taking the head-surgeon aside, while the nurses carried the poor young man back to his bed: "Monsieur," said Balsamo, "you heard what your poor patient said?"

"Yes, monsieur, that he would recover."

"He said something else; he said that God would take pity upon him, and would send him wherewithal to support his wife and children."

"Well?"

"Well, monsieur, he told the truth on this point, as on the others. Only you must undertake to be the charitable medium of affording him this assistance. Here is a diamond, worth about twenty thousand francs; when the poor man is cured, sell it, and give him the proceeds. In the meantime, since the soul, as your pupil Monsieur Marat said very truly, has a great influence upon the body, tell Havard, as soon as he is restored to consciousness, that his future comfort and that of his children is secured."

"But, monsieur," said the surgeon, hesitating to take the ring which Balsamo offered him, "if he should not recover?"

"He will recover."

"Then allow me at least to give you a receipt."

"Monsieur!"

"That is the only condition upon which I can receive a jewel of such value."

"Do as you think right, monsieur."

"Your name, if you please?"

"The Comte de Fenix."

The surgeon passed into the adjoining apartment, while Marat, overwhelmed, confounded, but still struggling against the evidence of his senses, approached Balsamo.

In five minutes the surgeon returned, holding in his hand the following receipt, which he gave Balsamo:

"I have received from the Comte de Fenix a diamond, which he affirms to be worth twenty thousand francs, the value of which is to be given to the man Havard when he leaves the Hôtel Dieu.
This Fifteenth of September, 1771.

DR. GUILLOTIN, M.D."

Balsamo bowed to the doctor, took the receipt, and left the room, followed by Marat.

"You are forgetting your head," said Balsamo, for whom the wandering of the young student's thoughts was a great triumph.

"Ah, true!" said he; and he again picked up his dismal burden.

Chapter IX

HUMANITY AND OUTRAGE

Dumas's mind was encyclopedic, not merely in its range, but in ability to include different and seemingly antagonistic attitudes. He was like the earth, which will grow weeds, useful plants, poisonous mushrooms, and delectable fruit, all equally well in the same space.

The result was that in a way he could do better justice to history than historians. Like Larousse of the Grand Dictionnaire Universel, he admired Bonaparte and hated Napoleon. He loved royalty and hated the pomp and the cruelty that went with most of it. He could take part in a revolution to unseat a king and thus gain the enthusiasm of the masses, and then protest against the king's statue being torn down, and thus lose that enthusiasm.

Here is a characteristic bit from Dumas's *Memoirs*, Volume IV.

Whilst waiting, I explored all the town and the surrounding neighborhood under the guidance of Pavie. Excellent companion, that Pavie! Pointed out to me, with indignation that revealed both his love of art and his love of France, how some workmen, under orders issued by the prefect, and following the directions given by a local architect, were busy beautifying the cathedral.

Those grotesque figures, for example, sculptured into the supporting stones, were being trimmed down into brackets. So that you no longer have to look at those wonderful grimacing faces that the Middle Ages liked to stick into every nook of their cathedrals, but can gaze your fill on a Roman entablature upheld by Grecian brackets, exactly like those you can see on the Paris stock exchange building, which itself is one of those modern marvels, part Greek and part Roman, with nothing French about it but the sheet iron stovepipes sticking out of the roof.

Furthermore Pavie could show me how they were scraping the
cathedral clean. No more of that brown color that eight centuries
of weather had laid over every inch of it. It was now "rejuvenated"
to a sickly paleness.

There you are. It takes twenty-five years to bring a child to man-
hood, and then some good Swiss mercenary, who has left his republic
to serve some king, can fire on this man, and then he is dead.
Matter of minutes.

It takes six or eight centuries to give a building a color that is
inimitable, and along comes an architect with good taste, and he
scrapes it! Matter of weeks and the cathedral is dead.

Why doesn't the Swiss kill the architect instead? Or why doesn't
the architect scrape the Swiss?

We went down to the promenade, and I walked past the tenth-
century castle, an ancient hulk, circled by a moat, and flanked by a
dozen massive towers, the labor of a whole population, the asylum
for an army.

"But don't you see that it spoils the view?" my poor Pavie said
with a sigh. "It is scheduled to be pulled down."

But just as Dumas could be outraged about ancient architecture
being mutilated and destroyed, he could be equally outraged by
ancient customs not giving way to modern intelligence. As in this
bit from his *Memoirs*, Volume V:

Everybody knows Lyons, a poor, dirty town with a canopy of
smoke and a jumble of wealth and misery, where people dare not
drive through the streets in carriages, not for fear of running over
some pedestrian, but for fear of being insulted. Because here, for
forty thousand unfortunate human beings, the twenty-four hours of
the day contain eighteen hours of work, of noise, and of agony.

Lyons? Imagine a spiral composed of three turns. On the top
turn: eight hundred manufacturers. In the middle turn: ten thousand foremen. At the base: forty thousand workmen who support
the whole structure.

And buzzing, gleaning, picking about this spiral of human flesh,
like hornets about a hive, are the factors, the middlemen, the

suppliers, who bring the raw material and take away the finished product.

The mechanism of all this? The commissionaires live on the manufacturers, the manufacturers live on the foremen, the foremen live on the workers. Once upon a time this system functioned. But that was before England, instead of being a buyer of Lyons magnificent textiles, became a producer of her own, and then went on from that to becoming the banker for setting up looms in Zurich, in Basel, in Cologne, and in Berne.

Forty years ago, during Napoleon's continental system, the whole of France had to come to Lyons for her materials, and workmen there earned anywhere from four to six francs a day. That enabled him easily to provide for his wife and his numerous offspring which always come into being when there's prosperity for the workingman.

But with the fall of the Empire, things began to slide. Wages went from four francs to forty sous, then to thirty-five sous, then thirty, and then twenty-five. And now, in our own day the Lyons operative can earn only eighteen sous for an eighteen-hour day of work! One sou per hour! It is a starvation wage.

The unfortunate workmen of Lyons struggled in silence for a long time, trying, as each quarter came around, to move into smaller rooms, to more noxious quarters. Trying, day by day, to economize something in the diet of their meals and those of their children. But at last, when they came face to face with the deadening effect of bad air and bad food, and even total lack of bread, there went up from the working area of the town—the Croix-Rousse (the Red Cross, Rousse is also slang for police) an appropriate name, isn't it? that is to say, from the working portion of the city—a great sob, like that which Dante heard when he was passing through the first circle of the Inferno.

It was the cry of one hundred thousand sufferers!

When I wrote about the series of novels that Dumas published on the downfall of the French monarchy and the revolution, I said: "Maquet was in general the collaborator on all these works." The words "in general" referred in particular to the last volume of this series, the one called *The Countess de Charny*. This one Dumas wrote alone, because he wrote it after his rupture with Maquet, and indeed when he was in his self-imposed exile in Brussels.

It is therefore a good novel for those to study who think that all of Dumas's talent came from his collaborators. Though of course one may quibble by saying that this time it was the historian Jules Michelet who was his collaborator, since Dumas certainly inspired himself from that man's many volumed *Histoire de France*.

It must be pointed out, however, that Michelet was just then himself in exile in Brussels, and a good friend of Dumas. Dumas was to start his *Countess de Charny*, but needed Michelet's works on that period, and sent away to Paris for them. Meanwhile he read a work by a Flemish writer that had just recently appeared, a slight thing called *The Conscript* by Hendrik Conscience. In that little book Dumas found an incident that charmed him and that he wished to use, so he wrote away to the author for permission, and that being granted, he produced in a short time a book called *Conscience the Innocent*, a small thing which, however, Dumas long regarded as his favorite bit of writing.

Just as he called his character Conscience, as a tribute to the original writer, so Dumas dedicated this book to Michelet, whose work he was now about to use for his *Countess de Charny*. His dedication reads: "To Michelet the historian, Michelet the philosopher, Michelet the poet."

And Michelet himself certainly bore Dumas no grudge. He wrote to him: "I love and admire you, for you are one of the forces of nature."

Here then is the extract, dealing with the end of Louis XVI.

Though this is printed on the form of fiction, my readers can see with what impartiality I have placed before their eyes not only the terrible, the cruel, the bloodthirsty, the debased features of the Revolutionists, and the events which they fostered, but also the good, the beautiful, the sublime elements of those very same people and events.

Today those persons are dead of whom I write. The events only remain. Immortalized by history, they can never die.

I would gladly summon from the grave all those of whom I speak —so few of whom filled out the appointed measure of their days— and ask them if I have not pictured their careers, not perhaps exactly as they were—for who can claim to know all mysteries?—but as they have seemed to my studied and honest convictions.

I would say to Mirabeau: "Tribune, arise!" to Louis XVI: "Martyr, arise!" I would say: "Rise, all of you—Favras, Lafayette, Bailly, Fournier the American, Jourdan the Headsman, Maillard, Théroigne de Méricourt, Barnave, Bouille, Gamain, Pétion, Manuel, Danton, Robespierre, Marat, Vergniaud, Dumouriez, Marie Antoinette, Madame Campan, Barbaroux, Roland, Madame Roland—king, queen, artisan, orators, generals, murderers, politicians! Rise, and declare if I have not candidly presented you to my own generation—to the low, to the exalted, especially to women—that is, to the mothers of our sons, whom we would gladly instruct in history."

To the long lines of events, standing on either side of the road we have traveled together, I would thus appeal: "Great and luminous Fourteenth of July! Dark and threatening Fifth and Sixth of October! Thou crimson storm in the Champ de Mars, when powder was mixed with lightning, and the thunder of cannon mingled with heaven's artillery! thou prophetic invasion of the Twentieth of June! thou terrible victory of the Tenth of August; thou awful memory of the Second and Third of September! To all of you I say: Have I truthfully represented you? Have I told your story well? Have I wittingly lied about you? Have I unfairly tried to calumniate or defend you?"

The men and women would reply, the events would reply: "No. You have sought the truth, without hatred or passion. You believed, or you would not have spoken. You have been faithful to the glories of the past, insensible to the allurements of the present, confident in the hopes of the future. We pronounce you absolved! Acquitted!"

Well, what I have so far done, not as an appointed judge, but as an impartial narrator, I shall continue to do unto the end; and that end we are approaching rapidly. We are sliding down the steep incline of events, and there are few breathing places between September 21, 1792—the day of the monarchy's demise—and January 21, 1793—the day of the monarch's doom.

We have heard the proclamation of the Republic, made beneath the royal prison house, by the strong voice of Municipal Lubin; and that proclamation naturally summons us to that prison—the Temple.

Let us enter into that gloomy edifice, wherein is confined a king who is fast becoming a man, and a queen who still remains a queen, also one virgin martyr, and two poor children, innocent by their years, if not by their birth.

The King was in the Temple. How came he there? Was it deliberately planned to send him to this shameful prison? No!

To begin with, Pétion had an idea of transporting Louis to the interior of France, assigning him Chambord for his estate, and treating him as a sort of used-up sovereign.

If all the European monarchs had curbed their generals, their ministers, and their manifestoes, and had been content to note what was going on in France without meddling with her politics, then the throne forfeiture of August 10, this secluded residence in a beautiful palace, with a fine climate, in the midst of what is well called the Garden of France—all this would not have been a very severe retribution for a man expiating, not merely his own faults, but those of the two Louises preceding him, the Fourteenth and Fifteenth.

However, there had had just been a Royalist revolt in the Vendée, and it was objected that there might be a rescuing dash along the Loire. This reason appeared weighty, and so Chambord was passed by.

The Assembly then suggested the Luxembourg, in Paris itself. The Luxembourg, a Florentine palace which had belonged to Marie de Médicis—with its lovely solitude, and gardens which rivaled those of the Tuileries—would have been a residence not less desirable than Chambord for a deposed ruler.

To this place it was objected that the cellars under the palace opened into the catacombs, which had recently been found both unsafe and unwholesome. Perhaps this was only a pretext on the part of the Commune, because the Council wished to have the King directly under its fist; but it was nevertheless a plausible pretext.

The Commune decided for the Temple, the edifice which had formerly belonged to the Order of Knights Templar, that organization so cruelly persecuted by Philip the Fair. This decision did not refer to the Grand Tower, which was the dungeon of the Temple, but to that part called the Palace, which in the old days had been the Commandery of the Chiefs of the Templars, and had later become a pleasure house for Count d'Artois, the youngest brother of Louis the Sixteenth, afterward himself King of France.

Then, at the very moment when Pétion was taking the royal prisoners to the Temple Palace, just as they were being installed there, and Louis was making his household arrangements, a denunciation reached the Commune, which led the Council to send Manuel to make a change in the municipal arrangements for the King. And the Tower was substituted for the Palace.

Manuel came and inspected the place designed as the home of King Louis and Marie Antoinette, and went away somewhat mortified.

The Donjon was really uninhabitable, and lately had been occupied only by a sort of janitor. Its narrow apartments did not afford sufficient room. The beds were inconvenient and alive with vermin.

All this arose less from reprehensible premeditation on the part of the judges, than from that fatality which weighs down a dying race.

The National Assembly did not dicker about the expense of gratifying the royal palate. The King was a hearty eater. This is not adduced by way of reproach. It belongs to the temperament of the Bourbons to be great eaters! Louis Sixteenth, however, ate at awkward times. He ate, and with a good appetite, even while the slaughter was going on at the Tuileries. During his trial, not only did his judges reproach him with his unseasonable repast, but—what is worse—implacable history recorded the facts in her archives.

The National Assembly granted 500,000 francs for the expenses of the royal appetite. During the four months the King remained in the Temple, the cost was 40,000 francs—10,000 francs per month, over 333 francs a day. This was to be reckoned in paper assignats, it is true; but at that date the assignats had only fallen off some six or eight per cent in their purchasing value.

In the Temple, Louis had three personal and thirteen table servants. He had four courses every day at dinner. There were six roasts, four side dishes, three varieties of jam, three dishes of fruit, a decanter of bordeaux, a decanter of malvoisie, a decanter of madeira. He and his little son drank wine. The Queen and the princesses drank only water.

On the gastronomical side, therefore, the King had nothing to complain of; but he woefully lacked air and exercise, sunshine and shade.

Formerly accustomed to the chase at Compiègne and Rambouillet to the parks of Versailles and the Grand Trianon, and latterly to the drives and walks from and around the Tuileries, Louis now found himself reduced, not to a courtyard merely, not to a garden, nor even to a small park, but to a little piece of dry and barren earth, with four beds of exhausted turf, some decaying and stunted trees, made leafless by the autumnal gales.

In this place, every day at two o'clock, the royal family promenaded; or rather, let us say, that there, at two daily, the royal family were led up and down.

This was something unfamiliar, disagreeable, harsh; but it was less harsh and disagreeable than the cellars of the Inquisition at Madrid, the Leads established by the Council of Ten at Venice, or the dungeons at Spielberg, where monarchs often sent their political offenders.

Let it be well understood that while we do not excuse the Commune, neither do we excuse the kings. We simply say that the Temple was a reprisal—a fatal, ill-advised, a terrible reprisal; whereas this penalty has been represented as persecution, and thus the culprit has been transformed into a martyr.

Meanwhile, what was the present aspect of the different personages whom we have undertaken to follow in the principal phases of their lives?

The King, with his nearsightedness, his flaccid cheeks, his hanging lips, his heavy and uncertain gait, seemed like some worthy farmer, bowed down by misfortune. His sadness was like that of an agriculturist, when a hailstorm has bruised his crops and the lightning has fired his barns.

The Queen's attitude was as usual, quiet, supercilious and highly antagonistic. In the days of her grandeur, Marie Antoinette inspired love. In the hour of her downfall, she inspired devotion, yes, but never pity. Pity is born of sympathy, and sympathy the Queen did not win.

Madame Elizabeth, the self-sacrificing virgin, with her white robe, symbolic of her moral and physical purity, with her blond hair, which was all the more beautiful, now that she was forced to wear it loose and unpowdered—with blue ribbons on her cap and about her waist—seemed like the guardian angel of the family.

Despite the charm of her youth, Madame Royale was not very interesting. A complete Austrian, like her mother—another Marie Antoinette or Maria Theresa—she already displayed that contempt and pride which belong alike to royal families and birds of prey.

The little Dauphin was somewhat interesting, with his golden locks and his fair but rather sickly complexion; yet his blue eye was stern and bold, and he often wore an expression beyond his age. He understood everything, and could catch the suggestions which his mother gave him in a single glance. He had all the juvenile trickery and witchery which often draws tears from executioners themselves. He even touched Chaumette—poor child!—Chaumette, that marten with a pointed snout, that weasel in spectacles.

"I would give him an education," said the ex-clerk to Hue, the King's valet; "but it would be necessary to take him away from his family, so that he would forget his rank."

The Commune officers were both cruel and imprudent—cruel in subjecting the royal family to such harsh treatment, to such vexations, and even insults; imprudent in letting the royal family be seen in its feeble and crushed condition.

Every day new guardians were sent to the Temple, who were called *municipals*. They entered the Temple sworn enemies of the King. They came out the sworn enemies of Marie Antoinette, but feeling softer toward the King, pitying the children, and glorifying Madame Elizabeth.

In place of the *wolf*, the *she-wolf*, and the *cubs*, whom did they find in the Temple? They found a middle-class family. They found the mother somewhat lofty—a sort of Elmira, who would not allow anybody to touch the hem of her gown; but they found no trace of a tyrant.

How did the day pass with this family? Let us see how the time was employed, as we learn it from Cléry, the valet devoted to his master till the last minute.

First let us look about the prison, and afterward return to the prisoners.

The King was confined in the Small Tower. The Small Tower was back to back with the Large Tower, but there was no interior connection between them. The Small Tower was square, and flanked by two turrets. In one of these turrets was a small staircase, which ran from the main story to the gallery on the flat roof. In the other turret were small rooms, mere nooks or alcoves, corresponding to each floor of the Small Tower.

There were four stories in the main part of this Small Tower. The main story, up one flight from the courtyard, was divided into an antechamber, an eating room, and the small room, or cabinet, in the turret.

The next story was divided in much the same way. Here the large room served for the bedroom of the Queen and Dauphin. The second room separated from the first by a dark little entry, was occupied by Madame Elizabeth and Madame Royale. In order to enter the cabinet in the turret, it was necessary to pass through this bedroom; and as for this turret cabinet—which by the way, was only what the English call a toilet closet—it was used in common by the royal family, the municipal guardians, and the soldiers.

The King occupied the suite up three flights, which contained the same number of rooms. He slept in the largest. The cabinet in the adjoining turret served him for a little study. Beside it was a kitchen, with a little anteroom, which at first, before they were separated from him, was occupied by Chamilly and Hue, but was afterward sealed up.

As for the upper story, it was closed. And the basement was consecrated to old kitchens and sculleries, long disused.

How did the royal family manage to live in such narrow quarters, half tenement and half prison? We shall see.

The King rose regularly at six o'clock in the morning. He shaved himself, as long as he was allowed to do so. Cléry brushed his hair and helped him dress. As soon as he was brushed and dressed he went into his study—that is, into a library, in which were fifteen or sixteen hundred volumes, besides the ancient archives of the Knights of the Order of Malta.

One day the King found the works of Voltaire and Rousseau among these books, and pointed them out to Hue. "These," he said, in a low voice, "are the men who have ruined France!"

When he entered this room each morning, Louis usually knelt five or six minutes in prayer. Then he read till nine. During this time Cléry put the King's chamber in order, arranged breakfast, and went downstairs to the Queen's apartments.

While alone in this little retreat, Louis amused himself by translating from Virgil or the *Odes* of Horace; for in order to keep up the Dauphin's education, he had resumed his study of Latin.

This cabinet was very small. The door was always open; and a municipal officer was always in the bedroom, whence he could look through the open door, and see what the King was about.

The Queen did not open her door till Cléry's arrival; in order that the municipal officer might not come in.

Cléry would dress the young Prince's hair, arrange the Queen's toilet and then go into the other chamber to render Madame Royale and Madame Elizabeth the same service. This moment of toilet was both rapid and precious, for it was the only time when Cléry could tell the ladies whatever outside information he had gleaned. If he made a certain sign, which meant that he had something to say, the Queen, or one of the ladies, would enter into some conversation with the official, and Cléry would take advantage of this distraction to whisper what he had to say.

At nine the ladies and children went up to the King's chamber, where breakfast was served. During the dessert Cléry went downstairs again, and put the Queen's apartment in order.

A man named Tison, with his wife, had been ordered to join Cléry, under the pretense of aiding him in his work, but really to act as spies, not only upon the royal family, but upon the guards also. The husband, formerly a clerk in the city excise office at one of the barriers, was a harsh and malicious old fellow, incapable of any humane sentiments. The woman, made more womanly by the love she bore for her daughter, carried that love to such an extreme that once, when separated from her child, she denounced the Queen, thinking that thus her daughter might be restored to her.

At ten o'clock in the morning, after breakfast, the King went down to the Queen's room, and there passed the day. He occupied himself almost exclusively with the Dauphin, making him repeat passages from Corneille or Racine, giving him a lesson in geography, and letting him draw maps. For three or four years France had been divided into departments instead of the old ducal provinces, but it was the geography of the kingdom which the King instructed to his son.

On her part the Queen busied herself with teaching Madame Royale. These lessons were often interrupted by the mother's relapse into deep and gloomy reveries. When this happened, her daughter would leave her alone in that mysterious grief, unblessed with tears, and withdraw on tiptoe, making a sign for her brother to keep silence. The Queen would remain some time thus absorbed. Then a tear would appear on her eyelash, steal down her cheek, and fall upon her yellow hand, which had taken on an ivory tint. Then the poor prisoner—who had been for a while set free in an immense domain of thought, in the limitless field of remembrance—would emerge abruptly from her dream; and, looking about her, she would find herself again in her prison house, her heart bruised, and her head bowed with shame.

At noon the three ladies assembled in Madame Elizabeth's room, in order to change their morning gowns, this being the one moment when the modesty of the Commune left them alone, and no guard was present.

At one o'clock, when the weather permitted, the royal family were taken down into the garden. Four municipals and an officer of the National Guards accompanied them, or rather watched them. As there were many workmen about the temple, employed in demolishing old buildings and putting up new walls, the prisoners were only allowed to use that part called the Allée des Marroniers.

Cléry was also present at these outings, and gave the young Prince a little exercise at playing ball and quoits.

At three they all returned to the Small Tower. Cléry served the dinner. Every day at that hour Commander Santerre came to the Temple, accompanied by two aides, and examined scrupulously the apartments both of the King and Queen.

Sometimes the King spoke to him; but the Queen, never. She had forgotten June 20, and what she owed to that man's friendship the first time the mob overran the Tuileries.

After dinner they all went upstairs again. The King played a game of piquet or backgammon with the Queen or his sister, while Cléry took his turn at dining.

At four o'clock the King stretched himself for a siesta, on a lounge or in a big armchair. Then the profoundest silence reigned. The ladies took their work or some books, and everybody was mute, even the little Dauphin.

Louis Sixteenth passed from wakefulness to slumber almost without an interval—such was the tyrannical rule over him of his corporeal needs. He slept usually from an hour and a half to two hours.

When he awoke, conversation was resumed. Cléry was called, for he was never far off, and gave the little Dauphin a writing lesson. Then he took him into Madame Elizabeth's room, and made him play battledore and shuttlecock.

When evening came, the royal family gathered about a table. The Queen read aloud something to amuse and instruct the children. Aunt Elizabeth took the Queen's place when she was weary. This reading lasted till eight o'clock.

At eight the Prince had his supper in Aunt Elizabeth's chamber. The family were in the room while he ate; and from a set of the *French Mercury*, which the King had found in the library, he gave out enigmas and conundrums for his children to guess.

After the Dauphin's supper, the Queen heard him say his little prayer:

"All-powerful God, who has created and redeemed me, thee I adore. Prolong the days of the King my father, and also those of all my family. Protect us from our enemies. Give Madame de Tourzel the strength she needs to bear what she endures on our account."

Then Cléry undressed the boy and put him to bed, and one of the younger ladies remained near him until he fell asleep.

Every night about that hour a newspaper carrier went along the street crying aloud the news of the day. Cléry would be on the alert, and then repeat to the King the crier's words.

At nine the King took his supper. On a tray, Cléry carried some food to whichever lady was still watching with the Dauphin.

His repast finished, the King would go into the Queen's chamber, to wave an adieu to her and his sister, and kiss the children, and then would go up to his own apartments, where he would sit in the little library and read till midnight.

When the King had gone the ladies would shut themselves in, an official staying in the small entry which separated their two chambers. The other official always followed the King upstairs.

Cléry placed his bed near the King's; but before lying down Louis always waited till the new official came upstairs, in order to ascertain who he was, and if he had ever been on duty before. There was always a change of guards at eleven in the forenoon, five in the afternoon, and at midnight.

This sort of life lasted, without any change, as long as the King remained in the Small Tower—that is, till September 30.

As one can see, the situation was sad, and the worthier of pity because borne so nobly. The most hostile onlookers were softened by the sight. They came to keep watch over an abominable tyrant, who had ruined France, slaughtered Frenchmen, and appealed to foreign armies—over a Queen who united the sensuality of Messalina with the depravity of Catherine Second. They found a man clad in gray, whom they might readily mistake for his valet—a man who ate well, drank well, slept well, played backgammon and piquet, taught his boy Latin and geography, and made his children solve riddles. They found a woman undoubtedly proud and disdainful, but noble, calm, resigned, and still beautiful, teaching her girl embroidery and her boy his prayers, speaking softly to the servants, and saying *my friend*, even to a humble and a deferential valet.

The first hours were full of hatred. Each guard came with sentiments of vengeance and animosity in his heart, and gave free course to these sentiments. Gradually he relented. He might leave his home in the morning with a high head and threatening aspect, but he would return to his home in the evening with a gloomy air and bowed head.

The wife of one of these men waited for her husband with much curiosity.

"Ah, it's thee!" she cried.

"Yes!" responded the municipal, laconically.

"Well, hast thou seen the tyrant?"

"Yes, I've seen him!"

"Has he a ferocious look?"

"He looks like a retired grocer in the Marais District."

"What was he doing? Swearing, cursing the Republic—?"

"He passes his time in studying with his younkers, teaching them Latin, playing piquet with his sister, and propounding enigmas to amuse his wife."

"Hasn't he any remorse, the wretch?"

"I saw him eat. He eats like a man with a tranquil conscience. I saw him sleep, and I'll bet he never has a nightmare."

Then the wife would become pensive in her turn, and presently she would say: "So he can't be as cruel and guilty as folks say?"

"Guilty? Well I don't know— Cruel? I should say not!— Unhappy? Most decidedly!"

"Poor man!" the wife would ejaculate.

This is what happened. The more the communists humiliated the prisoner, the more they tried to show that he was only a man like any other, the more those other men pitied one in whom they recognized a fellow man.

Sometimes this sympathy manifested itself directly to the King, or to Cléry and the Dauphin.

One day a stonecutter was busy making holes in the wall of the antechamber, where some enormous bolts were to be inserted. While the workman was taking his breakfast, the Dauphin amused himself by playing with the tools. Then the King took the chisel and mallet from the boy, and handled them in such a way as to show that he was a skillful locksmith and mechanic.

The mason looked on in amazement, from the corner where he was munching his bread and cheese. He had not shown the King and the Prince the courtesy of rising, but now he rose in respect for the man and his child. Approaching them, with his mouth full of bread, but with his cap in his hand, he said to the King: "When you go out of this donjon you can say you worked at your own prison bars!"

"Ah! When and how shall I go out?" said the King.

The Dauphin began to cry. The mason dried a tear. The King dropped chisel and hammer, and went into his chamber, where he walked the room for a long time.

Another day a suburban was acting as sentinel at the Queen's door—a man coarsely dressed, but with a strong sense of propriety. Cléry was alone in the room, reading. The sentinel watched him very attentively. Presently, called elsewhere by his duties, Cléry rose and started to go out; but the sentinel presented arms, and said in a low and timid voice, almost trembling: "You can't pass here!"

"Why not?" asked Cléry.

"Because my orders are to keep my eye on you."

"On me? Surely you must be mistaken!"

"Aren't you the King?"

"Then you don't know the King?"

"I have never seen him, monsieur; and, if I must say it, if I see him at all, I would rather see him somewhere else."

"Speak low!" said Cléry. Then pointing to a door he added: "I'm going into that chamber, and then you can see the King. He sits at a table, reading."

Cléry went in, and told the King what had happened; so the King rose and walked into the other room, that the good fellow might see him more readily.

Suspecting that it was solely on his account that the King was taking this trouble, the sentinel said to Cléry: "Ah monsieur! how good the King is. As for me, I don't believe he has done half so much mischief as they say!"

A sentinel, stationed at the end of the alley which served as the promenade for the royal family, one day gave them to understand that he had some information to communicate. At the first turn in their walk, nobody appeared to give any attention to these signs; but at the second turn Madame Elizabeth approached the soldier, to see if he would speak to her. Unhappily the young man, who had a distinguished bearing, remained mute, either through fear or respect; but tears filled his eyes, and he pointed to a pile of rubbish, where a letter was probably concealed.

Under pretense of finding some stones for the little Prince's quoits, Cléry began to search among the dirt, but the officials, doubtless suspecting what he was after, ordered Cléry to desist and forbade his ever talking with the sentinels, under pain of being separated from his master.

All who came near the prisoners did not show the same sentiments of respect and pity. Hatred and vengeance were so strongly rooted in many minds as not to be eradicable by the sight of royal misfortunes, though borne with middle-class virtue, and consequently both King and Queen had to hear gross remarks and insults.

One day the official on duty near the King was a man named James, a teacher of English. This man stuck to the King like his shadow, never leaving him. When the King went into his little library to read, this official followed, and sat down near the prisoner.

"Monsieur," said the King, with his habitual mildness, "your comrades have usually left me alone when I came into this little room, so small that I cannot elude their watch when the door is open."

"My colleagues can take their own way, and I'll take mine."

"Notice if you please, monsieur, that the room is not large enough for two."

"Then go into the larger room!" harshly replied the official.

Without saying another word the King rose and went into the bedroom. The Englishman followed, and was in Louis's way till the guard was relieved.

The sentinels were regularly changed at midnight. One morning the King supposed the official on duty was the same who had been there the evening before; so he went to him, and said, with some interest: "Ah, monsieur, I'm sorry they forgot to relieve you from duty!"

"What do you mean?" was the surly reply.

"I only meant to say that you must be tired."

"Citizen," answered the fellow, whose name was Meunier, "I'm here to watch you, and not for you to concern yourself with my affairs." Putting on his cap, he went closer to the King, and added: "Nobody, and you less than anybody else, has any right to meddle with me!"

One day the Queen ventured to speak to an official who was present during dinner. "In what section do you live, monsieur?"

"In my own country!" he proudly replied.

"But it seems to me that your country is all France," replied the Queen.

"Except the part occupied by the enemies whom you have brought into it."

Some of the commissioners would never speak to any member of the royal family without adding some obscene epithet or ringing oath.

One day an official named Turlot said to Cléry, loud enough for the King to hear every word: "If the headsman won't guillotine this blooming family pretty soon, I'll guillotine 'em myself."

In going out for their walk the royal family had to pass by a large number of sentinels, several of whom were stationed in the interior of the Small Tower. When the military chiefs and the municipals passed by, the guards presented arms; but when the King came along, they would ground their arms or turn their backs.

It was the same with the outside guards on duty at the foot of the Tower. When the King came along, they would ostentatiously keep their caps on, or sit down, but as soon as he had passed by, they would stand up again, and take off their caps.

These insults were carried yet farther. One day a sentinel, not content with presenting arms to the military and municipal officers, while he refused to do so to the King, wrote as follows on the interior of the prison door:

The guillotine is a fixture, and awaits the tyrant, Louis XVI!

This was a new device, and became very popular. This writer had many imitators. Very soon the walls of the Temple, especially on the staircase used by the royal family, were covered with such inscriptions as these:

"We must put the fat hog on short allowance."

"Down with the red ribbon! Strangle the Cubs!"

Other inscriptions, like the title under a picture, explained some impertinent sketch.

Under the drawing of a hangman's noose was this sentence:

"Madame Veto will dance!"

Beneath the picture of a man on the gallows was the motto: "Louis taking an airbath!"

The most aggravating tormentors were two men who were always at the Temple—Simon the shoemaker and Rocher the sapper.

Simon was a monopolist. He held all sorts of places. Not only was he a shoemaker, but a municipal official. Moreover he was one of six commissioners, charged with inspecting the work and surroundings of the Temple. By virtue of these three occupations he never left the donjon.

This man, celebrated for his subsequent ill-treatment of the little Dauphin, was the personification of impudence. Every time he came into the presence of the prisoners, it was for the purpose of inflicting some new outrage.

If the valet asked for something for the King, Simon would say: "Let Capet ask for what he wants all at once. I can't run up and down to please him!"

In impertinence Rocher was his equal, but he was not so bad a man. On August 10 it was Rocher who caught up the little Prince, outside the Assembly door, and placed him in safety on the President's table.

From being a saddler, Rocher became a military officer under San-terre, and then a janitor in the Temple. He usually wore his sapper's uniform and a black fur cap, and carried a large saber. His beard and mustache were long. About his waist was a belt, from which de-pended his great bunch of keys.

He was placed in the Tower by Manuel, to watch over the royal prisoners, and prevent others from doing them any mischief—not for the sake of harming them himself. He resembled a child, set to guard a cageful of birds, with directions not to let anybody harm them, but who amuses himself by pulling out their feathers.

When the King wished to go out, Rocher would appear at the door, but he would not open the door till he had made the King wait, while the janitor jingled his big bunch of keys. Then he would pull the bolts with a bang. When the bolts were drawn and the door was open, Rocher would rush downstairs, and place himself by the last wicket, at the end of the archway, with a pipe in his mouth. As each member of the royal family came out, but particularly the ladies, he would blow a puff of smoke into their faces.

These miserable cowards did these things in the presence of Na-tional Guards, who, instead of checking them, often brought their chairs, and sat down to enjoy the fun, like spectators at a play.

This encouraged Rocher, who went everywhere bragging: "Marie Antoinette may be awfully proud, but I've brought her down, I have! Elizabeth and the girl have to knock down to me, in spite of them-selves. The wicket is so low that they have to bow down when they go through it! Every day I give one or t'other of them a taste of my pipe. One day the sister says to the commissioner, says she: 'Why does Rocher smoke all the time?'—'Apparently because he chooses!' says the commissioner."

In all such great expiations, besides the penalty inflicted upon the victims, there is always some fellow who makes them drink the gall to its very dregs. For Louis Sixteenth this tormentor was Simon or Rocher. For Napoleon it was Hudson Lowe. These are the very men whose behavior causes others to idealize the victim's suffering, and sanctify his death, when he has submitted to the last penalty, and is done with life. Would Saint Helena be Saint Helena without the jailer in his red coat? Would the Temple be the Temple without its sapper and its cobbler? Such men are genuine parts of the romance.

They rightfully make a part of long and lugubrious popular stories.

It is difficult for ideality to control deeds. What the members of the Convention could not understand—or, at least, what only a few of them could understand, some clearly and others intuitively—was this: that they should have proceeded against Royalism, not against the King.

Royalty was a gloomy abstraction, a mysterious peril, which nobody wanted. It was an idol, gilded on the outside; but, like the whited sepulchers of which Jesus spoke, it was full of "dead men's bones, and all uncleanness."

The King was another matter. The King was a man—a man not very interesting in the days of his prosperity, but a man purified by misfortune and broadened by captivity. His humanity was developed through his disgrace. The brightening influence of adversity over him was such that even the Queen—either from new intuition or from repentance of the past—now that she was a poor prisoner in the Temple, almost adored, worshiped—in a religious sense of the word— this king, this prince, this man, whose plebeian instincts and sensuous appetites had often sent the blood to her face. It cannot be said that she loved him, however; for her poor broken heart had lost all the love it had ever contained—like a leaking vase which has lost its precious liquor drop by drop.

One day the King entered the Queen's rooms, and found her sweeping the chamber where the little Dauphin lay ill. He paused on the threshold, let his head fall on his breast, and said with a sigh; "Ah madame, what an occupation for the Queen of France! What if Vienna could see what you are doing? Who would have believed that I should cause you such a downfall, by linking your fate with mine!"

"And do you count as nothing," replied the Queen, "the glory of being the wife of the best and most persecuted of men?"

This is what Marie Antoinette said, and without a witness, as she believed, not knowing that a poor valet, who had followed the King's fortunes, gathered up these words like black pearls that they might form a diadem, not for the brow of a king, but for a condemned prisoner.

Another day Louis saw Sister Elizabeth cutting with her teeth, for want of scissors, the thread with which she was repairing the Queen's gown.

"Poor sister!" said he. "What a contrast to that pretty mansion at Montreuil, where you once lacked nothing!"

"Ah, my brother," said this saintly lady, "can I regret anything, when I share your misfortunes?"

All this became known. All this was noised abroad. All this embellished, with golden arabesques, the sad romance of the royal martyr.

Royalty was smitten to the death; but the King, living and imprisoned, suggested a great and powerful thought—so great and forcible that it entered the brains of but few men, who found it so unpopular that they hardly dared to give it utterance.

"People need salvation, but they do not need vengeance," said Danton to the Cordelier Club.

"Assuredly the King must be tried," said Grégoire to the Convention, "but he is regarded with so much contempt, that there is no place left for hatred."

This is what Thomas Paine wrote:

"I wish the prosecution could be drawn up, not against Louis Sixteenth, but against the whole tribe of kings. One of them we have in our power. He will put us on the track of conspiracy everywhere . . . Louis Sixteenth will be very useful to prove the necessity of revolutions."

Lofty minds like Paine's, and great hearts like Danton's and Grégoire's, were in accord on this point. Not one king, but kings as a whole should be indicted, and Louis should be summoned only as a witness.

Republican France—that is, a nation which had attained its majority—should proceed, not only in her own name, but in the name of nations still submissive to royalty—that is, still under age. France should sit in judgment, not as an earthly magistrate, but as a divine arbiter. She should look down from the higher spheres, and her word should no longer rise to the throne like a splash of mud and blood, but it should fall upon the kings of earth like a thunderclap.

Suppose a public prosecution, supported by proofs, had been begun against Catherine II—murderess of her husband, the plunderer of Poland. Suppose the monstrous details of her life had been openly exposed, like Madame de Lamballe's corpse. Imagine that Pasiphae of the North chained in the pillory of public opinion, and say what would have been the result of teaching the nations by such a prosecution.

We will cite only one phrase of the condemned King's will:

"I close by declaring before God, and expecting to appear before Him, that I cannot reproach myself with the crimes charged against me."

This sentence has won for Louis XVI, in the eyes of posterity, the reputation of being an honest man. Yes, this man perjured in all his oaths, this traitor who fled towards a foreign land, leaving behind him a protest against the very oaths he had solemnly taken. This man who had discussed, appreciated, and recorded the plans of Lafayette and Mirabeau for his own safety, yet had called upon the enemy to strike a mortal blow at the heart of France; this man, being now ready to appear before God, who must be his judge, and believing that God would reward both good and bad actions, was able to say: "I cannot reproach myself with the crimes charged against me."

Perhaps the construction of the phrase may help explain the matter. The King did not say: "The allegations against me are false," but he said: "I cannot reproach myself with the crimes charged against me," which is not exactly the same thing.

To say, "The allegations against me are false," would be to deny those allegations, and Louis could not deny them; but to say, "I cannot reproach myself with the crimes charged against me," might mean, strictly interpreted: "These crimes may exist, but I do not reproach myself with them."

Why did not Louis XVI reproach himself? Because his point of view, as we have just said, was the standpoint of royalty. Because, thanks to the influences under which he was reared, thanks to his belief in the sanctity of hereditary rights, and the infallibility of the royal right divine, kings cannot see crimes, especially political crimes, in the same light as other people.

In the eye of Louis XI, his revolt against his father was no crime. It was a war for the public welfare.

To Charles IX, the Saint Bartholomew Massacre was no crime. It was a measure dictated by public security.

This same Malesherbes, who now defended the King, had tried in former days, when he belonged to the Royal Council, to persuade the King to reinstate the Protestants in their old political rights; but he found Louis XVI very obstinate on this subject.

"No," said the King, "no! The proscription of Protestants is a law of the state, a law of Louis Fourteenth. Never disturb the ancient landmarks."

"Sire," replied Malesherbes, "politics should never override justice."

"But," cried the King, like a man who could not understand, "where was there any proscription of justice in the Revocation of the Edict of Nantes. Was not the Revocation of the Edict of Nantes necessary to the welfare of the state?"

In the eyes of Louis XVI, therefore, this persecution of the Protestants, devised by an old devotee and a revengeful Jesuit—an atrocious measure, which made the blood run in the streams of the Cévennes valleys, and kindled the pyres at Nîmes, Albi, and Béziers—this persecution was not a crime, but, on the contrary, a state necessity.

There is another matter which has to be urged for the royal standpoint—that a king is a man who is almost always born of a foreign princess, from whom he therefore derives the best part of his blood, and is thus almost a stranger to his people. He governs them—that is all. But he is not one of them. By whom does he govern? By his ministers.

So that not only are his subjects considered unworthy of being related to him, unworthy of being allied to him by marriage, but they are not even worthy of being directly governed by their king. It is foreign sovereigns, on the contrary, who are the relatives and allies of a king, who himself has neither kinsfolk nor allies in his kingdom. And with these foreign kinsmen he can correspond without the intervention of public officers.

The Spanish Bourbons, the Neapolitan Bourbons, the Italian Bourbons, all came from the same stock, Henry IV. They were all cousins. The Emperor of Austria was Louis XVI's brother-in-law. The Savoy princes were his kinsfolk, for Louis was Saxon on his mother's side.

When the people reached a point where they wished to impose upon the King conditions which he did not believe to be for his interest, to whom did Louis appeal for support against his revolted subjects? Why, to his cousins, his brothers-in-law, of course. To his kinsfolk. To him the Spanish and the Austrians were not the enemies of France, because they were the relatives and the friends of himself, the King; and from the Royalist point of view, the King was the state, was France. "The state? It is I!" said his great predecessor.

And these kings whom Louis XVI called upon to come to his aid, what did they gather to defend? The sacred, infallible, almost divine cause of royalty.

This is why Louis XVI could not reproach himself with the crimes charged against him.

Chapter X

THE WINGS OF BENVENUTO CELLINI

Oυτ oF Benvenuto Cellini's *Memoirs*, Dumas drew, in 1843, a historical romance, *Ascanio*, which was first published serially in *Le Siècle*, then in five volumes and subsequently in two, and in other reprints. And in English under different titles, in at least three different translations.

Paul Meurice, brother of Froment Meurice, one of the greatest goldsmiths and jewelers of the nineteenth century, is said to have brought Dumas the idea of doing a novel from Cellini's *Memoirs*. Some, for example, Larousse, in his article on Paul Meurice, even maintained that Dumas merely signed his name to the Meurice book, and there was no Dumas in it at all.

Bearing out the idea that Dumas had no hand in it, is the fact that in 1852 the Porte Saint-Martin theater announced that it was doing a prose drama in five acts and eight scenes based on Dumas's *Ascanio*, the adaptation being the work of Paul Meurice.

Dumas wrote a protest to be published in *Le Pays*, saying: "I hear they are rehearsing *Ascanio* at the Porte Saint-Martin without my authorization. Kindly announce that I positively oppose the production of my drama. By placing it in rehearsal they have omitted only one thing from the book: *the necessity of consulting me.*"

In spite of this the drama was produced under the title of *Benvenuto Cellini*. The famous actor Mélingue starred in it, and it was a success. In fact a brilliant one.

Whether Dumas protested any further, or whether he and Meurice subsequently came to some understanding, or whether because the book was really Meurice's Dumas could not do anything more than just protest for form's sake, I don't know.

In 1891, an opera was made out of this same drama, and brought out under the old title of *Ascanio*. Meurice was still alive, since he lived to 1905, but Dumas was long dead.

Nevertheless F. W. Reed, than whom no one has a better right to say so, declares: "Paul Meurice had some hand in assisting Dumas, but the work is in the main the master's own."

Meurice was a writer of some talent. As brother of the goldsmith, it sounds quite logical that he should call Dumas's attention to Cellini. He was the author of a play *Fanfan la Tulipe*, which was made into a fine French movie some ten or more years ago. He was not only Dumas's friend, but also so close a friend of Victor Hugo that the latter appointed him as his literary executor.

If the following extract is not pure Dumas, it certainly has the Dumas touch, even in this stilted translation that I have hastily brushed up to remove its worst faults. By the Dumas touch I mean a story both informative and exciting. History dressed up and going places.

Since we have drawn the portrait and mentioned the name of Benvenuto Cellini, we crave the reader's permission (so that he may the more understandingly approach the artistic subject of which we propose to treat) to indulge in a short digression upon this extraordinary man, who at this time had been living in France for two months, and who is destined to become one of the principal characters of this history.

But first of all let us say a word as to the goldsmiths of the sixteenth century.

There is at Florence a bridge called the Ponte-Vecchio, which is covered with houses to this day; these houses were in the old days goldsmiths' shops.

But the word is not to be understood as we understand it today. The goldsmith of our day follows a trade; formerly, the goldsmith was an artist.

So it was that there was nothing in the world so wondrously beautiful as these shops, or rather as the articles with which they were stocked. There were round cups of onyx, around which dragons' tails were twined, while heads and bodies of those fabulous creatures confronting one another with gold-bespangled sky-blue wings outspread, and with jaws wide open like chimeras, shot threatening glances from their ruby eyes. There were ewers of agate, with a festoon of ivy clinging around the base, and climbing up in guise of handle well above the orifice, concealing amidst emerald foliage some marvelous bird from the tropics, in brilliant plumage of enamel, seemingly alive and ready to burst forth in song. There were urns of lapis lazuli, over the edge of which leaned, as if to drink, lizards chiseled with such art that one could almost see the changing reflection of their golden cuirasses, and might have thought that they would fly at the least sound, and seek shelter in some crevice in the wall. Then there were chalices and monstrances, and bronze and gold and silver medallions, all studded with precious stones, as if in those days rubies, topazes, carbuncles, and diamonds could be found by searching in the sand on river banks, or in the dust of the highroad; and there were nymphs, naiads, gods, goddesses, a whole resplendent Olympus, mingled with crucifixes, crosses, and Calvarys; Mater Dolorosas, Venuses, Christs, Apollos, Jupiters launching thunderbolts, and Jehovahs creating the world; and all this not only cleverly executed, but poetically conceived; not only admirable, viewed as ornaments for a woman's boudoir, but magnificent masterpieces fit to immortalize the reign of a king or the genius of a nation.

To be sure, the goldsmiths of that epoch bore the names of Donatello, Ghiberti, Ghirlandajo, and Benvenuto Cellini.

Now, Benvenuto Cellini has himself described in his memoirs, which are more interesting than the most interesting novel, the adventurous life of the artists of the fifteenth and sixteenth centuries, when Titian was painting in coat of mail, when Michelangelo was sculpturing with his sword at his side, when Massaccio and Domenichino died of poison, and Cosmo I secluded himself in his laboratory to discover the mode of tempering steel so that it would cut porphyry.

To show the character of the man, we will take a single episode in his life—that which was the occasion of his coming to France.

Benvenuto was at Rome, where Pope Clement VII had summoned him, and was at work with characteristic ardor upon the beautiful chalice which His Holiness had ordered; but as he desired to display his talent at its best upon the precious work, he made but slow progress. Now, Benvenuto, as may well be imagined, had many rivals, who envied him the many valuable orders he received from the Pope, as well as the marvelous skill with which he executed them. The result was that one of his confreres, named Pompeo, who had nothing to do but slander his betters, took advantage of the delay to do him all possible injury in the Pope's sight, and kept at work persistently, day in and day out, without truce or relaxation, sometimes in undertones, sometimes aloud, assuring him that he would never finish it, and that he was so overwhelmed with orders that he executed those of other people to the neglect of His Holiness's.

He said and did so much, did good Pompeo, that when Benvenuto Cellini saw him enter his workshop one day with smiling face, he divined at once that he was the bearer of bad news for him.

"Well, my dear confrere," Pompeo began, "I have come to relieve you from a heavy burden. His Holiness realizes that your neglect in completing his chalice is not due to lack of zeal, but to lack of time; he therefore considers it no more than just to relieve you from some one of your important duties, and of his own motion he dismisses you from the post of Engraver to the Mint.

"It will be nine paltry ducats a month less in your pocket, but an hour more each day at your disposal."

Benvenuto was conscious of an intense longing to throw the jeering varlet out of the window, but he restrained his feelings, and Pompeo, seeing that not a muscle of his face moved, thought that he had missed his aim.

"Furthermore," he continued, "why, I know not, but in spite of all that I could say in your behalf, His Holiness demands his chalice at once, in whatever condition it may be. Verily, I am afraid, dear Benvenuto, I say it in all friendliness, that it is his purpose to have some other finish it."

"Oh no, not that!" cried the goldsmith, starting up like one bitten by a serpent. "My chalice is my own, even as the office at the mint is the Pope's. His Holiness has no right to do more than bid me return the five hundred crowns paid to me in advance, and I will dispose of my work as may seem good to me."

"Beware, my master," said Pompeo; "imprisonment may be the sequel of your refusal."

"Signore Pompeo, you're an ass!" retorted Benvenuto.

Pompeo left the shop in a rage.

On the following day two of the Holy Father's chamberlains called upon Benvenuto Cellini.

"The Pope has sent us," said one of them, "either to receive the chalice at your hands, or to take you to prison."

"Monsignori," rejoined Benvenuto, "an artist like myself deserved no less than to be given in charge to functionaries like yourselves. Here I am; take me to prison. But I give you fair warning that all this will not put the Pope's chalice forward one stroke of the graver."

Benvenuto went with them to the governor of the prison, who, having doubtless received his instructions in advance, invited him to dine with him. Throughout the repast the governor used every conceivable argument to induce Benvenuto to satisfy the Pope by carrying the chalice to him, assuring him that, if he would make that concession, Clement VII, violent and obstinate as he was, would forget his displeasure. But the artist replied that he had already shown the Holy Father his chalice six times since he began it, and that that was all that could justly be required of him; moreover, he said he knew His Holiness, and that he was not to be trusted; that he might very well, when he had the chalice in his hands, take it from him altogether, and give it to some idiot to finish, who would spoil it. He reiterated his readiness to return the five hundred crowns paid in advance.

Having said so much, Benvenuto met all subsequent arguments of the governor by exalting his cook to the skies, and praising his wines.

After dinner, all his compatriots, all his dearest friends, all his apprentices, led by Ascanio, called upon him to implore him not to rush headlong to destruction by resisting the commands of Clement VII; but Benvenuto told them that he had long desired to establish the great truth that a goldsmith can be more obstinate than a Pope; and as the most favorable opportunity he could ask for was now at hand, he certainly would not let it pass, for fear that it might not return.

His compatriots withdrew, shrugging their shoulders, his friends vowing that he was mad, and Ascanio weeping bitterly.

Fortunately Pompeo did not forget Cellini, and meanwhile he was saying slyly to the Pope:

"Most Holy Father, give your servant a free hand; I will send word to this obstinate fellow that, since he is so determined, he may send me the five hundred crowns; as he is a notorious spendthrift he will not have that sum at his disposal, and will be compelled to give up the chalice to me."

Clement considered this an excellent device, and bade Pompeo do as he suggested. And so, that same evening, as Cellini was about to be taken to the cell assigned him, a chamberlain made his appearance, and informed the goldsmith that His Holiness accepted his ultimatum, and demanded the delivery of the chalice or the five hundred crowns without delay.

Benvenuto replied that they had but to take him to his workshop, and he would give them the five hundred crowns.

He was escorted there by four Swiss, accompanied by the chamberlain. He entered his bedroom, drew a key from his pocket, opened a small iron closet built into the wall, plunged his hand into a large bag, took out five hundred crowns, and, having given them to the chamberlain, showed him and the four Swiss the door. It should be said, in justice to Benvenuto Cellini, that they received four crowns for their trouble, and in justice to the Swiss, that they kissed his hands as they took their leave.

The chamberlain returned forthwith to the Holy Father, and delivered the five hundred crowns, whereupon His Holiness, in his desperation, flew into a violent rage, and began to abuse Pompeo.

"Go to my great engraver at his workshop, animal," he said. "Employ all the soothing arguments of which your ignorant folly is capable, and say to him that if he will consent to finish my chalice, I will give him whatever facilities he may require."

"But, Your Holiness," said Pompeo, "will it not be time tomorrow morning?"

"I fear lest it be already too late this evening, imbecile, and I do not choose that Benvenuto shall sleep upon his wrath; therefore do my bidding on the instant, and let me not fail to have a favorable reply tomorrow morning at my levee."

Pompeo thereupon left the Vatican with drooping feathers, and repaired to Benvenuto's workshop. The place was locked.

He peered through the keyhole and through the cracks in the door, and scrutinized all the windows, one after another, to see if there was not one which showed a light; but all were dark. He ventured to knock a second time somewhat louder than at first, and then a third time, still louder.

Thereupon a window on the first floor opened, and Benvenuto appeared in his shirt, harquebus in hand.

"Who's there?" he demanded.

"I," the messenger replied.

"Who is I?" rejoined the goldsmith, although he recognized his man at once.

"Pompeo."

"You lie!" said Benvenuto. "I know Pompeo well, and he is far too great a coward to venture out into the streets of Rome at this hour."

"But, my dear Cellini, I swear—"

"Hold your peace, villain! You're someone who has taken the poor devil's name to induce me to open my door, and then to rob me."

"Master Benvenuto, may I die—"

"Say but another word," cried Benvenuto, pointing the harquebus toward his interlocutor, "and that wish of yours will be gratified."

Pompeo fled at full speed, crying "Murder!" and disappeared around the corner of the nearest street.

Benvenuto thereupon closed his window, hung his harquebus on its nail, and went to bed once more, laughing in his beard at poor Pompeo's fright.

The next morning, as he went down to his shop, which had been opened an hour earlier by his apprentices, he spied Pompeo on the opposite side of the street, where he had been doing sentry duty since daybreak, waiting to see him descend.

As soon as he saw Cellini, Pompeo waved his hand to him in the most affectionately friendly way imaginable.

"Aha!" said Cellini, "is it you, my dear Pompeo? By my faith! I was within an ace last night of making a churl pay dearly for his insolence in assuming your name."

"Indeed!" said Pompeo, forcing himself to smile, and drawing gradually nearer to the shop; "how did it happen, pray?"

Benvenuto thereupon described the incident to His Holiness's messenger; but as his friend Benvenuto had described him in their nocturnal interview as a coward, Pompeo did not dare confess his identity with the visitor. When his tale was finished, Cellini asked Pompeo to what happy circumstance he was indebted for the honor of so early a visit from him.

Pompeo thereupon acquitted himself, but in somewhat different terms, be it understood, of the errand upon which Clement VII had sent him to his goldsmith. Benvenuto's features expanded as he proceeded. Clement VII yielded; *ergo* the goldsmith had been more obstinate than the Pope.

"Say to His Holiness," said Benvenuto, when the message was duly delivered, "that I shall be very happy to obey him, and to do anything in my power to regain his favor, which I have lost, not by any fault of my own, but through the evil machinations of envious rivals. As for yourself, Signore Pompeo, as the Pope does not lack retainers, I counsel you, in your own interest, to look to it that another than you is sent to me hereafter; for your health's sake, Signore Pompeo, interfere no more in my affairs; in pity for yourself, never happen in my path, and for the welfare of my soul, Pompeo, pray God that I be not your Caesar."

Pompeo waited to hear no more, but returned to Clement VII with Cellini's reply, of which, however, he suppressed the peroration.

Sometime thereafter, in order to put the seal to his reconciliation with Benvenuto, Clement VII ordered the papal medallion struck by him. Benvenuto struck it in bronze, in silver, and in gold, and then carried it to him. The Pope was so enraptured with it that he cried out in his admiration, saying that so beautiful a medallion had never been produced by the ancients.

"Ah, well, Your Holiness," said Benvenuto, "had not I displayed some firmness, we should have been at enmity today; for I would never have forgiven you, and you would have lost a devoted servant. Look you, Holy Father," he continued, by way of good counsel, "Your Holiness would not do ill to remember now and then the opinion of many discreet folk, that one should bleed seven times before cutting once. And you would do well also to allow yourself to be something less easily made the dupe of lying tongues and envious detractors. So much for your guidance in the future, and we will say no more about it, Most Holy Father."

Thus did Benvenuto pardon Clement VII, which he certainly would not have done had he loved him less; but, as his compatriot, he was deeply attached to him. Great, therefore, was his sorrow when the Pope suddenly died, a few months subsequent to the episode we have described. The man of iron burst into tears at the news, and for a week he wept like a child. The Pontiff's demise was doubly calamitous to poor Cellini. On the very day of his burial he met Pompeo, whom he had not seen since the day when he bade him spare him the too frequent infliction of his presence.

It should be said that since Cellini's dire threats, the unhappy

Pompeo had not dared to go out unless accompanied by a dozen men, well armed, to whom he gave the same pay that the Pope gave his Swiss guards; so that every walk that he took in the city cost him two or three crowns. And even when surrounded by his twelve sbirri, he trembled at the thought of meeting Benvenuto Cellini, for he knew that if the meeting should result in an affray, and any mishap should befall Cellini, the Pope would make him, Pompeo, pay dearly for it. But, as we have said, Clement VII was dead, and his death restored some little courage to Pompeo.

Benvenuto had been to St. Peter's to kiss the feet of the deceased Pontiff, and was returning through the street Dei Banchi, accompanied by Pagolo and Ascanio, when he found himself face to face with Pompeo and his twelve men. At the sight of his enemy, Pompeo became very pale; but as he looked around and saw how amply provided he was with defenders, while Benvenuto had only two boys with him, he took heart of grace, halted, and nodded his head mockingly, while he toyed with the hilt of his dagger with his right hand.

At sight of this group of men by whom his master was threatened, Ascanio put his hand to his sword, while Pagolo pretended to be looking in another direction. But Benvenuto did not choose to expose his beloved pupil to so unequal a conflict. He laid his hand upon Ascanio's, pushing the half-drawn blade back into the scabbard, and walked on as if he had seen nothing, or as if he had taken no offense at what he saw. Ascanio could hardly recognize his master in such guise, but as his master withdrew, he withdrew with him.

Pompeo triumphantly made a deep salutation to Benvenuto, and pursued his way, still surrounded by his sbirri, who imitated his bravado.

Benvenuto bit his lips till the blood came, while externally his features wore a smile. His behavior was inexplicable to anyone who knew the irascible nature of the illustrious goldsmith.

But they had not proceeded a hundred yards when he stopped before the workshop of one of his confreres, and went in, alleging as a pretext his desire to see an antique vase which had recently been found in the Etruscan tombs of Corneto. He bade his pupils go on to the shop, and promised to join them there in a few moments.

As the reader will understand, this was only a pretext to get Ascanio out of the way, for as soon as he thought that the young man and his companion (concerning whom he was less anxious because he was sure that such courage as the latter possessed would not carry him too far), had turned the corner of the street, he replaced the vase upon the shelf from which he had taken it, and darted out of the shop.

With three strides Benvenuto was in the street where he had met Pompeo; but Pompeo was no longer there. Luckily, or rather unluckily, this man, encompassed by his twelve sbirri, was a noticeable object, and so when Benvenuto inquired as to the direction he had taken, the first person to whom he applied was able to give him the information, and like a bloodhound that has recovered a lost scent, Benvenuto started in pursuit.

Pompeo had stopped at a druggist's door, at the corner of the Chiavica, and was vaunting to the worthy compounder of drugs the prowess he had shown in his meeting with Benvenuto Cellini, when his eye suddenly fell upon the latter turning the corner of the street, with fire in his eye, and the perspiration streaming down his forehead.

Benvenuto shouted exultantly as he caught sight of him, and Pompeo stopped short in the middle of his sentence. It was evident that something terrible was about to happen. The bravos formed a group around Pompeo and drew their swords.

It was an insane performance for one man to attack thirteen, but Benvenuto was, as we have said, one of those leonine creatures who do not count their enemies. Against the thirteen swords which threatened him, he drew a small keen-edged dagger which he always wore in his girdle, and rushed into the center of the group, sweeping aside two or three swords with one arm, overturning two or three men with the other, until he made his way to where Pompeo stood, and seized him by the collar. But the group at once closed upon him.

Thereupon naught could be seen save a confused struggling mass, whence issued loud shouts, and above which swords were waving. For a moment the living mass rolled on the ground, in shapeless, inextricable confusion, then a man sprang to his feet with a shout of triumph, and, with a mighty effort, forced his way out of the group as he made his way in, bleeding himself, but triumphantly waving his bloodstained dagger. It was Benvenuto Cellini.

Another man remained upon the pavement, writhing in the agony of death. He had received two blows from the dagger, one below the ear, the other at the base of the neck behind the collar bone. In a few seconds he breathed his last—it was Pompeo.

Any other than Benvenuto, after such a deed, would have taken himself off at full speed, but he passed his dagger to his left hand, drew his sword, and resolutely awaited the sbirri.

But the sbirri had no further business with Benvenuto; he who paid them was dead, and consequently could pay them no more. They ran off like a flock of frightened rabbits, leaving Pompeo's body where it lay.

At that juncture Ascanio appeared, and rushed into his master's arms; he was not deceived by the ruse of the Etruscan vase, but although he had made all possible speed he had arrived a few seconds too late.

Benvenuto returned to his abode with Ascanio, somewhat ill at ease, not because of the three wounds he had received, which were all too slight to occasion him any anxiety, but because of the possible results of the affray. Six months before, he had killed Guasconti, his brother's murderer, but had come off scot free by virtue of the protection of Pope Clement VII; moreover, that act was committed by way of reprisal, but now Benvenuto's old protector had gone the way of all flesh, and the prospect was much more ominous.

Remorse, be it understood, did not disturb him for one moment. But we beg our readers not for that reason to form an unfavorable opinion of our worthy goldsmith, who, after killing a man, after killing two men perhaps—indeed, if we search his past very carefully, after killing three men—although he had a wholesome dread of the police, did not for one instant fear to meet his God.

For this man, in the year of grace 1540, was an ordinary man, an everyday man, as the Germans say. Men thought so little of dying in those days, that they naturally came to think very little of killing. We are brave today, but the men of those days were foolhardy. We are men grown, they were hotheaded youths. Life was so abundant in those days that men lost it, gave it, sold it, nay, even took it, with absolute indifference and recklessness.

There was once an author who was calumniated and abused for many years, whose name was made a synonym for treachery, cruelty, and all the words which mean infamy, and it needed this nineteenth century, the most impartial since the birth of humanity, to rehabilitate that author as the grand patriot and noblehearted man he was. And yet Nicolò Machiavelli's only crime was that he lived at an epoch when brute strength and success were all in all, when folk judged by deeds, not words, and when such men as Cesar Borgia the sovereign, Machiavelli the thinker, and Benvenuto Cellini the artisan, marched straight to their goal, without thought of methods or reasons.

One day a body was found in the public square of Cesena, cut in four pieces; it was the body of Ramiro d'Orco. Now, as Ramiro d'Orco was a considerable personage in Italy, the Florentine Republic sought to ascertain the causes of his death. The Eight of the Signoria therefore wrote to Machiavelli, their ambassador at Cesena, to satisfy their curiosity.

But Machiavelli made no other reply than this:

"Magnificent Signoria: I have naught to say anent the death of Ramiro d'Orco, save this: that no prince in the world is so skillful as Cesar Borgia in the art of making and unmaking men according to their deserts."

MACHIAVELLI.

Benvenuto was an exponent of the theory enunciated by the illustrious secretary of the Florentine Republic. Benvenuto the genius, Cesar Borgia the prince, both considered themselves above the laws by virtue of their power. In their eyes the distinction between what was just and what was unjust was identical with the distinction between what they could and what they could not do. Of right and duty they had not the slightest conception. A man stood in their path, they suppressed the man. Today civilization does him the honor of purchasing him.

But in those old days the blood was boiling so abundantly in the veins of the young nations that they shed it for their health's sake.

They fought by instinct, not for their country to any great extent, not for women, to any great extent, but largely for the sake of fighting, nation against nation, man against man. Benvenuto made war upon Pompeo as François I did upon Charles V. France and Spain fought an intermittent duel, now at Marignano, and again at Pavia; all as if it were the most natural thing in the world, without preamble, without long harangues, without lamentation.

In the same way genius was exercised by those who possessed it as an innate faculty, as an absolute royal power, based upon divine right; art in the sixteenth century was looked upon as the natural birthright of man.

We must not therefore wonder at these men who wondered at nothing. We have, to explain their homicides, their whims, and their faults, an expression which explains and justifies everything in our country, especially in these days of ours:

That was the fashion.

Benvenuto therefore had done nothing but that which was fashionable. Pompeo had annoyed Benvenuto Cellini, and Benvenuto had suppressed Pompeo.

But the police occasionally investigated these acts of suppression; they were very careful not to protect a man when he was alive, but perhaps once in ten times they showed a feeble desire to avenge him when he was dead.

And such a desire they experienced in the matter of Pompeo and Benvenuto Cellini. As the goldsmith, having returned to his shop, was putting certain papers in the fire, and some money in his pocket, he was arrested by the pontifical sbirri, and taken to the castle of San Angelo—an occurrence for which he was almost consoled by the reflection that the castle of San Angelo was where noblemen were imprisoned.

But another thought that was no less efficacious in bringing consolation to Cellini as he entered the castle was this—that a man endowed with so inventive a mind as his need not long delay about leaving it, in one way or another. And so, when he was taken before the governor, who was sitting at a table covered with a green cloth, and looking through a great pile of papers, he said:

"Sir Governor, multiply your locks and bolts and sentinels threefold; confine me in your highest cell or in your deepest dungeon; keep close watch upon me all day, and lie awake all night; and yet I warn you that, despite all that, I will escape."

The governor looked up at the prisoner who addressed him with such unheard-of assurance, and recognized Benvenuto Cellini, whom he had had the honor of entertaining three months before.

Notwithstanding his acquaintance with the man, perhaps because of it, Benvenuto's allocution caused the worthy governor the most profound dismay. He was a Florentine, one Master Georgio, a knight of the Ugolini, and an excellent man, but somewhat weak in the head. However, he soon recovered from his first surprise, and ordered Benvenuto to be taken to the highest cell in the castle. The platform was immediately above it; a sentinel was stationed on the platform and another sentinel at the foot of the wall.

The governor called the prisoner's attention to these details, and when he thought that he had had time to digest them, he said:

"My dear Benvenuto, one may open locks, force doors, dig out from an underground dungeon, make a hole through a wall, bribe sentinels and put jailers to sleep; but without wings one cannot descend to earth from this height."

"I will do it, nevertheless," said Cellini.

The governor looked him in the eye, and began to think that his prisoner was mad.

"Why, in that case, you propose to fly?"

"Why not? I have always believed that man can fly, but I have lacked time to make the experiment. Here I shall have time enough, and, pardieu! I mean to solve the problem. The adventure of Daedalus is history, not fable."

"Beware the sun, dear Benvenuto," sneeringly replied the governor; "beware the sun."

"I will fly away by night," said Benvenuto.

The governor was not expecting that reply, so that he had no suitable repartee at hand, and withdrew in a rage.

In good sooth it was most important that Benvenuto should make his escape, at any price. At another time he would not have been at all perturbed because he had killed a man, and would have been quit of all responsibility by following the procession of the Virgin in August, clad in a doublet and cloak of blue armoisin. But the new Pope, Paul III, was vindictive to the last degree, and when he was still Monsignore Farnese, Benvenuto had had a crow to pluck with him, apropos of a vase which the goldsmith refused to deliver until paid for, and which His Eminence sought to procure by force, the result being to subject Benvenuto to the dire necessity of using His Eminence's retainers somewhat roughly. Moreover, the Holy Father was jealous because King François I had commanded Monseigneur de Montluc, his ambassador to the Holy See, to request that Benvenuto be sent to France.

When he was informed of Benvenuto's imprisonment Monseigneur de Montluc urged the request more strenuously than before, thinking thereby to render the unfortunate prisoner a service; but he was entirely unfamiliar with the character of the new Pope, who was even more obstinate than his predecessor, Clement VII. Now Paul III had sworn that Benvenuto should pay dearly for his escapade, and if he was not precisely in danger of death—a pope would have thought twice in those days before ordering such an artist to the gallows— he was in great danger of being forgotten in his prison. It was therefore of the utmost importance that Benvenuto should not forget himself, and that was why he was determined to take flight without awaiting the interrogatories and judgment, which might never have arrived; for the Pope, angered by the intervention of François I, refused even to hear Benvenuto Cellini's name mentioned.

The prisoner knew all this from Ascanio, who was managing his establishment, and who, by dint of persistent entreaties, had obtained permission to visit his master. Their interviews, of course, were held through two iron gratings, and in presence of witnesses watching to see that the pupil passed neither file, nor rope, nor knife to his master.

As soon as the door of his cell was locked behind the governor, Benvenuto set about inspecting his surroundings.

The following articles were contained within the four walls of his new abiding place: a bed, a fireplace, a table, and two chairs. Two days after his installation there, he obtained a supply of clay and a modeling tool. The governor at first declined to allow him to have these means of distraction, but he changed his mind upon reflecting that, if the artist's mind were thus employed, he might perhaps abandon the idea of escape, to which he clung so tenaciously. The same day, Benvenuto sketched a colossal Venus.

All this of itself was no great matter; but in conjunction with imagination, patience, and energy, it was much.

On a certain very cold day in December, when the fire was lighted on the hearth, the servant changed the sheets on his bed and left the soiled ones upon a chair. As soon as the door was closed, Benvenuto made one bound from the chair on which he was sitting to the bed, took out of the mattress two enormous handfuls of the maize leaves which are used to stuff mattresses in Italy, stowed the sheets away in their place, returned to his statue, took up his tool, and resumed his work. At that moment the servant returned for the forgotten sheets, and, after looking everywhere for them, asked Benvenuto if he had not seen them. But he replied carelessly, as if absorbed by his work, that some of his fellows doubtless had taken them, or that he carried them away himself without knowing it. The servant had no suspicion of the truth, so little time had elapsed since he left the room, and Benvenuto played his part so naturally; and as the sheets were never found, he was very careful to say nothing for fear of being obliged to pay for them or of losing his employment.

One who has never lived through some supreme crisis can form no idea of the possibilities of such a time in the way of terrible catastrophes and poignant anguish. The most trivial accidents of life arouse in us joy or despair. As soon as the servant left the room, Benvenuto fell upon his knees, and thanked God for the help He had sent him.

As his bed was never touched until the next morning after it was once made, he quietly left the sheets in the mattress.

When the night came he began to cut the sheets, which luckily were new and strong, in strips three or four inches wide, then tied them together as securely as he could; lastly, he cut open his statue, which was of clay, hollowed it out, placed his treasure in the cavity, then spread clay over the wound and smoothed it off with his finger and his modeling tool, until the most skillful artist could not have discovered that poor Venus had been made to undergo an operation known as the Caesarean.

The next morning the governor entered the prisoner's cell unexpectedly, as he was accustomed to do, but found him as usual calm and hard at work. Every morning the poor man, who had been specially threatened for the night, trembled lest he should find the cell empty; and it should be said, in justice to his frankness, that he did not conceal his joy every morning when he found it occupied.

"I confess that you make me terribly anxious, Benvenuto," said the poor man; "however, I begin to think that your threats of escape amount to nothing."

"I didn't threaten you, Master Georgio," rejoined Benvenuto, "I warned you."

"Do you still hope to fly away?"

"I'm not hoping," Benvenuto explained, "I'm informing you."

"Demonio! how will you do it?" cried the poor governor, dismayed beyond measure by Benvenuto's real or pretended confidence in his means of escape.

"That's my secret, master. But I give you fair warning that my wings are growing."

The governor instinctively turned his eye upon the prisoner's shoulders.

"'Tis thus," continued Benvenuto, working away at his statue, and rounding the hips in such fashion that one would have thought he proposed to rival the Venus Callipyge. "Betwixt us there is a duel. You have on your side enormous towers, thick doors, strong bolts, innumerable keepers always on the alert; I have on my side my brain and these poor hands, and I warn you very frankly that you will be beaten. But as you are a very clever man, as you have taken every possible precaution, you will at least, when I am gone, have the consolation of knowing that it is through no fault of yours, Master Georgio, that you have no occasion to reproach yourself at all, Master Georgio, and that you neglected nothing that could help you to detain me, Master Georgio. And now what do you say to this hip, for you are a lover of art, I know."

Such unblushing assurance enraged the unhappy official. His prisoner had become his idée fixe, upon which all his faculties were centered. He grew melancholy, lost his appetite, and started constantly, like one suddenly aroused from sleep. One night Benvenuto heard a great noise upon the platform; then it was transferred to his corridor, and finally stopped at his door. The door opened, and he saw Master Georgio, in dressing gown and nightcap, attended by four jailers and eight guards. The governor rushed to his bedside with distorted features. Benvenuto sat up in bed and laughed in his face. The governor, without taking offense at his hilarity, breathed like a diver returning to the surface.

"Ah! God be praised!" he cried; "he is still here! There's much good sense in the saying, *songe—mensonge* (dream—lie)."

"In God's name, what's the matter?" demanded Benvenuto, "and what happy circumstance affords me the pleasure of a visit from you at such an hour, Master Georgio?"

"*Jésus Dieu!* it's nothing at all, and I am quit of it this time for the fright. Did I not dream that your accursed wings had grown— huge wings, whereon you tranquilly hovered above the castle of San Angelo, saying: 'Adieu, my dear governor, adieu! I did not wish to go away without taking leave of you. I go; I pray that I may be so blessed as never to see you more.'"

"What! did I say that to you, Master Georgio?"

"Those were your very words. Ah, Benvenuto, you are a sorry guest for me!"

"Oh! I trust that you do not deem me so ill-bred as that. Happily it was but a dream; for otherwise I would not forgive you."

"Happily it is not true. I hold you fast, my dear friend, and although truth compels me to say that your society is not the most agreeable to me, I hope to hold you for a long time yet to come."

"I do not think it," retorted Benvenuto, with the confident smile which caused his host to use strong language.

The governor went out, cursing Benvenuto roundly, and the next morning he issued orders that his cell should be inspected every two hours, night and day. This rigid inspection was continued for a month; but at the end of that time, as there was no apparent reason to believe that Benvenuto was even thinking of escape, the vigilance of his keepers was somewhat relaxed.

Benvenuto, however, had employed the month in accomplishing a terrible task.

As we have said, he minutely examined his cell immediately after he was first consigned to it, and from that moment his mind was made up as to the manner of his escape. His window was barred, and the bars were too strong to be removed with the hand or with his modeling tool, the only iron instrument he possessed. The chimney narrowed so toward the top that the prisoner must needs have had the fairy Melusina's power of transforming herself into a serpent to pass through it.

The door remained. Ah, the door! Let us see how the door was made.

It was a heavy oaken door two fingers thick, secured by two locks and four bolts, and sheathed on the inside with iron plates kept in place by nails at the top and bottom. It was through that door that the escape must be effected.

Benvenuto had noticed in the corridor, a few steps from the door, the stairway leading to the platform. At intervals of two hours he heard the footsteps of the relieving sentinel going up, then the steps of the other coming down; after which he would hear nothing more for another two hours.

The question for him to solve, then, was simply this: how to reach the other side of that door, which was secured by two locks and four bolts, and furthermore sheathed on the inside with iron plates kept in place by nails at the top and bottom. The solution of this problem was the task to which Benvenuto had devoted the month in question.

With his modeling tool, which was of iron, he removed, one by one, the heads of all the nails, save four above and four below, which he left until the last day: then, in order that his work might not be detected, he replaced the missing heads with exactly similar ones, modeled in clay and covered with iron filings, so that it was impossible for the keenest eye to distinguish the false from the true. As there were, at top and bottom together, some sixty nails, and as it took at least one hour, and sometimes two, to decapitate each nail, the magnitude of the task may be understood.

Every evening, when everybody had retired, and nothing could be heard save the footsteps of the sentinel walking back and forth overhead, he built a great fire on the hearth, and piled glowing embers against the iron plates on his door; the iron became red hot, and gradually transformed to charcoal the wood upon which it was applied; but no indication of the carbonizing process appeared on the other side of the door.

For a whole month Benvenuto devoted himself to this task, as we have said; but at the end of the month it was finished, and he only awaited a favorable opportunity to make his escape. He was compelled, however, to wait a few days, for the moon was near the full when the work was done.

There was nothing more to be done to the nails, so Benvenuto continued to char the door, and drive the governor to desperation. That every day the functionary entered his cell more preoccupied than ever.

"My dear prisoner," said the worthy man, whose mind constantly recurred to his fixed idea, "do you still propose to fly away? Come, tell me frankly."

"More than ever, my dear host," replied Benvenuto.

"Look you," said the governor, "you may say what you choose, but upon my word, I believe it's impossible."

"Impossible, Master Georgio, impossible!" rejoined the artist; "why, you know full well that that word does not exist for me, who have always exerted myself to do those things which are the most impossible for other men, and that with success. Impossible, my dear host! Why, have I not sometimes amused myself by making nature jealous, by fashioning with gold and emeralds and diamonds a flower fairer far than all the flowers that the dew empearls? Think you that he who can make flowers can not make wings?"

"May God help me!" said the governor; "with your insolent assurance you'll make me lose my wits! But tell me, in order that these wings may sustain your weight in the air—a thing which seems impossible to me, I confess—what form shall you give them?"

"I have thought deeply thereupon, as you may well imagine, since my safety depends entirely upon the shape of my wings."

"With what result?"

"After examining all flying things, I have concluded that, if I wish to reproduce by art what they have received from God, I can copy the bat most successfully."

"But when all is said, Benvenuto," continued the governor, "even if you had the materials with which to make a pair of wings, would not your courage fail you when the time came to use them?"

"Give me what I need for their construction, my dear governor, and I'll reply by flying away."

"What do you need, in God's name?"

"Oh! mon Dieu! almost nothing; a little forge, an anvil, files, tongs, and pincers to make the springs, and twenty yards of oiled silk for the membranes."

"Good! very good!" said Master Georgio; "that reassures me somewhat, for, clever as you may be, you never will succeed in obtaining all those things here."

" 'Tis done already," rejoined Benvenuto.

The governor leaped from his chair; but he instantly reflected that it was a material impossibility. And yet, for all that, his poor brain had not a moment's respite. Every bird that flew by his window he imagined to be Benvenuto Cellini, so great is the influence of a master mind over one of moderate capacity.

The same day, Master Georgio sent for the most skillful machinist in all Rome, and ordered him to measure him for a pair of bat's wings.

The machinist stared at the governor in blank amazement, without replying, thinking, with some reason, that Master Georgio had gone mad.

But as Master Georgio insisted, as Master Georgio was wealthy, and as Master Georgio had the wherewithal to pay for insane freaks, if he chose to indulge in them, the machinist set about the task, and a week later brought him a pair of magnificent wings fitted to an iron waist to be worn upon the body and worked by means of an extremely ingenious arrangement of springs, with most encouraging regularity.

Master Georgio paid his man the stipulated price, measured the space required to accommodate the apparatus, went up to Benvenuto's cell, and without a word overturned everything therein, looking under the bed, peering up the chimney, fumbling in the mattress, and leaving not the smallest corner unvisited.

Then he went out, still without speaking, convinced that, unless Benvenuto was a sorcerer, no pair of wings similar to his own could be hidden in his cell.

It was clear that the unhappy governor's brain was becoming more and more disordered.

Upon descending to his own quarters, Master Georgio found the machinist waiting for him; he had returned to call his attention to the fact that there was an iron ring at the end of each wing, intended to support the legs of a man flying in a horizontal position.

The machinist had no sooner left him than Master Georgio locked himself in, donned the iron waist, unfolded his wings, hung up his legs, and, lying flat upon his stomach, made his first attempt at flying.

But, try as he would, he could not succeed in rising above the floor.

After two or three trials, always with the same result, he sent for the mechanic once more.

"Master," said he, "I have tried your wings, but they won't work."

"How did you try them?"

Master Georgio described his repeated experiments in detail. The mechanic listened with a sober face, and said, when he had concluded:

"I am not surprised; as you lay on the floor, you hadn't a sufficient quantity of air under your wings. You must go to the top of the castle of San Angelo, and boldly launch yourself into space."

"And you think that in that way I can fly?"

"I am sure of it."

"If you are so sure of it, would it not be as well to make the experiment yourself?"

"The wings are proportioned to the weight of your body and not of mine," replied the machinist. "Wings to carry my weight would need to measure a foot and a half more from tip to tip."

And with that he bowed and took his leave.

"The devil!" exclaimed Master Georgio.

Throughout the day Master Georgio indulged in various vagaries, which tended to prove that his reason, like Roland's, was penetrating farther and farther into imaginary realms.

In the evening, just at bedtime, he summoned all the servants, all the jailers, all the guards.

"If," said he, "you learn that Benvenuto Cellini is intending to fly away, let him go, and notify me, nothing more; for I shall know where to go to capture him, even in the dark, since I am myself a veritable bat, while he whatever he may say, is only a false bat."

The poor governor was quite mad; but as they hoped that a night's rest would have a soothing effect upon him, they decided to wait until morning before advising the Pope.

Moreover it was an abominable night, dark and rainy, and no one cared to go out in such weather; always excepting Benvenuto Cellini, who had selected that very night for his escape, doubtless in a spirit of contrariety.

And so, as soon as he heard the clock strike ten, and the footsteps indicating that the sentinel had been relieved, he fell on his knees and offered a fervent prayer, after which he set to work.

In the first place he removed the heads of the four nails, which alone held the iron plates in place. The last yielded to his efforts just at midnight.

He heard the steps of the sentinel going up to the platform; he stood with his ear glued to the door, without breathing, until the relieved sentinel came down, the steps died away in the distance, and silence reigned once more.

The rain fell with redoubled force, and Benvenuto's heart leaped for joy as he heard it beating against the window.

He at once tried to remove the iron plates; as there was nothing to hold them, they yielded to his efforts, and he placed them, one by one, against the wall.

He then lay flat upon the floor, and attacked the bottom of the door with his modeling tool, sharpened like a dagger, and fitted to a wooden handle. The oak was entirely changed to carbon, and give way at the first touch.

In an instant Benvenuto had made an aperture at the bottom of the door sufficiently large to allow him to crawl through it. He reopened the belly of his statue, took out the strips of line, coiled them around his waist like a girdle, armed himself with his modeling tool, of which he had, as we have said, made a dagger, and fell on his knees once more and prayed.

Then he passed his head through the hole, then his shoulders, then the rest of his body, and found himself in the corridor.

He stood erect; but his legs trembled so that he was compelled to lean against the wall for support. His heart was beating as if it would burst, and his head was on fire. A drop of perspiration trembled at the end of each hair, and he clutched the handle of his dagger in his hand, as if someone were trying to tear it away from him.

However, as everything was quiet, as nothing was stirring and not a sound was to be heard, Benvenuto soon recovered himself, and felt his way along the wall of the corridor with his hand, until the wall came to an end. Then he put out his foot and felt the first step of the staircase, or, more properly speaking, the ladder, which led to the platform.

He mounted the rungs, one by one, shivering as the wood creaked under his feet, until he felt a breath of air; then the rain beat against his face as his head rose above the level of the platform, and as he had been in most intense darkness for a quarter of an hour, he was able to judge at once what reason he had to fear or hope.

The balance seemed to incline toward hope.

The sentinel had taken refuge from the storm in his sentry box. Now, as the sentinels who mounted guard upon the castle of San Angelo were stationed there, not to inspect the platform, but to look down into the moat and survey the surrounding country, the closed side of the sentry box faced the top of the ladder by which Benvenuto ascended.

The artist crept cautiously on his hands and knees toward that part of the platform which was farthest removed from the sentry box. There he securely fastened one end of his improvised rope to a jutting projection some six inches in length, and then knelt for the third time.

"Oh Lord!" he muttered, "O Lord! do Thou help me, since I am seeking to help myself."

With that prayer upon his lips, he let himself down by his hands, heedless of the bruises upon his knees and his forehead, which, from time to time, rubbed against the face of the wall, and at last reached the solid earth.

When he felt the ground beneath his feet, his breast swelled with an infinitude of joy and pride. He contemplated the immense height from which he had descended, and could not avoid saying in an undertone: "Free at last!" But his joy was short-lived.

As he turned away from the tower, his knees trembled under him; directly in front of him rose a wall recently built, and of which he knew nothing; he was lost.

Everything seemed to give way within him, and in his despair he fell to the ground; but as he fell, his foot struck against something hard—it was a long beam; he gave a slight exclamation of surprise and delight; he was saved.

Ah! no one knows what heart-rending alternations of joy and hope one short minute of life can contain.

Benvenuto seized the beam as a shipwrecked sailor seizes the spar which may save him from drowning. Under ordinary circumstances two strong men would have found difficulty in lifting it; he dragged it to the wall, and stood it on end against it. Then he climbed to the top of the wall, clinging to the beam with his hands and knees, but when he arrived there his strength was insufficient to raise the beam and lower it on the other side.

For a moment his head swam; he closed his eyes, and it seemed as if he were struggling in a lake of flames.

Suddenly he remembered his strips of linen, by means of which he had descended from the platform.

He slid down the beam to the ground once more, and ran to the spot where he had left them hanging; but he had fastened them so securely at the opposite end that he could not detach them. In his desperation he raised himself from the ground by hanging to them, pulling with all his strength, and hoping to break them. Fortunately one of the knots slipped at last, and Benvenuto fell to the ground, grasping a fragment some twelve feet long.

This was all that he needed; he rose with a bound, and, filled with fresh vigor, climbed up to the top of the wall once more, fastened the cord to the end of the beam, and slid down on the other side.

When he reached the end of the cord he felt in vain for the ground with his feet, and, upon looking over his shoulder, saw that it was still some six feet away. He let go the cord, and dropped.

He lay still for an instant; he was completely exhausted, and there was no skin left on his legs and hands. For some moments he gazed stupidly at his bleeding flesh; but five o'clock struck, and he saw that the stars were beginning to pale.

He rose; but as he rose, a sentinel whom he had not noticed, but who had undoubtedly witnessed his performance, walked toward him. Benvenuto saw that he was lost, and that he must either kill or be killed. He drew his modeling tool from his belt, and marched straight toward the guard, with such a determined expression that that worthy doubtless realized that he had not only a powerful man, but a deathly despair, to contend with. Benvenuto was determined not to give ground, but suddenly the soldier turned his back upon him as if he had not seen him. The prisoner understood what that meant.

He ran to the last rampart, and found himself some twelve or fifteen feet above the moat. Such a trifle was not likely to stop a man like Benvenuto Cellini, in his present predicament, when he had left part of his cord hanging from the top of the tower, and the other part attached to the beam, so that he had nothing left with which to lower himself, and there was no time to lose.

He hung by his hands from a ring in the masonry, and, with a mental prayer, let himself drop.

This time he fainted outright.

An hour passed before he came to himself; but the coolness, which is always noticeable in the air as dawn approaches, revived him. He lay for an instant with his mind in confusion, then passed his hand over his forehead and remembered everything.

He felt a sharp pain in his head, and saw blood upon the stones where he lay, which had trickled down from his face. He put his hand to his forehead a second time, not to collect his thoughts, but to investigate his wounds, which he found were but skin deep. He smiled and tried to stand up, but fell heavily back; his right leg was broken three inches above the ankle. The leg was so benumbed that at first he felt no pain.

He at once removed his shirt and tore it into strips, then put the ends of the bone together as well as he could, and applied the bandage, binding it with all his strength, and passing it under the sole of his foot now and then in order to keep the bones in place.

Then he dragged himself on all fours toward one of the city gates which was within five hundred yards. After half an hour of atrocious suffering, he reached the gate only to find that it was closed. But he noticed a large stone under the gate, which yielded to his first attempt to remove it, and he passed through the hole left by it.

He had not taken twenty steps beyond the gate when he was attacked by a pack of famished dogs, who were attracted by the odor of blood. He drew his modeling tool, and dispatched the largest and most savage with a blow in the side. The others immediately threw themselves upon their defunct comrade and devoured him.

Benvenuto dragged himself along to the church of La Transpontina where he fell in with a water carrier who had just filled his jars and loaded his donkey. He called him.

"Look you," he said; "I was with my mistress; circumstances compelled me, although I went in at the door, to come out through the window. I leaped from the first floor, and broke my leg; carry me to the steps of Saint Peter's, and I will give you a golden crown."

The water carrier, without a word, took the wounded man on his shoulder, and carried him to the designated spot. Having received his pay, he went his way without so much as looking behind.

Thereupon Benvenuto, still on all fours, made his way to the palace of Monseigneur de Montluc, the French ambassador, who lived only a few steps away.

Monseigneur de Montluc exerted himself so zealously in his behalf that at the end of a month Benvenuto was cured, at the end of two months he was pardoned, and at the end of four months he started for France with Ascanio and Pagolo.

The poor governor, who had gone mad, lived and died a madman, constantly imagining that he was a bat, and making the most violent efforts to fly.

Chapter XI

TO MEET THE DOOM

Dumas was right in becoming incensed when people cavalierly assumed that as a writer of fiction he had no need either for the research or the intelligence expected of writers of nonfiction. For this not only insulted him, as author, but also insulted his readers, dismissing them—merely because they enjoyed novels—as people of no brains, satisfied with any kind of trash.

It was only jokingly that he sometimes referred to himself as "Dumas the ignorant" because France at that time boasted of a savant of the same name, J-B. Dumas, whose *Chemistry in Art and Industry* is one of the major contributions of the nineteenth century to that science.

The following two selections have been chosen because they illustrate a keenness of mind that deserves respect. The first is a sly treatment of the subject of ghosts, and the second a flaming exposition of the human forces in the French revolution. In both cases the subject is argued in dialogue which gives it both vivacity and drama.

Today this method of exposition is scorned. But Socrates (or rather Plato) used that method for expounding his philosophy, and Galileo thought it fit for presenting his great scientific discoveries.

Here is the first selection, taken from *The Companions of Jehu*, a book from which we have already quoted the introduction, showing Dumas carrying on research for his novel. And the second is another passage from *The Countess de Charny*.

"I own a place in England," Sir John said, "where ghosts come occasionally for a visit."

"Did you ever see them, my lord?"

"Yes, when I was a little fellow; unfortunately, by the time I had grown up the ghosts had disappeared."

"That's the way with ghosts," said Roland, gayly; "they come and go. Was I not fortunate to get home just as there were ghosts to be seen in the monastery of Seillon?"

"Yes," said Sir John, "it was very fortunate; but are you sure they were real ghosts?"

"No; but by the day after tomorrow I shall know what to think."

"What do you mean?"

"I intend to pass tomorrow night there."

"And you will allow me to accompany you?"

"I should be very glad to have you, my lord; but unfortunately it will be impossible."

"Impossible? Why?"

"Are you acquainted with the peculiarities of ghosts, my lord?" asked Roland, gravely.

"No."

"Well, I am. Ghosts will not show themselves except under certain conditions."

"What are those conditions?"

"Well, for example, in Italy and Spain, which are essentially superstitious countries, they don't have a ghost once in ten, twenty, a hundred years."

"And how do you account for the absence of ghosts among them?"

"I attribute it to the lack of fogs, my lord."

"Ah!"

"Not a doubt of it. You see the atmosphere of ghosts is fog. In Scotland, Denmark, and England, countries that are always foggy, they are surfeited with ghosts. There is the ghost of Hamlet's father, the ghost of Banquo, the ghosts of the victims of Richard III. In Italy they have only one ghost, that of Caesar; and where did he appear to Brutus? At Philippi in Macedonia, and in Thrace, which is the Denmark of Greece, the Scotland of the Orient, where the fog made Ovid so melancholy that he entitled his very verses 'Tristes.' Why did Virgil make the ghost of Anchises appear to Aeneas? Because Virgil was from Mantua. Do you know Mantua?—a country of marshes, a regular fen, a manufactory of rheumatism, an atmosphere of vapors—consequently a hotbed for ghosts."

"Go on, I am listening."

"Have you seen the borders of the Rhine?"

"Yes."

"In Germany, is it not?"

"Yes."

"There's another country that's right for fairies, undines, sylphs, and consequently ghosts, and every bit of it caused by fogs. But in Italy or Spain, where would the ghosts take refuge? There is not the least little bit of fog there. And therefore if I were in Spain or Italy, I should not even attempt tomorrow night's adventure."

"But all this does not explain why you refuse my company," insisted Sir John.

"Wait; I have explained to you why ghosts do not venture into certain countries, for want of certain atmospheric conditions; now let me explain what must be done, if one would see them."

"Explain! explain!" said Sir John. "I would rather hear you talk than anyone I know."

Sir John stretched himself out on a sofa, and prepared to enjoy the improvisations of the fantastic mind which he had already seen under so many aspects during the last few days.

Roland bowed his thanks. "Well, I will tell you. I have heard so much about ghosts in my life that I know the rogues as well as if I had made them. Why do ghosts show themselves?"

"Do you ask me that?" said Sir John.

"Yes, I ask you."

"I must confess that, not having made a study of ghosts like yourself, I am not in a position to give you a positive answer."

"My dear lord, ghosts show themselves for the purpose of frightening the people to whom they appear."

"Not a doubt of it."

"And if they do not frighten those to whom they appear, they are frightened by them. There is Monsieur de Turenne, for example, whose ghosts turned out to be impostors. Did you ever hear that story?"

"No."

"I will tell you it some day; we will not bother with it now. That is the reason that when they do make up their minds to appear, which is very seldom, they choose stormy nights, with thunder, lightning, and wind; that is their stage setting."

"You certainly must be right."

"Wait; there are moments when the bravest will feel cold shivers. Before I had an aneurism, I felt them myself, many times, when I saw the flash of sabers over my head, and heard in my ears the thunder of cannon. To be sure, since I have had this aneurism I have sought the flash of steel and the roar of cannon; but there is a chance that the ghosts may not know this fact, and that they may think I will be afraid of them."

"But it is impossible that you should be, is it not?" said Sir John.

"How can it be otherwise? When instead of fearing death a man believes, whether right or wrong, that he has a reason for seeking it, there is no occasion for him to be afraid; but as I have said, it is possible that the ghosts, although they certainly must know a great deal, do not happen to know this. But there is one thing that they must know; and that is, that external objects have a great deal to do with augmenting or diminishing fear. For example, where do ghosts prefer to appear? Why, in out-of-the-way places, in cemeteries, in old cloisters, in ruins, in subterranean passages, because the very sight of these localities predisposes the mind to fear. And by what is their appearance heralded? By the rattling of chains, by groanings, by sighs, because there is nothing cheerful about all this. They take good care never to appear in the midst of a brilliant light, nor after dance music. No, fear is an abyss to which a man descends step by step, until vertigo seizes him, his foot slips, and he falls with closed eyes to the foot of the precipice.

"Read the history of all ghosts, and you will see how they proceed: at first the sky is obscured, the thunder rolls, the wind howls, the doors and windows creak, and the lamp, if there be one, flickers, pales, and dies. Complete obscurity! in the midst of which comes the sound of wails, groans, and clanking chains. Finally the door opens and the ghost appears. All the apparitions that I have read about have been produced under similar circumstances. Am I not right, Sir John?"

"Perfectly."

"And did you ever know a ghost to appear to two persons at once?"

"I don't believe I ever read or heard of such a thing."

"There is a very simple reason for it, my lord: when two persons are together, they are not afraid of anything. Fear is a strange thing independent of the will, and needing isolation, shadows, and solitude. A ghost is not as dangerous as a cannon ball; and yet a soldier is not afraid of a cannon ball in daylight, when he has the companionship of his comrades, and can touch elbows with them; he marches straight at the piece, and is either killed or he kills. But that is not what the ghosts want; that is why they never appear to two persons at once. That is why I must go alone to the monastery, my lord; your presence would prevent the most determined ghost from appearing. If I see nothing, or if I see anything that will pay me for my trouble, you shall have your turn tomorrow. Will that suit you?"

And here is the much more serious bit of dialogue from *The Countess de Charny*.

"Today," said the count, continuing to address the queen with intrepidity, "I have decided to give up my post at the Tuileries, and take up one at Versailles. In so doing I violate my orders, but I trust I am not thereby displeasing my queen in selecting service where I shall be able to defend her. So here I am, even though Madame de Charny may be alarmed by the bloody events now taking place, and may choose to emigrate. But I intend to stay here, that is unless the queen decides to break my sword for violating my duties as an officer in the royal army. In that case, I would no longer have the right to fight and die for her in her palace at Versailles, but I could not be denied the right to sacrifice my life outside, on the pavement just outside her threshold."

The young man pronounced these simple words so valiantly and so loyally, and they emanated so evidently from the depths of his heart, that the queen appeared suddenly to lose her usual haughtiness, a retreat behind which she had up to that moment been able to conceal feelings that were more human than royal.

"Count," said the queen, "never utter that word again. Do not say that you would die for me, for in truth I know that you would do as you say."

"Oh, on the contrary, I shall always say it!" exclaimed Monsieur de Charny. "I shall say it to everyone, and in every place. I shall say it and I shall do it, because the time has come, I fear, when all who have been attached to the kings of this earth must die."

"Count! Count!—what is it gives you this fatal forewarning?"

"Alas! Madame," replied De Charny, shaking his head, "I too, during the fatal American war, I too was affected like the rest with that fever of independence which pervaded all society. I too wished to take an active part in the emancipation of the slaves, as it was customary to say in those days; I too was initiated into the secrets of masonry. I became affiliated with a secret society, along with the Lafayettes and the Lameths. Do you know what the object of this society was, madame? The destruction of thrones. Do you know what it had for its motto? Three letters—L.P.D."

"And what did these letters signify?"

"*Lilia pedibus destrue!*—Trample the lilies underfoot!"

"You knew that?"

"I withdrew with honor. But for everyone who withdrew from the society, there were twenty who applied to be admitted into it. Well, then, what is happening today, madame, is the prologue to the grand drama which has been preparing in silence and in darkness for twenty years. At the head of the men who are stimulating Paris to resistance, who govern the Hôtel de Ville, who occupy the Palais-Royal, and who took the Bastille, I recognized the countenances of my former affiliated brethren. Do not deceive yourself, madame; all the events which have just taken place are not the results of chance; they are outbreaks which had been planned for years."

"Oh, you think so!—you really think so, my friend!" exclaimed the queen, bursting into tears.

"Do not weep, madame, but endeavor to comprehend the present crisis," said the count.

"You wish me to comprehend it!" continued Marie Antoinette. "I, the queen—I, who was born the sovereign of twenty-five million men—you wish me to understand how these twenty-five million subjects, born to obey me, should revolt and murder my friends! No—that I shall never comprehend."

"And yet it is absolutely necessary for you to understand it, madame; for the moment this obedience becomes a burden to these subjects, to these men born to obey you, you become their enemy;

and until they have the strength to devour you, until they have sharpened their famished teeth, they will devour your friends, still more detested than you are."

"And perhaps you will next tell me that they are right, most sage philosopher," exclaimed the queen, imperiously her eyes dilated, and her nostrils quivering with anger.

"Alas! yes, madame, they are right," said the count in his gentle and affectionate voice; "for when I drive along the boulevards, with my beautiful English horses, my coat glittering with gold, and my attendants bedecked with more silver than would be necessary to feed three families, your people, that is to say, those twenty-five million starving men, ask themselves of what use I am to them—I, who am only a man like themselves."

"You serve them with this, Marquis," exclaimed the queen, seizing the hilt of the count's sword; "you serve them with the sword that your father wielded so heroically at Fontenoy, your grandfather at Steinkirk, your great-grandfather at Lens and at Rocroi, your ancestors at Ivry, at Marignan, and at Agincourt. The nobility serves the French nation by waging war. By war, the nobility has earned, at the price of its blood, the gold which decks its garments, the silver which covers its liveries. Do not, therefore, ask yourself, Olivier, how you serve the people, you who wield in your turn, and bravely too, the sword which has descended to you from your forefathers."

"Madame!—madame!" said the count, shaking his head, "do not speak so much of the blood of the nobility; the people, too, have blood in their veins; go and see it running in streams on the Place de la Bastille; go and count their dead, stretched out on the crimsoned pavement, and consider that their hearts, which now no longer beat, throbbed with a feeling as noble as that of a knight on the day when your cannon were thundering against them; on the day when, seizing a new weapon in their unskillful hands, they sang in the midst of grapeshot—a thing which even our bravest grenadiers can not always do. Ah! madame, my sovereign, do not look on me, I entreat you, with that frowning eye. What is a grenadier? It is a gilt blue coat, covering the heart of which I was speaking to you a moment since. Of what importance is it to the bullet which pierces and kills, that the heart be covered with blue cloth or with a linen rag? Of what importance is it to the heart which is pierced through, whether the cuirass which protected it was cloth or canvas? The time is come to think of all that, madame. You have no longer twenty-five million slaves in France; you have no longer twenty-five million subjects; you have no longer even twenty-five million men. You have twenty-five million soldiers."

"Who will fight against me, Count?"

"Yes, against you; for they are fighting for liberty, and you stand between them and liberty."

A long silence followed the words of the count. The queen was the first to break it.

"In fine," said she, "you have told me this truth, which I had begged you not to tell me."

"Alas! Madame," replied De Charny, "under whatever form my devotion may conceal it, under whatever veil my respect disguises it, in spite of me, in spite of yourself, examine it, listen to it, think of it. The truth is there, madame, is there forever, and you can no longer banish it from your mind, whatever may be your efforts to the contrary. Sleep!—sleep, to forget it, and it will haunt your pillow; it will become the phantom of your dreams, and a reality at your awakening."

"Oh, Count," said the queen, proudly, "I know a sleep which it cannot disturb!"

"As for that sleep, madame, I fear it no more than does Your Majesty, and perhaps I desire it quite as much."

"Oh," exclaimed the queen, in despair, "according to you, it is, then, our sole refuge?"

"Yes; but let us do nothing rashly, madame. Let us go no faster than our enemies, and we shall go straight to that sleep by the fatigue which we shall have to endure during so many stormy days."

And a new silence, still more gloomy than the first, weighed down the spirits of the two speakers.

They were seated, he near her, and she near him. They touched each other, and yet between them there was an immense abyss, for their minds viewed the future in a different light.

"Most assuredly, Count, you make matters more than sufficiently gloomy. A successful riot—do you call that the downfall of the monarchy? What! Is it because the Bastille has been taken, Monsieur de Charny, that you say the monarchy is abolished? Have you not reflected that the Bastille was founded in France only in the fourteenth century, while monarchy has been taking root in the world during the last six thousand years."

I should be well pleased to deceive myself in this matter, madame," replied the count; "and then, instead of afflicting Your Majesty's mind, I should bring to you the most consoling news. Unfortunately, the instrument will not produce any other wounds but those for which it was intended."

"Let us see, let us see. So it is I who must sustain you—I who am but a woman. It is I who must put you on the right path."

"Alas! I ask for nothing better."

"The Parisians have revolted, have they not?"

"Yes."

"In what proportion?"

"In the proportion of twelve to fifteen."

"How do you arrive at this calculation?"

"Oh, very easily: the people form twelve-fifteenths of the body of the nation; there remain two-fifteenths for the nobility and one for the clergy."

"Your calculations are exact, Count, and you have them at your fingers' ends. Have you read the works of Monsieur and Madame de Necker?"

"Those of Monsieur de Necker? Yes, madame."

"Well, the proverb holds good," said the queen, gayly: "we are never betrayed but by our own friends. Well, then, here is my own calculation; will you listen to it?"

"With all respect."

"Among these twelve-fifteenths there are six of women, are there not?"

"Yes, Your Majesty. But—"

"Do not interrupt me. We said there were six-fifteenths of women, so let us say six; two of indifferent or incapable old men—is that too much?"

"No."

"There still remain four-fifteenths, of which you will allow that at least two are cowards or lukewarm individuals—I flatter the French nation. But finally, there remain two-fifteenths; I will grant you that they are furious, robust, brave, and warlike. These two-fifteenths, let us consider them as belonging to Paris only, for it is needless to speak of the provinces, is it not? It is only Paris that requires to be retaken?"

"Yes, madame. But—"

"Always but; wait a moment. You can reply when I have concluded."

Monsieur de Charny bowed.

"I therefore estimate," continued the queen, "the two-fifteenths of Paris at one hundred thousand men; is that sufficient?"

This time the count did not answer. The queen rejoined:

"Well, then! to these hundred thousand men, badly armed, badly disciplined, and but little accustomed to battle, hesitating because they know they are doing wrong, I can oppose fifty thousand men, known throughout Europe for their bravery, commanded by officers like you, Monsieur de Charny. And furthermore that sacred cause which is denominated divine right! And in addition to all this, my own firm soul, which it is easy to move, but difficult to break."

The count still remained silent.

"Do you think," continued the queen, "that in a battle fought in such a cause, two men of the people are worth more than one of my soldiers?"

Charny said nothing.

"Speak—answer me!— Do you think so?" exclaimed the queen, growing impatient.

"Madame," answered the count at last, throwing aside, on this order from the queen, the respectful reserve which he had so long maintained, "on a field of battle, where these hundred thousand men would be isolated, undisciplined and badly armed as they are, your fifty thousand soldiers would defeat them in half an hour."

"Ah!" said the queen, "I was then right."

"Wait a moment. But it is not as you imagine. And, in the first place, your hundred thousand insurgents in Paris are five hundred thousand."

"Five hundred thousand?"

"Quite as many. You had omitted the women and children in your calculation! Oh, Queen of France, proud and courageous woman! Consider them as so many men, these women of Paris! Or the day may come when they will compel you to consider them as so many demons."

"What can you mean, Count?"

"Madame, do you know what part a woman plays in a civil war? No, you do not. Well, I will tell you; and you will see that two soldiers against each woman would not be too many."

"Count, have you lost your senses?"

Charny smiled sadly.

"Did you see them at the Bastille?" asked he, "in the midst of the fire, in the midst of the shot, crying, 'To arms!' threatening with their fists your redoubtable Swiss soldiers, fully armed and equipped, uttering maledictions over the bodies of the slain, with that voice that excites the hearts of the living. Have we not seen them boiling the pitch, dragging cannon along the streets, giving cartridges to those who were eager for the combat, and to the timid combatants a cartridge and a kiss? Do you know that as many women as men trod the drawbridge of the Bastille, and that at this moment, if the stones of the Bastille are falling, it is by pickaxes wielded by women's hands? Ah! Madame, do not overlook the women of Paris; take them into consideration; think also of the children who cast bullets, who sharpen swords, who throw paving stones from a sixth story; yes, think of them, for the bullet which was cast by a child may kill your best general from afar off, and the sword which that child has sharpened will cut the hamstrings of your war horses, while the clouds of stones which fall as from the skies will crush your dragoons and your guards. Consider the old men, madame, for if they have no longer the strength to raise a sword, they have still enough to serve as shields. At the taking of the Bastille, madame, there were old men. Do you know what they did— these aged men whom you affect to despise? They placed themselves before the young men, who steadied their muskets on their shoulders, that they might take sure aim, so that the balls of your Swiss killed the helpless aged man, whose body served as a rampart to the vigorous youth. Include the aged men, for it is they who for the last three hundred years have related to succeeding generations the insults suffered by their mothers—the desolation of their fields, caused by the devouring of their crops by the nobleman's game; the odium attached to their caste, crushed down by feudal privileges; and when the sons seize a hatchet, a club, a gun, in short any weapon within their reach, and sally out to kill, they are fully charged with the curses of the aged against all this tyranny, just as cannons are loaded with powder and iron. At Paris, at this moment, men, women, old men, and children are all crying, 'Liberty, deliverance!' Count everything that has a throat to yell through, madame, and you will have to estimate the number of combatants in Paris at eight hundred thousand souls."

"Three hundred Spartans defeated the army of Xerxes, Monsieur de Charny."

"Yes; but today it is your three hundred Spartans who have increased to eight hundred thousand! While your fifty thousand soldiers compose the army of Xerxes."

The queen raised her head, her hands convulsively clinched, and her face burning with shame and anger.

"Oh, let me fall from my throne," said she, "let me be torn to pieces by your five hundred thousand Parisians, but do not suffer me to hear a Charny, a man devoted to me, speak to me thus."

"If he speaks to you thus, madame, it is because it is necessary. For this Charny has not in his veins a single drop of blood that is unworthy of his ancestors, or that is not all your own."

"Then let him march upon Paris with me, and there we will die together."

"Ignominiously," said the count, "without the possibility of a struggle. We shall not even fight; we shall disappear like the Philistines or the Amalakites. March upon Paris!—but you seem to be ignorant of a very important thing, that, at the moment we shall enter Paris, the houses will fall upon us as did the waves of the Red Sea upon Pharaoh; and you will leave in France a name which will be accursed, and your children will be killed like the cubs of a wolf."

No anthology of Dumas could have any self-respect if it did not quote the famous scene of the death of Porthos, one of the three (really four) musketeers. And so I will give it here, even though it seems to me, as I read it here again, that it must lack its full effect to those who have not read the volumes in which this tower of strength moved, and who have thus not become the friend of this man who "knew" that a case must weigh a thousand pounds because after picking it up and carrying it around for a while he felt rather "tired."

Here is the excerpt from the fourth volume of *The Vicomte de Bragelonne*, chapter 53, called "The Death of a Titan." (Part of this large novel, reprinted as a separate novel, is usually called *The Man in the Iron Mask*, and was based on the suggestion made once by Voltaire that this famous nameless prisoner was really a twin brother of Louis XV, put away forever lest he become the leader of an opposition movement.)

The scene is the large grotto of Locmaria by the sea, in which a bitter struggle is taking place between Porthos and Aramis on the one hand, and brigades of the King's Guard on the other. There is a barrel of gunpowder stored in one of the halls of the deep grotto.

At the moment when Porthos, already more accustomed to the darkness than his pursuers, just coming from open daylight, was looking around him to see if in this night Aramis might not be signaling him, he felt his arm gently touched, and a voice low as a breath murmured in his ear: "Come."

"Oh!" said Porthos.

"Hush!" said Aramis, still more softly.

And amid the noise of the third brigade, which continued to advance amid the imprecations of the guards left alive, of the dying breathing their last sigh, Aramis and Porthos glided imperceptibly along the granite walls of the cavern. Aramis led Porthos into the last compartment but one, and showed him in a hollow of the rocky wall a barrel of powder weighing from seventy to eighty pounds, to which he had just attached a match. "My friend," said he to Porthos, "you will take this barrel, the match of which I am going to set fire to, and throw it amid our enemies; can you do so?"

"*Parbleu!*" replied Porthos; and he lifted the barrel with one hand. "Light it!"

"Stop," said Aramis, "till they are all massed together, and then, my Jupiter, hurl your thunderbolt among them."

"Light it," repeated Porthos.

"For my part," continued Aramis, "I will join our Bretons, help them to get the canoe to the sea, and will wait for you on the shore. Throw your barrel strongly, and hasten to us."

"Light it," said Porthos, a third time.

"But don't you understand me?"

"*Parbleu!*" said Porthos, with laughter that he did not even attempt to restrain; "when a thing is explained to me, I understand it. Go, and give me the light."

Aramis gave the burning match to Porthos, who held out his arm to him to press, his hands being engaged. Aramis pressed the arm of Porthos with both his hands, and fell back to the outlet of the cavern, where the three rowers awaited him.

Porthos, left alone, applied the spark bravely to the match. The spark—a feeble spark, first principle of a conflagration—shone in the darkness like a firefly, then was deadened against the match which it inflamed. Porthos enlivened the flame with his breath. The smoke was a little dispersed, and by the light of the sparkling match objects might for two seconds be distinguished. It was a short but a splendid spectacle—that of this giant, pale, bloody, his countenance lighted by the fire of the match burning in surrounding darkness! The soldiers saw him; they saw the barrel he held in his hand; they at once understood what was going to happen. Then these men, already filled with fright at the sight of what had been accomplished, filled with terror at thinking of what was soon about to be accomplished, uttered together one shriek of agony. Some endeavored to fly, but they encountered the third brigade, which barred their passage; others mechanically took aim and attempted to fire their discharged muskets; others fell upon their knees. Two or three officers cried out to Porthos to promise him his liberty if he would spare their lives. The lieutenant of the third brigade commanded his men to fire; but the guards had before them their terrified companions, who served as a living rampart for Porthos.

We have said that the light produced by the spark and the match did not last more than two seconds; but during these two seconds this is what it illuminated: in the first place, the giant, enlarged in the darkness; then, at ten paces from him, a heap of bleeding bodies, crushed, mutilated, in the midst of which was still visible some last struggle of agony which lifted the mass as a last breath raises the sides of a shapeless monster expiring in the night. Every breath of Porthos, while enlivening the match, sent toward this heap of bodies a sulphurous hue mingled with streaks of purple. In addition to this principal group, scattered about the grotto as the chance of death or the surprise of the blow had stretched them, some isolated bodies seemed to threaten by their gaping wounds. Above the ground, soaked by pools of blood, rose, heavy and sparkling, the short, thick pillars of the cavern, of which the strongly marked shades threw out the luminous particles. And all this was seen by the tremulous light of a match attached to a barrel of powder—that is to say, a torch which, while casting a light upon the dead past, revealed at the same time the death to come.

As I have said, this spectacle did not last above two seconds. During this short space of time, an officer of the third brigade got together eight men armed with muskets, and, through an opening, ordered them to fire upon Porthos. But they who received the order to fire trembled so that three guards fell by the discharge, and the five other balls went hissing to splinter the vault, plough the ground, or indent the sides of the cavern.

A burst of laughter replied to this volley; then the arm of the giant swung around; then was seen to pass through the air, like a falling star, the train of fire. The barrel, hurled a distance of thirty feet, cleared the barricade of the dead bodies and fell amid a group of shrieking soldiers, who threw themselves on their faces. The officer had followed the brilliant train in the air; he endeavored to precipitate himself upon the barrel and tear out the match before it reached the powder it contained. Useless devotion! The air had made the flame attached to the conductor more active; the match, which at rest might have burned five minutes, was consumed in thirty seconds, and the infernal work exploded.

Furious vortices, hissings of sulphur and niter, devouring ravages of fire, the terrible thunder of the explosion—this is what the second which followed the two seconds we have described disclosed in that cavern, equal in horrors to a cavern of demons. The rocks split like planks of deal under the ax. A jet of fire, smoke, and debris sprang up from the middle of the grotto, enlarging as it mounted. The great walls of silex tottered and fell upon the sand; and the sand itself— an instrument of pain when launched from its hardened bed— riddled the face with its myriads of cutting atoms. Cries, howlings, imprecations, and lives—all were extinguished in one great crash.

The first three compartments became a gulf into which fell back again, according to its weight, every vegetable, mineral, or human fragment. Then the lighter sand and ashes began to fall in their turns, stretching like a gray winding sheet and smoking over these dismal remains. And now seek in this burning tomb, in this subterranean volcano—seek for the King's Guards with their blue coats laced with silver. Seek for the officers brilliant in gold; seek for the arms upon which they depended for their defense; seek among the stones that have killed them, upon the ground that bore them. One single man has made of all this a chaos more confused, more shapeless, more terrible than the chaos which existed an hour before God conceived the idea of creating the world. There remained nothing of these three compartments—nothing by which God could have recognized his own work.

As to Porthos, immediately after having hurled the barrel of powder amid his enemies, but before it exploded, he had fled as Aramis had directed him and had gained the last compartment, into which air, light, and sunshine penetrated through the opening. And scarcely had he turned the angle which separated the third compartment from the fourth, when he perceived at a hundred paces from him the boat dancing on the waves. There were his friends; there was liberty; there was life after victory. Six more of those formidable strides of his and he would be out of the vault; and once out of the vault, two or three vigorous springs and he would reach the canoe. Suddenly he felt his knees give way; his knees appeared powerless, his legs yielded under him.

"Oh, oh!" murmured he, "there is my fatigue seizing me again! I can walk no farther! What is this?"

Aramis perceived him through the opening; unable to conceive what could induce him to stop thus, he cried: "Come on, Porthos! come on! come quickly!"

"Oh!" replied the giant, making an effort which acted upon every muscle of his body, "oh! but I cannot!" While saying these words he fell upon his knees, but with his robust hands he clung to the rocks, and raised himself up again.

"Quick, quick!" repeated Aramis, bending forward toward the shore, as if to draw Porthos to him with his arms.

"Here I am," stammered Porthos, collecting all his strength to make one step more.

"In the name of heaven, Porthos, make haste! the barrel will blow up!"

"Make haste, monsieur!" shouted the Bretons to Porthos, who was floundering as in a dream.

But there was no longer time; the explosion, which we have already described, resounded, the earth gaped, the smoke which rushed through the large fissures obscured the sky; the sea flowed back as if driven by the blast of fire which darted from the grotto as if from the jaws of a gigantic chimera; the reflux carried the boat out twenty fathoms; the rocks cracked to their base, and separated like blocks under the operation of wedges; a portion of the vault was carried up toward heaven, as if by rapid currents; the rose-colored and green fire of the sulphur, the black lava of the argillaceous liquefactions clashed and combated for an instant beneath a majestic dome of smoke; then, after first oscillating, then declining, there fell successively the long angles of rock, which the violence of the explosion had not been able completely to uproot from their bed of ages; they bowed to one another like grave and slow old men, then prostrated themselves, and fell, embedding themselves forever in their dusty tomb.

The frightful shock seemed to restore to Porthos the strength he had lost. He arose, himself a giant among these giants. But at the moment he was flying between the double hedge of granite phantoms, these latter, which were no longer supported by the corresponding links, began to roll with a crash around this Titan, who looked as if precipitated from heaven amid the rocks which he had just been launching at it. Porthos felt the earth beneath his feet shaken by this long rending. He extended his vast hands to the right and left to repulse the falling rocks. A gigantic block was held back by each of his extended hands. He bent his head, and a third granite mass sank between his two shoulders. For an instant the arms of Porthos had given way, but the Hercules united all his forces, and the two walls of the prison in which he was buried fell back slowly and gave him place. For an instant he appeared in this frame of granite like the ancient angel of chaos; but in pushing back the lateral rocks, he lost his point of support for the monolith which weighed upon his strong shoulders, and this monolith, lying upon him with all its weight, slowly brought the giant down upon his knees. The lateral rocks, for an instant pushed back, drew together again and added their weight to that of the other, which would have been sufficient to crush ten men. The giant fell without crying for help; he fell while answering Aramis with words of encouragement and hope, for, thanks to the powerful arch of his hands, for an instant he might believe, that, like Enceladus, he should shake off the triple load. But by degrees Aramis saw the block sink; the hands contracted for an instant, the arms stiffened for a last effort, gave way, the extended shoulders sank wounded and torn, and the rock continued to lower gradually.

"Porthos! Porthos!" cried Aramis, tearing his hair, "Porthos! where are you? Speak!"

"There, there!" murmured Porthos, with a voice evidently weaker; "patience! patience!"

Scarcely had he pronounced these words, when the impulse of the fall augmented the weight; the enormous rock sank down, pressed by the two others which sank in from the sides, and, as it were, swallowed up Porthos in a sepulcher of broken stones. On hearing the dying voice of his friend, Aramis had sprung to land. Two of the Bretons followed him, each with a lever in his hand—one man being sufficient to take care of the boat. The last sighs of the valiant struggler guided them amid the ruins. Aramis, animated, active, and young as at twenty, sprang toward the triple mass, and with his hands, delicate as those of a woman, raised by a miracle of vigor a corner of the immense sepulcher of granite. Then he caught a glimpse, in the darkness of that grave, of the still-brilliant eye of his friend, to whom the momentary lifting of the mass restored a moment of respiration. The two men came rushing up, grasped their iron levers, united their triple strength, not merely to raise it, but to sustain it. All was useless. The three men slowly gave way with cries of grief, and the rough voice of Porthos, seeing them exhaust themselves in a useless struggle, murmured in a bantering tone those last words which came to his lips with the last breath: "Too heavy!"

After which the eye darkened and closed, the face became pale, the hand whitened, and the Titan sank quite down, breathing his last sigh. With him sank the rock, which even in his agony he had still held up. The three men dropped the levers, which rolled upon the tumulary stone. Then, breathless, pale, his brow covered with sweat, Aramis listened, his breast oppressed, his heart ready to break.

Nothing more! The giant slept the eternal sleep, in a sepulcher which God had carved to his measure.

Aramis, silent, icy, trembling like a timid child, arose shivering from the stone. A Christian does not walk upon tombs. But though capable of standing, he was not capable of walking. It might be said that something of Porthos, dead, had just died within him. His Bretons surrounded him; Aramis yielded to their kind exertions, and the three sailors, lifting him up, carried him into the canoe. Then, having laid him down upon the bench near the tiller, they took to their oars, preferring to get off by rowing rather than to hoist a sail, which might betray them.

Of all that leveled surface of the ancient grotto of Locmaria, of all that flattened shore, one single little hillock attracted their eyes. Aramis never removed his from it; and at a distance out in the sea, in proportion as the shore receded, the menacing and proud mass of rock seemed to draw itself up, as formerly Porthos used to do, and raise a smiling and invincible head toward heaven—like that of the honest and valiant friend, the strongest of the four, and yet the first dead. Strange destiny of these men of brass! The most simple of heart allied to the most crafty; strength of body guided by subtlety of mind; and in the decisive moment, when strength alone could save mind and body, a stone, a rock, a vile and material weight triumphed over strength, and, falling upon the body, drove out the mind.

Worthy Porthos! born to help other men, always ready to sacrifice himself for the safety of the weak, as if God had given him strength only for that purpose. In dying he thought he was only carrying out the condition of his compact with Aramis—a compact, however, which Aramis alone had drawn up, and which Porthos had known only to suffer by its terrible solidarity.

Noble Porthos! of what good are your many châteaux filled with sumptuous furniture, your forests abounding in game, your lakes teeming with fish, and cellars gorged with wealth? Of what good are your lackeys in brilliant liveries, and in the midst of them your faithful body servant, Mousqueton, proud of the power delegated to him? O noble Porthos! careful heaper up of treasures, was it worth while to labor to sweeten and gild life, to come upon a desert shore to the cries of sea birds, and lay yourself with broken bones beneath cold stone? Was it worth while, in short, noble Porthos, to heap so much gold, and not have even the distich of a poor poet engraven upon your monument?

Valiant Porthos! Without a doubt, he still sleeps, lost, forgotten, beneath the rock which the shepherds of the heath take for the gigantic abode of a *dolmen*. And so many twining branches, so many mosses, caressed by the bitter wind of the ocean, so many lichens have soldered the sepulcher to the earth, that the passer-by will never imagine that such a block of granite can ever have been supported by the shoulders of one man.

Skipping a couple of chapters, we come to the reading of Porthos's will.

At Pierrefonds everything was in mourning. The courtyards were deserted, the stables closed, the lawns and flower beds were neglected. In the basins, the fountains, formerly gushing so lavishly, so noisily and sparkling, had stopped of themselves.

Along the roads to the château came grave personages mounted upon mules or farm horses. These were country neighbors, curés, and bailiffs of adjacent estates. All these people entered the château silently, gave their horses to a melancholy-looking groom, and directed their steps, conducted by a huntsman in black, to the great dining room where Mousqueton received them at the door.

Mousqueton had become so thin in two days that his clothes moved upon him like scabbards which are too large, in which the blades of swords dance about at each motion. His face, composed of red and white, like that of the Madonna of Vandyke, was furrowed by two silver rivulets which had dug their beds in his cheeks, as full formerly as they had become thin since his grief began. At each fresh arrival Mousqueton shed fresh tears, and it was pitiful to see him press his throat with his fat hand to keep from bursting into sobs and lamentations. All these visits were for the purpose of hearing the reading of Porthos's will, announced for that day, and at which all the covetous and all who were allied by friendship with the deceased were anxious to be present, as he had left no relative behind him.

The visitors took their places as they arrived; and the great room had just been closed when the clock struck twelve, the hour fixed for the reading. Porthos's procurator—who was naturally the successor of Master Coquenard—began by slowly unfolding the vast parchment upon which the powerful hand of Porthos had traced his last wishes. The seal broken, the spectacles put on, the preliminary cough having sounded, everyone opened his ears. Mousqueton had squatted himself in a corner, the better to weep and the less to hear.

All at once the folding doors of the great room, which had been shut, were thrown open as if by miracle, and a manly figure appeared upon the threshold, resplendent in the full light of the sun. This was D'Artagnan, who had come alone to the gate, and, finding nobody to hold his stirrup, had tied his horse to a knocker and announced himself.

The splendor of the daylight suddenly invading the room, the murmur of all present, and more than all that an instinct as of a faithful dog drew Mousqueton from his revery. He raised his head, recognized the old friend of his master, and, crying out with grief, embraced the captain's knees, watering the floor with tears.

D'Artagnan raised up the poor intendant, embraced him as if he had been a brother, and, having nobly saluted the assembly, who all bowed as they whispered to one another his name, went and took his seat at the extremity of the great carved-oak hall, still holding by the hand poor Mousqueton, who was suffocating and sank down upon the steps. Then the procurator, who, like the rest, was considerably agitated, began the reading.

Porthos, after a profession of faith of the most Christian character, asked pardon of his enemies for all the injuries he might have done them. At this paragraph, a ray of inexpressible pride beamed from the eyes of D'Artagnan. He recalled to his mind the old soldier, all those enemies of Porthos brought to the earth by his valiant hand; he reckoned up the numbers of them, and said to himself that Porthos had acted wisely not to detail his enemies or the injuries done to them, or the task would have been too much for the reader. Then came the following enumeration:

"I possess at this present time, by the grace of God—

"1. The domain of Pierrefonds, lands, woods, meadows, waters, and forests, surrounded by good walls.

"2. The domain of Bracieux, château, forests, ploughed lands, forming three farms.

"3. The little estate Du Vallon, so named because it is in the valley. [Brave Porthos!]

"4. Fifty farms in Touraine, amounting to five hundred acres.

"5. Three mills upon the Cher, bringing in six hundred livres each.

"6. Three fishpools in Berry, producing two hundred livres a year.

"As to my personal or movable property, so called because it cannot be moved, as is so well explained by my learned friend the Bishop of Vannes [D'Artagnan shuddered at the dismal remembrance attached to that name. The procurator continued imperturbably], they consist—

"1. In goods which I cannot detail here for want of room, and which furnish all my châteaux, or houses, but of which the list is drawn up by my intendant."

Everyone turned his eyes towards Mousqueton, who was absorbed in his grief.

"2. In twenty horses for saddle and draught, which I have particularly at my château of Pierrefonds, and which are called Bayard, Roland, Charlemagne, Pepin, Dunois, La Hire, Ogier, Samson, Milon, Nemrod, Urgande, Armide, Falstrade, Dalila, Rebecca, Yolande, Finette, Grisette, Lisette, and Musette.

"3. In sixty dogs, forming six packs, divided as follows: the first, for the stag; the second, for the wolf; the third, for the wild boar; the fourth, for the hare; and the two others, for watch and guard.

"4. In arms for war and the chase, contained in my gallery of arms.

"5. My wines of Anjou, selected for Athos, who liked them formerly; my wines of Burgundy, Champagne, Bordeaux, and Spain, stocking eight cellars and twelve vaults in my various houses.

"6. My pictures and statues, which are said to be of great value and which are sufficiently numerous to fatigue the sight.

"7. My library, consisting of six thousand volumes, quite new, which have never been opened.

"8. My silver plate, which perhaps is a little worn, but which ought to weigh from a thousand to twelve hundred pounds, for I had great trouble in lifting the coffer that contained it, and could not carry it more than six times around my chamber.

"9. All these objects, in addition to the table and house linen, are divided in the residences I liked the best."

Here the reader stopped to take breath. Everyone sighed, coughed, and redoubled his attention. The procurator resumed:

"I have lived without having any children, and it is probable I never shall have any, which to me is a cutting grief. And yet I am mistaken, for I have a son, in common with my other friends: he is M. Raoul Auguste Jules de Bragelonne, the true son of Monsieur le Comte de la Fère.

"This young nobleman has appeared to me worthy to succeed to the three valiant gentlemen of whom I am the friend and the very humble servant."

Here a sharp sound interrupted the reader. It was D'Artagnan's sword, which, slipping from his baldric, had fallen on the sonorous flooring. Everyone turned his eyes that way, and saw that a large tear had rolled from the thick lid of D'Artagnan upon his aquiline nose, the luminous edge of which shone like a crescent enlightened by the sun. The procurator continued:

"This is why I have left all my property, movable or immovable, comprised in the above enumerations, to Monsieur le Vicomte Raoul Auguste Jules de Bragelonne, son of Monsieur le Comte de la Fère, to console him for the grief he seems to suffer, and enable him to support his name gloriously."

A long murmur ran through the auditory. The procurator continued, seconded by the flashing eye of D'Artagnan which, glancing over the assembly, quickly restored the interrupted silence:

"But on several conditions: first, that Monsieur le Vicomte de Bragelonne do give to Monsieur le Chevalier d'Artagnan, captain of the king's musketeers, whatever the said Chevalier d'Artagnan may demand of my property. And on condition that Monsieur le Vicomte de Bragelonne do pay a good pension to Monsieur le Chevalier d'Herblay, my friend, if he should be compelled to live in exile. I leave to my intendant Mousqueton all my clothes, of city, war, or chase, to the number of forty-seven suits, with the assurance that he will wear them till they are worn out, for the love of, and in remembrance of, his master. Moreover, I bequeath to Monsieur le Vicomte de Bragelonne my old servant and faithful friend, Mousqueton, already named, with the charge that the said viscount shall so act that Mousqueton shall be able to declare when dying that he has never ceased to be happy."

On hearing these words, Mousqueton bowed, pale and trembling; his large shoulders shook convulsively; his countenance, impressed by a frightful grief, appeared from between his icy hands, and the spectators saw him stagger and hesitate, as if, though wishing to leave the hall, he did not know the way.

"Mousqueton, my good friend," said D'Artagnan, "go and make your preparations. I will take you with me to Athos's house, where I shall go on leaving Pierrefonds."

Mousqueton made no reply. He scarcely breathed, feeling as if everything in that hall would from that time be strange to him. He opened the door, and disappeared slowly.

The procurator finished his reading, after which the greater part of those who had come to hear the last will of Porthos dispersed by degrees, many disappointed, but all penetrated with respect. As for D'Artagnan, left alone after having received the formal compliments of the procurator, he was lost in admiration of the wisdom of the testator, who had so judiciously bestowed his wealth upn the most necessitous and the most worthy, with a delicacy that none among the most refined courtiers and the most noble hearts could have displayed more becomingly.

When Porthos enjoined Raoul de Bragelonne to give to D'Artagnan all that he would ask, he knew well, did that worthy Porthos, that D'Artagnan would neither ask for anything, nor accept anything; and in case he did demand anything, none but himself could say what. Porthos had also left a pension to Aramis, who, if he should be inclined to ask too much, would be checked by the example of D'Artagnan; and that word "exile" thrown out by the testator without apparent intention—was it not the most mild, the most exquisite criticism upon that conduct of Aramis which had brought about the death of Porthos?

But there was no mention of Athos, the Comte de la Fère, in the testament of the dead man. Could the latter for a moment suppose that the son, to whom so much was given, would not offer the best part to the father? The rough mind of Porthos had judged all these causes, caught all these shades, better than the law, better than custom, better than taste.

"Porthos! There was a heart," said D'Artagnan to himself, with a sigh. As he made this reflection he fancied he heard a groan in the room above him, and he thought immediately of poor Mousqueton, whom it was necessary to divert from his grief. For this purpose he left the hall hastily to seek the worthy intendant. He ascended the staircase leading to the first story, and perceived in Porthos's own chamber a heap of clothes of all colors and all materials, upon which Mousqueton had laid himself down after heaping them together. It was the legacy of the faithful friend. These clothes were truly his own; they had been given to him. The hand of Mousqueton was stretched over these relics, which he kissed with all his lips, with all his face, which he covered with his whole body. D'Artagnan approached to console the poor fellow.

"My God!" said he; "he does not stir—he has fainted!"

But D'Artagnan was mistaken; Mousqueton was dead—dead, like the dog who, having lost his master, comes back to die upon his cloak.

Chapter XII

MANSIONS TOO STATELY

D UMAS had put into this giant Porthos some of the love he must have had for his father who was famous for his incredible strength, and who died when Dumas was four. That was the time when young Alexandre was seen by his mother going upstairs lugging heavy pistols.

"What are you doing with those guns?" his mother cried.

"I'm going up to kill God for killing my papa," said the four-year-old.

Dumas's son, later the author of *Camille*, is said to have discovered his father sitting at his desk one day, writing, while heaving great sighs, and with tears rolling from his eyes.

"I have just killed Porthos," Dumas explained in a voice broken by sobs.

The newspaper *Le Siècle*, in which the *Vicomte* was running serially, complained later that Dumas failed to supply installments for a week after this episode.

Dumas replied that he was so shocked by the death of Porthos that he had to go back to his old home town of Villers-Cotterêts to recuperate. But some of his backbiting friends pointed out that the hunting season had opened, and that a 25,000 acre preserve where Dumas loved to hunt adjoins Villers-Cotterêts.

That may be so, for Dumas never lost an opportunity to go hunting and knock off at least a rabbit, if not something more exciting. But the fact remains that, for all that, Dumas was an extremely sensitive man, and these charming bits from a number of little pieces he wrote first for his periodical *Le Mousquetaire* and his subsequent periodical *Les Nouvelles* (for Dumas tried his hand at publishing magazines too) are evidence of that sensitivity.

The original title was *Chats with My Readers Concerning a Dog,*

Two Roosters and Eleven Chickens. They were published as a volume, with a number of other smaller pieces about animals and hunting, a number of years later, in fact only two years before Dumas's death.

May I assume that you, dear reader, are a sportsman—*and* a poultry fancier to boot? Well, then, did it ever happen to you that your sporting dog, with the best intentions in the world, and fully believing he was after game, chivied and killed your fowls?

This is quite a likely thing to have occurred, and one you have no call to be ashamed of after all; so I will make bold to make all these several assumptions.

Such being the case, I have no doubt that, loving your dog and loving your fowls too, you deeply regretted you knew of no way of punishing the former adequately, short of beating him to death.

For beat your dog as you may, you cannot bring your poultry to life again. Besides which, the Bible expressly says that God desires not the death of a sinner, but his repentance.

You object that in this precept regarding sins and repentance, God was not thinking about dogs. I say you are puffed up with the insolence of your supposed human superiority.

I firmly believe God paid just as much attention as He did to man to every animal He endowed with life, from the tiniest insect to the elephant, from the hummingbird to the eagle.

However, I will make some concession to your prejudices, reader, and allow that *perhaps* God implanted a special liability to be tempted in this particular direction in the dog, which of all beasts is the one whose instinct comes nearest to human intelligence.

Perhaps we might even venture on the proposition that some dogs have more instinct than some men have intelligence.

Remember what Michelet said so pleasantly: "Dogs are candidates for humanity."

Finally, if the point is contested, we can allege this convincing proof—that dogs go mad, and bite.

This settled, let us to our story.

I own a dog, and I once owned fowls.

There! Just think what it is to be a dramatic author, and with what an artful touch a dramatic author can broach a subject! "I own a dog, and I once owned fowls!" Why, that single sentence, those nine simple words, imply a whole catastrophe in the past, and give the actual state of things here and now into the bargain.

I own a dog—yes, I have one still; my dog, therefore, is alive. *I once owned* fowls, but I do so no longer; ergo my fowls are dead.

Nay! it is plain that, if you have any powers of deduction at all —even though I had not told you, perhaps rather prematurely—by means of the phrase "I own a dog, I once owned fowls," you would know perfectly well not merely that my dog is alive and my poultry dead, but be able to guess, into the bargain, that in all probability it was my dog that killed my fowls.

So you see there is a whole tragedy implicit in the words: *I own a dog, I once owned fowls.*

If I could ever hope to be elected a member of the Academy, I should enjoy the certainty that one day at any rate my panegyric would be pronounced by my successor; and lauded by a great noble or a great poet of the future, a Noailles or a future Viennet, I could fall asleep in calm reliance on this one sentence: *I own a dog, and I once owned fowls,* confident that the fine implications involved would not be lost on an admiring posterity.

But, alas! I shall never join the Immortal Forty! A fellow Academician will never pronounce my panegyric after I am dead!

The simplest plan, therefore, is for me to do it for myself while I am still alive.

Now you are aware, dear reader, or possibly you are not aware, that in dramatic art everything depends on the *preparation*, the working-up.

To introduce and make known the *dramatis personae* is one of the surest ways of forcing the reader to be interested in them.

To force—it is a hard word, I know, but it is the proper technical expression; we must always *force* the reader to be interested in some person or some thing.

Only there are several different means of arriving at this result.

Remember Walter Scott—well, Walter Scott had a way of his own of attracting interest to his characters, one which, though it was with a very few exceptions always the same and of a kind to strike one at the first blush as very extraordinary, nevertheless proved highly successful.

His way was to be tiresome, deadly tiresome, often for half the first volume, sometimes for the whole of it.

But, in the course of this volume he was bringing his personages on the scene, and giving so minute and detailed a description of their personal appearance, their moral character, their habits and idiosyncrasies, the reader learned so exactly how they dressed and walked and talked, that when at the beginning of Volume II, one of these individuals found himself in some danger or emergency, you could not help exclaiming:

"Ah, dear! that poor gentleman who wore an apple-green coat, and limped as he walked, and lisped in speaking, however is he going to get out of this difficulty?"

And you were quite surprised, after being bored to death for half a volume or a whole volume, sometimes even for a volume and a half, you were quite astonished to find yourself deeply interested in the gentleman who lisped in speaking, who limped as he walked, and who wore an apple-green coat.

You may possibly observe, reader:

"This method, sir, which I see you commend so highly, is the one you follow yourself, is it?"

In the first place, I do not commend it; I only explain and describe and discuss it. Secondly, my own is precisely the opposite.

"Ah! so you have a method of your own?" Mr. This or Mr. That will ask me, with a pretty air of polished sarcasm.

"Certainly—and why not, my good friends?"

Well, then, here is *my* method: I give it you for what it is worth.

Only I am bound to be honest by telling you I think it is a bad one.

"But," you naturally object, "if your way is a bad one, why employ it?"

Because one is not always in a position to employ or not to employ a method at will; and sometimes, I strongly suspect, it is the method uses us rather than we the method.

Men dream that it is they who have ideas; I have a shrewd notion myself it is the ideas that often possess the men. There is many an idea has used up two or three generations of mankind and, before working itself out, is going to use up three or four more.

Anyhow, whether it is I who own my method or my method that owns me, here it is, such as it is:

To begin by being interesting, instead of beginning by being tiresome; to begin with action, instead of beginning with preparation for action; to describe the characters after having brought them on the stage, instead of bringing them on the stage after describing them.

Well, you will likely enough say at the first go off:

"Really, I see nothing so very perilous about this way of going to work."

All I can say to that is: you are mistaken. In reading a book or watching a play—comedy, tragedy, theatrical piece of any sort—a *Schauspiel*, as they say in German—we must always be bored more or less.

There is no fire without smoke, no sunlight without shadow. Well, boredom, ennui, is the shadow, the smoke, in this case.

Now experience has shown this much: it is better to be bored at the start than the finish.

More than that: some of my fellow novelists and dramatists, uncertain which of the two plans to adopt, have chosen that of boring the reader all through the romance or the spectator all through the play.

And they have been quite successful; while I, I have found my method pretty nearly fatal to me, consisting as it does in being amusing right from the start!

Consider my first acts, look at my first volumes; the pains I have always taken to make them as amusing as possible have frequently been prejudicial to the four others where a play has been concerned, the fifteen or twenty others where a novel has been in question.

Witness the prologue of *Caligula*, which kills that tragedy, and the first act of *Mademoiselle de Belle-Isle*, which came near ruining that comedy.

Once people are amused in the first act or the first volume, they expect to be amused all through—and it is hard, extremely hard, well-nigh impossible, to be always amusing.

On the contrary, when ennui is the order of the day in the first act or first volume, a change becomes highly desirable—and then the reader or spectator, as the case may be, is endlessly grateful for whatever is done with a view to bringing that about.

A novel or a play is like a dinner. Your guests are hungry; they want to eat, and don't much care what they eat so long as their appetite is satisfied.

Give them a dish of good plain onion soup. Some will make a face, perhaps; but all will take a plateful, never fear. Next, give them pork and pickled cabbage—any coarse food you please; provided there's plenty of it, they ask nothing better, and dine without a grumble, finally leaving the table with the words: "Well, it wasn't very delicate fare, to be sure, but, 'pon my word, I've dined, anyway."

That is why authors are often successful who are always tiresome, from the beginning of the novel or play to the end.

This method is the least usual and the most uncertain; I do not advise its adoption.

You serve, as at the dinner just described, onion soup to begin with, pickled cabbage, and common coarse dishes. But next come game, partridges, and pheasants, or perhaps poultry, say a goose, and lo! everybody begins to applaud, and forgets the unappetizing beginning of the meal, and all declare they have dined like Lucullus.

My own particular system is the worst of all—I said so before.

I serve up my partridges and pheasants, my turbot and lobster at once, and even my pineapples, which I do not reserve for dessert; then later on you come to the jugged hare and Gruyère cheese, and make a wry face. Indeed, I am very lucky if you don't go and cry on the housetops that my kitchen is a thousand yards below the lowest suburban cookshop and the level of the sea.

However, I begin to see, reader mine, that I have wandered a long way from the dog I own and the fowls I once owned.

I really think today I have been using Walter Scott's method.

Well, we ought to try everything, you know.

This next extract from Dumas's chats about his pets requires a bit of a commentary, so I shall interrupt myself after the first two paragraphs.

On my return to France, I found my house, which I was building on the Marly road, pretty nearly finished. In a few weeks' time I had the papering and woodwork of the whole of one floor completed, so that I was able to satisfy the wishes of my landlord at the *Villa Medicis* who, finding I had spent between seven and eight thousand francs on improvements to his property, had conceived the very natural desire of going back to it himself and thus enjoying life there all the more considering that it was at the expense of someone else.

I left Saint-Germain, therefore, to go and live at the Porte-Marly, in the much-discussed house which was subsequently christened Monte-Cristo by Madame Mélingue, and which later on made such a noise in the world.

Dumas always made a noise, so that in itself was nothing unusual. In his *Memoirs* Dumas tells of how he roused the neighborhood of Saint-Germain, when he went to live there in the *Villa Medicis.*

It's a fact that I can't explain, but it's a fact all the same, that I carry about with me, wherever I go, an atmosphere of life and stir which has become proverbial about me. For example: I moved to Saint-Germain and lived there for three years. It didn't take long before the respectable denizens of this Sleepy Hollow could no longer recognize themselves.

I communicated to the place a go and a liveliness which the inhabitants at first took to be some sort of epidemic or contagious fever, like that produced by the bite of the Neapolitan spider. I purchased the local theater, and the best actors and actresses from Paris would come down to have supper with me and to put on Shakespeare's *Hamlet,* or else my *Mademoiselle de Belle-Isle,* or my *Les Demoiselles de Saint Cyr,* for the benefit of the poor.

Ravelet, of the local livery stable, kept running out of horses. Collinet of the local inn never had enough rooms. And the railway company admitted to me one day an increase in their receipts of 20,000 francs each year since I had come to live at Saint-Germain.

It is true that, at the time of the elections, Saint-Germain nevertheless considered me too much of a wastrel to have the honor of representing them in the Chamber. But all the same Saint-Germain was now awake, or almost awake. There was the forest for horse riding, the theater for the evening, and fireworks at night, which were sent for from Paris.

Our fireworks were the great astonishment of Versailles, which from time to time would rise out of its tomb and stare with vacant

eyes over the Louvenciennes hills and murmur in dying tones: "What
is all that commotion over in Saint-Germain? What are those people
up to? Look at me. Do I move? Good Lord when one is dead, is
that the proper time for shooting off rockets, going to plays,
riding horseback? Look at me, I sleep like a member of the French
Academy, and take care, even in my sleep, not to disturb anyone by
so much as a snore."

One day the king was annoyed by all this noise coming from the
direction of Saint-Germain. He sent for M. de Montalivet. "My
dear Count," said Louis-Philippe, "do you know what has happened?"

"What, Sire?"

"Why, don't you see that our presence in Versailles has succeeded
in waking up Saint-Germain? [The king had been led to believe that
it was he who had brought about this miracle.] Now why can't we
galvanize Versailles into life by opening up our picture gallery and
playing the fountains, on each first Sunday of every month?"

"Sire," replied Montalivet, "would you really like Versailles to be
merry to the point of folly? Instead of being gloomy as death."

"My dear Count," the king replied to his minister, "that would
indeed give me the greatest pleasure."

"Very well, Sire. Dumas is due to serve his two weeks in the National Guard. Order that those two weeks be served at Versailles.
That will stir up life hereabouts."

The king turned his back on M. de Montalivet and did not speak
to him for a month after. Versailles became more and more gloomy
and after passing from melancholy to darkness, passed from darkness
to funeral depths.

(To be sure there must have been an additional reason for the
king's displeasure—as well as other reasons why the kingdom fell and
Louis-Philippe grabbed up his money and his wife and her jewelry
and both hotfooted it off to England—for the former Duke of Orleans could hardly have liked the idea that the part-Negro clerk who
used to copy letters for him had somehow managed to achieve a
success in life that was denied to him who had become king of France.
Yes, that must have hurt.)

In his *Memoirs* Dumas tells of a fancy dress ball he once gave, and
of how for him "that meant three or four hundred invitations." For

this ball the best artists of France painted special murals for him, and the best sculptors did decorations. The ball was such a success that Dumas would have loved to repeat it, but being the showman he was he knew that he would have to top it, for he would not have been able to stand people saying: "Yes, but you should have seen the ball he gave last year," or something of that sort. So that he never gave another one.

Nevertheless he continued to be a constant and generous host. So much so that he found it difficult to find a place in his own house where he could work in peace. Often he would serve a wonderful meal, and then take advantage of everyone being immersed in the business of eating, to disappear into his workroom. If he saw to it that the supply of champagne was sufficient, he, who himself rarely drank and never smoked, could count on his guests forgetting about him, and he could catch up with the never-ending demand for his serials and his plays.

In 1844, when the press of visitors was finally too much for him, Dumas found not far away, between Saint-Germain and Pecq, close to Marly-le-Roi, a piece of ground on an elevation called Mont Ferrand, overlooking the Seine valley, which he decided was just the place for him.

That very night he began to sketch what he thought would be a little retreat for himself. Just a place for work. But as he began to think of certain necessary comforts, he added a kitchen and a dining room. Then he thought of his son and of other possible guests, and he added a spare room or two.

He saw that a single story, which was all that he had wanted at first, would be insufficient. But the moment he got into a two-story affair, he saw no reason for not including a billiard room, a drawing room, more bedrooms, etc. The very next day he took himself to an architect named Plante, and he figured that such a house, along with a half acre of ground, would cost about 12,000 francs.

"A bagatelle," is the way that Dumas described the matter of cost at this time. And he gave orders to go ahead. Estimated time for construction: six weeks.

But he had just begun. No sooner had he bought half an acre than adjoining property owners came to offer him additional land. After all he wanted to be private, didn't he? What better way than to buy more land? Dumas bought. First this piece, then that. Until finally he owned six acres. And as the land grew, so naturally did the plans for his house.

In digging the foundations the architect expressed some doubts about the security of the structure. Plans for an elaborate cellar were immediately decided upon. In excavating for this cellar, springs of water were encountered. Dumas ordered them piped for his own water supply, and to ensure a pond.

That which had started out to be a retreat turned into a show place. And the price went up accordingly. First it had been 12,000 francs. Then 15,000. Then it soared to 30,000. Then to 60,000. And to 150,000. Naturally that meant the finest artists and craftsmen to do the designing and the execution.

And so, instead of six weeks, Dumas began to figure on three years. And it wasn't long before people by the hundreds were streaming out of Paris to watch Dumas's château going up.

The place had at first no name, but one day when Mélingue, the famous actor who had made such a success in Dumas's La Dame de Monsoreau, and in his D'Artagnan plays, took a carriage at Pecq, the nearest railroad stop, and the coachman asked whereto, Madame Mélingue said: "To Monte-Cristo," and the driver understood. So the name stuck.

During the construction Dumas and his son went off to Spain and came back not only with material for books but with several Moorish craftsmen in woodcarving and cabinetry to work on his house.

The result was a hodgepodge, architecturally speaking, but a sound building. (That still exists, and would still be a lovely place if it hadn't been used as a school for boys. At latest reports it is vacant.) Dumas opened it with a huge party to which some six hundred people came. They saw a château that had in general the appearance of a Renaissance mansion, but with some Moorish overtones in the shape of towers and turrets, and some Medieval grace notes in the banners that waved from the weathercocks, on which one could read Dumas's favorite device: "Au vent la flamme! Au Seigneur l'âme!" Which might mean: the fire of your life to the winds of fate! your soul to God!

On that opening day the two Moorish craftsmen, whose services, since they were slaves, Dumas had obtained as a gift from the Bey of Tunis, were turned into welcoming Moslems, in fine robes and turbans. Dumas himself had decked himself in his uniform as National Guardsman.

On the outside the guests saw a façade of beautifully carved white stone, breaking out into large bay windows, surrounded by an ornate iron balcony. Prominent in these carvings were the arms of the house of Pailleterie with Dumas's motto: *J'aime qui m'aime.* I love those who love me.

The exterior of the large entrance hall was topped with a frieze showing the busts of all the most famous writers from Homer to the time of Dumas, done in bas-relief on medallions.

"Why don't I find your bust there?" the journalist Léon Gozlan asked, looking at the outside of the house.

"Because I'll be inside," said Dumas.

As for the rooms, they were of every style. Gothic, Renaissance, Louis XIV, and in particular one small room *"la chambre arabe,"* with such superb carvings, arabesques, arches, and fretworks, in the Alhambra style, that the eye was lost in admiration of its intricacies. Special lamps and mirrors scattered and dimmed the light. Dark velvet drapes and tapestries added to the effect. Nothing north of the Mediterranean, so it was said, rivaled this haremlike boudoir in inviting man (and woman) to linger in dreams and sensuality.

All the rooms, the Louis XV room, the Henri II room, all were crowded with furniture and hangings and art works to fit and enhance the architecture. At every turn the guests discovered new wonders in the way of vases, statues, clocks, old weapons, furniture, rugs, and tapestries.

The garden was a similar enchantment, with artificial streams falling here and there in cascades, or forming a pond over which ran a bridge to an island where stood a delightful kiosk built of bricks—and on each brick in red letters a title—and each title the name of a work by Dumas.

Guests stood amazed before this evidence of the work that Dumas had accomplished. Inside the place was beautifully draped with blue hangings. But there was no furniture except a plain deal table, a chair, and a supply of ink, quills, and paper. The master may have written enough works so that their titles could build a small house, but he was by no means finished.

He was writing more. And indeed he had to. When you have a conservatory, flower and fruit gardens, an aviary, a coach house and stables, plus a poultry yard, a monkey house, and dog kennels . . . and mistresses, one after the other, and friends dropping in at all hours, with the table spread with food and wine night and day, when you have all that, you must work.

Dumas worked like a madman. Flinging serial after serial, book after book, play after play against his mountainous expenses. But he couldn't meet them. Each time one of his mistresses went—a mistress who for a time had functioned as if she were his wife, not only sleeping with him, but taking charge of his household—each time such an affair came to a crisis and a split, the beauty would move out with a good part of his furnishings.

His son would one day report that he had overheard his father screaming: "Take! Take whatever you like—only leave me my genius!"

In the end the house had to go too. And what Dumas had spent hundreds of thousands of francs for, went for a tenth of the cost.

But Dumas kept his genius. Nobody could take that from him. Nor his good humor. The proof of which is in this extract which we would have quoted in full, if we had not interrupted ourselves in order to explain what Dumas meant by that opening paragraph or two, and which we now repeat:

On my return to France, I found my house, which I was building on the Marly road, pretty nearly finished. In a few weeks' time I had the papering and woodwork of the whole of one floor completed, so that I was able to satisfy the wishes of my landlord at the *Villa Medicis*, who, finding that I had spent between seven and eight thousand francs on improvements to his property, had conceived the very natural desire of going back to it himself and thus enjoying life there all the more considering that it was at the expense of someone else.

I left Saint-Germain, therefore, to go and live at the Porte-Marly, in the much-discussed house which was subsequently christened Monte-Carlo by Madame Mélingue, and which later on made such a noise in the world.

Michel, my head gardener, had long before this made all his arrangements for the accommodation of my animals. I am bound to say that he paid far more attention to their comfort, than he did to mine, or for that matter, to his own.

I do not know what is the condition of Monte-Cristo nowadays; but I do know that, in the time of my occupancy, there was neither wall nor ditch nor hedge nor enclosure of any sort about the place. Consequently men as well as animals could enter at their own sweet will, walk about where they pleased, pluck the flowers and gather the fruits, without any fear of being charged with trespass or burglary. As for the animals—and it is to the dogs I would specially refer—Pritchard, who was naturally of a very hospitable disposition, did the honors of the house with an agreeable freedom from any formality, a disinterestedness that was quite Highland in its character.

This hospitality was practiced by Pritchard in the most simple and antique fashion. He would squat well in the middle of the Marly road, go up to every dog that passed with that low growling that is half a threat and half a friendly greeting, and is the canine manner of saying "How d'ye do?"—smell the newcomer in the orthodox way, and submit to the same ceremony himself.

Then, as soon as a proper understanding had been reached by dint of these little familiarities, conversation would begin on something like the following lines:

"Have you a good master?" the strange dog would ask.

"Oh, not bad," Pritchard would say.

"And are you well fed at your place?"

"Why, we have a meat pie twice a day, bones for breakfast and dinner, and all through the day anything we can prig from the kitchen."

The strange dog would lick his chops at the mere thought.

"Plague on't!" he would say, "you've nothing to complain of!"

"I'm not complaining," Pritchard would declare.

Then, seeing the strange dog looking pensive:

"Would you like to dine with me?" Pritchard would invite him.

Dogs never have the silly habit men are prone to of waiting to be pressed.

The guest always accepted eagerly, and at dinnertime I was greatly surprised to see an animal I knew nothing about walk in under Pritchard's escort, sit down on my right, if Pritchard took the left, and paw my knee coaxingly in a fashion that told me plainly what flattering accounts he had received of my kindly and Christian disposition.

No doubt invited by his host to spend the evening with him, as he had spent the day, the dog stayed on, and presently, finding it was too late for him to get home, found a comfortable place for himself somewhere about the premises, and there slept off his heavy meal.

Next morning, when the time came to go, the dog would stroll once or twice in the direction of the road, then, thinking better of it, would remark to Pritchard:

"Would it be making very bold if I stayed on in the house?"

To which Pritchard would reply:

"With a little care and ingenuity you can very easily make them think you are the dog from next door. Then in a day or two nobody will think any more about you, and you will be one of the household, every bit the same as those lazy apes that do nothing whatever all day long, and that greedy vulture that does nothing but gobble guts, and that squalling macaw that shouts all the time without ever knowing what it's talking about."

So the dog would stay where it was, hiding itself a bit the first day, wagging its tail at me the second, gamboling at my heels the third, and there would be an inmate the more of my establishment.

This sort of thing went on. Until one day Michel asked me:

"Does Monsieur know how many dogs we have on the premises?"

"No, Michel, I don't."

"Sir, there are thirteen of them."

"It is an unlucky number, Michel, and we must take care they don't all sit down to table together; there would infallibly be one that would die first."

"But that's not the point, sir," insisted Michel.

"Well, what is it, then?"

"Why, these fine chaps could eat up an ox a day, horns and all."

"Do you really think they would eat the horns, Michel? I cannot believe it myself."

"Oh! if Monsieur takes it like that, I've no more to say."

"You are wrong, Michel; speak out, and I will take it exactly as you prefer."

"Well, sir, if you give me a free hand, I'll just take a good whip and I'll turn the whole crew out of doors this very morning."

"Come, Michel, let us be reasonable. All these dogs, after all, are paying a compliment to the house by staying here. Give them a grand dinner today and tell them it's a farewell feast; then at dessert you will put them all out at the door."

"How does Monsieur think I am going to put them out at the door? There *is* no door."

"Michel," I replied gravely, "we must put up with certain conditions of locality and social position and inherited disposition, such as we have unfortunately been endowed with by fate. The dogs are in the house, and, by the Lord! they must just stay there. I don't suppose, anyhow, it's the dogs will ever ruin me, Michel. Only, for their own welfare, see to it they are not thirteen for the future."

"Well, sir, I'll drive one away, and make them a dozen."

"No, Michel, let another one come in, so as to make fourteen."

Michel heaved a sigh.

"If it were a pack, that would be something," he muttered.

Well, it was a pack—and a very strange pack at that. There was a wolf dog, a poodle, a water spaniel, a mastiff, a basset hound with twisty legs, a mongrel terrier, a mongrel King Charles—there was even an unbelievable dog with never a hair on his body except a tuft on the top of the head and a plume at tip of his tail.

Well, all this crew lived together on the very best of terms, and might have given an example of brotherly love to a phalanstery or a community of Moravian brethren. True, at mealtimes there would be a snap now and then to right or left; there would be some love quarrels between rivals, in which, as always, the weaker would go to the wall; but the most touching harmony would be instantly restored the moment I appeared in the garden. Not an animal, no matter how lazily stretched in the sun, no matter how luxuriously curled up on the soft turf, no matter how amorously engaged in conversation with a canine mistress, but would break off his sleep or love-making to sidle up to me with affectionate eye and waving tail. All did their best to manifest their gratitude, each in his own way— some by slipping familiarly between my legs, others by getting up on their hind paws and begging, others by jumping over the stick I held for them, whether for the Czar of Russia or the Queen of Spain, but positively refusing to leap for the poor King of Prussia, the humblest and most hackneyed of all monarchs, not only at home but among the canine population of all Europe.

We recruited a little spaniel bitch named Lisette, and the number of our pack was duly raised to fourteen.

Well, these fourteen dogs, when all was said and done, cost me say fifty or sixty francs a month. A single dinner to five or six of my literary brethren would have demanded three times the sum, and then they would have left my house, saying, very likely, "his wine is decent enough, but that doesn't make his books any less the rubbish that they are."

Among all the pack Pritchard had chosen out a comrade and Michel a favorite. This was the basset hound with twisty legs, a short, thickset animal, that seemed to walk on his stomach, and at utmost speed might perhaps have covered a league in an hour and a half, but, as Michel was never tired of saying, the finest organ (I mean for barking) in all the department of the Seine-et-Oise.

It was quite true; Portugo—that was the basset's name—had one of the finest bass voices ever uttered by dog in pursuit of rabbit, hare, or roebuck. Sometimes at night, as I sat at work, these majestic tones would make themselves heard about the neighborhood, and it was a sound to rejoice the heart of St. Hubert in his grave. Now, what was Portugo after at this hour of the night, and why was he up and about when the rest of the pack were sleeping? The mystery was resolved one morning.

"Would Monsieur like," Michel asked me, "would Monsieur like to have a nice dish of stewed rabbit for his breakfast?"

"Very good," I said; "has Vatrin sent us some rabbits, then?"

"Oh, Monsieur Vatrin! why it's over a year since I've set eyes on him."

"Well, where did they come from, then?"

"Monsieur doesn't need to know where the rabbit came from, provided the stew is all right."

"Take care, Michel, take care; you will get yourself caught one of these days."

"Why, what *do* you mean, sir? I have not so much as touched my gun since the end of the shooting season."

I could see that Michel had made up his mind to tell me nothing that time; but I knew him well enough to be quite sure he would open his lips one day or another.

"Why, yes, Michel," I told him, answering his original question, "I should be very glad to eat a good dish of stewed rabbit."

"Does Monsieur prefer to cook it himself or to let Augustine see to it?"

"Let Augustine attend to it, Michel; I have work to do this morning."

It was Michel who waited at breakfast that morning instead of Paul; he wished to see how much I liked his stew.

The much-talked-of dish appeared in due course, and I finished it to the last scrap.

"So Monsieur liked it?" Michel asked, beaming with satisfaction.

"Excellent, excellent!"

"Well, Monsieur can have one like that every morning, if he so pleases."

"What, Michel, every morning? It seems to me you are going ahead pretty fast, my friend."

"I know what I'm talking about."

"Well, Michel, we shall see. Stewed rabbit is very good; but there is a certain tale entitled *Eel-pie*, the moral of which is we must never abuse a good thing—not even stewed rabbit. Besides, before consuming such a lot of rabbits, I should like to know where they come from?"

"Sir, you shall know this very night, if you will condescend to come with me."

"Did I not say you were a poacher, Michel?"

"Oh no, sir! I'm as innocent as a newborn babe. As I said before, if only Monsieur will come with me tonight . . ."

"Is it far, Michel?"

"Only a hundred yards from this spot, sir."

"What time?"

"When Monsieur hears Portugo's first bark."

"Well, so be it, Michel; if you see a light in my room when Portugo first gives cry, I am your man."

I had almost forgotten I had pledged my word to Michel, and was working away as usual, when about eleven o'clock of a magnificent moonlight night Michel walked into my room.

"Well," said I, "I don't think Portugo has given voice, has he?"

"No," he told me; "but it struck me that, if Monsieur waited till then, he would miss the most curious part of all."

"Why, what should I miss, Michel?"

"Monsieur would not see the Council of War."

"Council of War! What Council of War?"

"The Council of War between Pritchard and Portugo."

"You are quite right; it must be a curious sight."

"If Monsieur will come down now, he can see it."

I followed Michel, and presently, as he had led me to expect, I saw in the midst of the encampment of the fourteen dogs, lying each as he found most comfortable, Portugo and Pritchard sitting up solemnly on their tails and apparently debating some question of the last importance.

This point decided, the pair separated. Portugo darted out of the gate, struck into the upper Marly road, which bounded the property on that side, and disappeared.

As for Pritchard, he showed every sign of having time to spare, and started off at a leisurely pace to follow the bypath that, after passing alongside the island in the river, mounted the hill behind the quarry.

We in turn set off after Pritchard, who appeared to pay no attention to us, though he had evidently scented our presence.

The dog climbed to the top of the quarry, which was planted with vines extending as far as the Marly road above. There he examined the ground with the utmost care, keeping to the line of the quarry, until he lighted on a scent, sniffed and found it fresh, advanced a few yards along a furrow formed by a double line of vinestakes, crouched flat on his belly, and waited.

Almost at the same moment, Portugo's first bark could be heard five hundred yards away. The plan of campaign was now clear. At nightfall the rabbits always quitted the quarry and scattered to feed. Pritchard would then nose out the scent of one of them, while Portugo, making a wide detour, chased the rabbit. Now rabbits and hares invariably hark back on their own track, and Pritchard, enscreened treacherously in ambush, awaited the creature's return.

And so it was; the nearer Portugo's barks approached, the more brilliantly we saw Pritchard's yellow eyes gleam. Then suddenly, using all four paws as a sort of quadruple spring, he gave a leap, and we heard a little scream of surprise and distress from the victim.

"The trick's done!" exclaimed Michel, and going up to Pritchard, he took a very fine rabbit out of his jaws, and finished it with a sharp blow on the back of the neck. He disemboweled it there and then, dividing the entrails between the two dogs, who shared them amicably, feeling presumably only one regret, that Michel's interference, backed by my authority, robbed them of the whole to leave them only a part. As Michel said, I might, if I had so desired, have had every morning for breakfast a nice dish of stewed rabbit.

Chapter XIII

THE WIT AND THE TRAVELER

Impossible to compile an anthology of Dumas and not do him an injustice in some field or other. The man was just too prolific. I have explained my injustice to Dumas with respect to his plays; and I shall here and now apologize to him for my injustice to his verse (which critics claim isn't much good anyhow, though I haven't given it the attention I ought in order to be sure, and furthermore wouldn't be able to translate if I wanted to include any); and as for his short stories, I shall simply plead guilty of having skimped him there and take whatever punishment I deserve; nor have I given a single extract from his great Valois series of novels; but I think it is chiefly in the matter of his travel writings that I have done him the greatest injustice.

I have done justice neither to his Swiss travel impressions, nor to his Spanish and Algerian. I have quoted nothing from his travels to Russia down to the Caucasus. And only a bit (concerning the corricolo) from his Italian travels. And an even smaller bit from his later Italian voyages that include the story of Dumas and Garibaldi.

So I shall give a small piece from *The Speronara* of 1835, that may atone in part for my many omissions from those still very readable and sprightly travel books.

But before I do so, I wish to bring up another area in which I would not want to do an injustice to Dumas. Because excerpts from his written works are still not enough to convey the whole of this man. I refer to Dumas's ability as a conversationalist. Concerning which I quoted in my own novel, *King of Paris*, the following paragraph from the diary of the Goncourt brothers:

"Dumas is a kind of giant with the hair of a Negro, the salt beginning to mix with the pepper, and with little blue eyes buried in his flesh like those of a hippopotamus, clear and mischievous; and an enormous moon-face, exactly the way cartoonists love to draw him.

"No doubt about it: there's a magnetism that radiates from him. A king of mesmerism. You sense at once the showman of freaks and prodigies; the vender of wonders; the traveling salesman for the *Arabian Nights*. He talks volubly and, it must be admitted, engagingly; but what holds you is not brilliance, nor mordancy, nor color; it is an endless array of facts, astounding facts, facts that he keeps dredging up in a pleasantly hoarse voice from a memory that is like a bottomless ocean."

I feel that this is a rather grudging admission of genius, torn from the unwilling Goncourts. They hold it against him that he fascinates his audience, and find that it cannot be ascribed to brilliance, nor mordancy, nor color. But simply to quantity and astounding strangeness.

But some wit the man certainly had. And there exists at least one book that is nothing but a compilation of Dumas's ability at repartee, for which he was in fact famous in his time.

At the age of sixty, being backstage while one of his plays was being rehearsed, he held three young actresses in gallant conversation, so that the director felt forced to say to this old roué: "Aren't you ashamed of yourself. At your age?"

To which Dumas replied: "My age? Why I'm exactly twenty years old for each of them."

With the rival playwright Alexandre Soumet, Dumas had the following experience. (Incidentally Soumet was in that time the greater man. The French Academy had elected Soumet to its membership, an honor which it never gave to Dumas. In his day Soumet was looked up to as the great man who had written a poem rivaling Milton and Dante, a poem depicting how Christ, after having died for mankind, decided to save the damned in Hell, and expiate for their sins too. Today Soumet and his great *Divine Epos* have lost their place in literature, and the space that used to be given to them is now given to Dumas. Lanson, for example, in his history of French literature, doesn't even mention Soumet, and Marcel Braunschvig in his compilation, scarcely does more than print his name.)

But this Soumet once sat with Dumas while one of Soumet's plays was being given its last performance. Dumas nudged Soumet and drew his attention to a spectator who was obviously asleep.

"You see, my dear Soumet," said Dumas, "why your play must close."

The next night, in the same theater, one of Dumas's plays was being given, and both men sat together again. And now Soumet, to his delight, was also able to discover a sleeping spectator.

"It seems, my dear Dumas," Soumet said triumphantly, "that one can be put to sleep by your plays too."

Dumas didn't hesitate for a moment: "Why that's the same man who was asleep last night. He hasn't been able to wake up yet!"

Many stories are told of the relations of the two Dumases, Dumas *père* and Dumas *fils*. Cartoons were drawn in which the older man was depicted as a baby in the arms of the younger one, with the caption: "What trouble this child gives to his son."

Dumas *fils* was even in the habit of introducing his father in this manner: "Here is my grown-up child whom I had when I was very small."

The escapades of the older man often humiliated the son, who early in life took to writing plays that were filled with preaching against the sinful life. And one of these escapades of the father drew a reproving: "What a great boy you are!" from the son. To which the father answered: "That's more than I was ever able to say of you, Alexandre."

Once, when the two men had set off on a trip together they discovered at their first stopping place that they had left behind the keys to their trunks.

"What a pair of idiots we are!" Dumas exclaimed.

"No need to couple the two of us in this," Alexandre said with some irritation.

"Very well then: what an idiot you are!" said the father.

Best known perhaps is the story of Dumas being solicited for a donation to help bury a poor man. When he heard that the man had been a bailiff, one of those process servers who had been the bane of his existence, since Dumas was in perpetual financial confusion and perpetually being sued, Dumas asked:

"How much should I give?"

"Five francs," he was told, "would be a suitable gift."

"Five francs to bury a bailiff?" Dumas exclaimed. "Here are ten. Bury two of them!"

But now back to our piece from *La Speronara*, to make up slightly for our injustice to Dumas's travel books.

Since the eruption of 1781, Etna has had now and then some occasional slight notion of upsetting things in Sicily. But these have been mere whims, as is shown from the fact that they have had no serious results. We have the right to assume, therefore, that what she has done has been merely for the sake of self-respect, and to preserve and defend her position as not just some hill or other, but a volcano.

Among the many minor eruptions, the most noteworthy, because the most terrible, was that of 1669. As this eruption issued from the Monte-Rosso which is only half a mile from where we were, in Nicolosi, Jadin and I started out to see this crater, after promising our host, Signore Gemellaro, to dine with him.

It should be distinctly understood that Etna considers herself too far above all other volcanoes to behave as routinely as they do. Vesuvius, Stromboli, and even Hecla pour the lava from the top of their craters, as wine overflows too full a glass. Etna does not give herself that trouble. Her crater is merely a show crater, a crater of ceremony, which contents itself with playing cup-and-ball, tossing off incandescent rocks as large as ordinary houses, which the eye can follow in their aerial ascension just as it can follow the flight of shells from a mortar; but during that exhibition the real eruption is going on elsewhere.

When Etna is in travail there rises on her back, in one spot or another, a species of boil about the size of Montmartre; then the boil bursts, and a river of lava pours down following the slope, burning or overthrowing everything on its way until it ends in the sea. This method of proceeding is the reason why Etna is covered with a quantity of little crater cones that look like huge haycocks; each of these secondary volcanoes has its name and its own particular date, and all have made in their time more or less noise, and done more or less damage.

The Monte-Rosso is in the first rank of this secondary aristocracy; it would be considered, in any neighborhood but that of the Andes, the Cordilleras, and the Alps, a very pretty little mountain, of an altitude of nine hundred feet; that is to say, three times the height of the towers of Notre-Dame. This volcano owes its name to the terrous scoriae of which it is formed; the ascent is easy, and a climb of half an hour brings one to the crater. This is a species of well, with a division at the bottom like a salt-and-pepper cellar, which at the present time has a good-natured air of perfect tranquillity. Although there is no path into it, persons can, if necessary, be lowered down by ropes; its depth is about two hundred feet, its circumference five or six hundred.

This was the mouth, now mute and cold, from which there issued, in 1669, such a rain of stones and ashes that the sun was, literally, obscured for three months, and the wind blew the ashes to Malta. The violence of the evacuation was such that a rock fifty feet long was flung to a distance of one thousand feet from the crater whence it came, to where it plunged into the ground to a depth of twenty-five feet. Then the lava followed the rock, rose boiling to the orifice, overflowed on the southern slope, and, leaving Nicolosi to right and Boriello to left, began to flow, not as a torrent but as a river of fire, covering with its burning current the villages of Campo-Rotondo, San Pietro, and Gigganeo, till it threw itself into the harbor of Catania, driving before it a portion of the town.

There a terrible struggle between fire and water began; the sea, forced back, at first gave way and recoiled three-quarters of a mile disclosing its depths to the human eye. Ships were burned in port, large fish floated dead to the surface of the water. Then, as if furious at its defeat, the sea returned to attack the lava. The struggle lasted fifteen days; finally, the vanquished lava stopped, and from its molten state passed to a solid one. Fifteen days longer the sea boiled still, stiffening the new shore it was forced to accept; then, little by little, the ebullition ceased. But the entire region was devastated; three villages were annihilated, Catania was three-fourths destroyed, and its port more than half filled up.

From the top of Monte-Rosso, or rather the Monti-Rossi, for this crater divides into two summits like Vesuvius, one sees the whole of this flow of lava, five leagues long and at places three leagues wide, which two centuries have been unable to cover with more than two inches of earth. From the point where I stood, to right, to left, before and behind me, within the circumference my eye could take in, I counted twenty-six mountains, all produced by volcanic eruptions and similar in form and height to the one on which I was.

In turning my eyes around me I observed at the foot of another extinct volcano, the remains of the famous convent of San Nicolà il

Vecchio, and on our way down from the Monti-Rossi we visited its ruins. It was built, according to Farello, by Count Simon, grandson of the Norman, Roger, the most popular conqueror of Sicily, known to this day by every peasant as the "Comte Ruggiero." Some *savants* insist that the monastery stands on the site of the ancient city of Inessa; others declare that the said ancient city stood on the opposite slope of Etna; volumes on the subject have been exchanged between the erudites of Catania, Taormina, and Messina, with the result that the facts are more obscure than before; each and all having such excellent proofs for their own opinion. On my return to Catania one of these savants asked me what was thought on the subject by the Academy of Sciences in Paris. I replied that the Academy of Sciences, after pondering this grave question for some time, had recognized the fact that two cities of Inessa may have existed, built in rivalry to each other; one by the Naxians on the southern slope of Etna, the other by the Siccans on the northern slope. The *savant* struck his brow as though he felt illuminated by a sudden idea, ran to his desk, took a pen, and began a volume which, as I have since been told, throws a flood of light on this important question.

This monastery, where, according to the intentions of its pious founder, the Benedictines were condemned to live exposed to the ravages of the volcano which their prayers ought to have exorcised, is now little more than a ruin. The parts best preserved are the chapel and the famous hall where Count Weder, a second Faust, was present at the saturnalia of Gaetano-Mephistopheles. A plateau which overhangs the monastery is nothing else than a mass of black lava rent into deep gulfs, from the upper part of which we could look down upon an amphitheater of extinct craters.

After inspecting the ruins of this doubly interesting monastery we descended to dine, at half past four o'clock, with our excellent host, Gemellaro, and with all the more alacrity because our morning meal had well prepared us for a second. We found the table laid, having hit upon the rare and fleeting moment when no one waits or causes others to do so.

Signore Gemellaro is one of those learned men in whom I delight; skilled experimenters, who detest all theories and talk only of what they have seen. During dinner the conversation rolled, of course, upon the mountain of our host. I say *his* mountain, for he is well convinced that Etna belongs to him, and he would be much astonished if the King of the Two Sicilies set up a counterclaim. After Etna, that which Signore Gemellaro thinks grandest and finest is Napoleon, that other extinct volcano, which, during an eruption of fourteen years, caused such earthquakes under thrones and empires. His dream was to possess a complete collection of all the engravings made upon his hero. I distressed him by telling him there were enough to load four vessels, and that the crater of Monte-Rosso could not contain them.

After dinner our host inquired into the preparations we had made for ascending Etna. We told him they were limited to a bottle of rum and the roasting of two or three chickens. Signore Gemellaro then cast his eyes on our costumes, and observing Jadin with a woollen shirt and me with a linen jacket, he asked us, shivering, if we had neither cloaks nor overcoats. We told him that for the moment we possessed absolutely nothing but what was on our backs. "True Frenchmen!" he muttered, rising. "No German or Englishman would start in that way. Wait, wait!" And he fetched us two heavy overcoats with hoods, like our military greatcoats, assuring us that we should not be a couple of miles above Nicolosi before we did homage to his foresight.

Our talk lasted till nine that night, when the guide came around with our mules. We asked him if he had succeeded in procuring provisions. He showed us four of those miserable fowls that exist only in Italy; all four were not worth a good tame pigeon. He had also bought two bottles of wine, bread, grapes, and pears; with that, he said, anyone could make the tour of the world.

We mounted our animals and set out into a night that seemed to us, coming from a lighted room, to be frightfully dark; but, little by little, we began to distinguish the landscape, thanks to the myriad of stars that strewed the sky. At first we felt, by the way our mules sank beneath us, that we were crossing sand. Soon we reached the second region, that of forests, if indeed a few sparse, sickly, stunted trees deserved that name. We rode through it for nearly two hours, following with confidence the path our guide, or rather our mules, had taken; a path which, to judge by its eternal ups and downs, seemed frightfully rugged.

Already, for more than an hour, we had felt the justice of Signore

Gemellaro's predictions with regard to cold, so that when we arrived
at a species of hut without a roof, where our mules stopped of
themselves, we put on our hooded coats. This hut was called the
"Casa del Bosco" or "della Neve"—house of the wood or the snow—
names that suit it successively, summer and winter. This, said our
guide, was our halting place. We were now halfway up the path to
the Casa Inglese, only we had, as the peasants say, eaten our white
bread first.

The Casa della Neve was a prelude to the desolation that awaited
us higher up. Without roof, without shutters, without doors, it offered
us no shelter but its four walls. Fortunately, our guide had supplied
himself with a little axe; he brought us an armful of wood, and with
the help of a phosphorus match we kindled a roaring fire. The
reader will understand how welcome it was when I tell him that a
little pocket thermometer that I carried with me went down 18
degrees (Réaumur) since leaving Catania.

Our fire lighted, the guide advised us to go to sleep, and he left
us alone to attend to his mules. We tried to follow his advice; but
no! we were as wide-awake as mice; it was impossible to close an eye;
but we made up for sleep by several glasses of rum and a variety of
jokes on Parisian friends, who were at that hour snugly taking their
tea and little thinking that Jadin and I were gadding among the
forests and craters of Etna. We remained, sleepless, in the hut till
half past twelve o'clock, at which hour our guide requested us to
remount our mules.

During our halt the heavens were enriched with a crescent moon;
slim as it was it cast a little light; the trees were becoming fewer and
fewer, until they ceased altogether. We were now entering the third
region, and we could feel by the feet of our mules when they were
walking on lava, when they crossed over ashes, or when they were
trampling a species of moss, the only vegetation that grows at that
height. As for our eyes, they were of little or no utility; the ground
appeared to them more or less colored, and that was all; we were
quite unable in such obscurity to distinguish details.

The higher we went, the more intense became the cold, and in
spite of our coats and hoods we were frozen. This change of temperature had suspended conversation; each of us, concentrated within
himself as if to preserve what warmth he had, rode on silently. I went

first, and though I could not see the ground on which we advanced, I could perfectly distinguish on our right gigantic escarpments and vast peaks rising like giants, their black forms defined upon the indigo sky. The farther we advanced, the more these apparitions took on a weird, phantasmal aspect; one felt that nature had never made these mountains thus; but that some long and mighty struggle had despoiled them. We were crossing the battlefield of Titans; we were climbing Pelion piled on Ossa.

It was all terrible, somber, majestic; I saw and felt the poesy of this noctural journey, but I was so cold that I had no courage to exchange a word with Jadin to ask him if these visions were the effect of torpor, or whether I was dreaming. From time to time strange mysterious noises, resembling no noises that I had ever heard, came from the bowels of the earth, which seemed to moan and groan like a living being. These noises had something unexpected, lugubrious, and solemn that made one shiver. Often, at the sound, the mules would stop and bring their smoking nostrils to the soil, then, raising their heads, neigh sadly, as if they wanted to make it known that they comprehended that great voice of the Solitude, and that it was not of their own will they had come there to trouble its mysteries.

Ever as we rose, minute by minute the cold became more intense; scarcely had I strength to lift my flask of rum to my lips. Moreover, that operation was followed by another more difficult still—that of corking the flask; my hands were so frozen that they had no sensation of the things they touched, and my feet were so heavy they seemed to have an iron weight attached to each leg.

At last, feeling that I was stiffening into torpidity more and more, I made an effort over myself, stopped my mule, and dismounted. While doing this, Jadin passed me on his animal. I asked him if he did not want to do likewise; he shook his head in sign of refusal and rode on. At first it was impossible to walk; I seemed to be setting my naked feet on millions of pins and needles. The idea occurred to me to use my mule, and I grasped his tail. But he was too well satisfied at having got rid of me not to preserve his independence if he could. Hardly had he felt the contact of my hand when he flung out his two hind legs; one of them struck me in the thigh and threw me ten feet back. My guide ran to help me and lifted me up.

Nothing was broken; moreover, the commotion had put my blood in circulation; I felt almost no pain, although my fall showed that the blow had been violent. I began to walk and I felt much better. A hundred steps farther on I found Jadin waiting for me. My mule, which had joined his without me or the guide, told him that an accident of some kind had happened. I reassured him, and we went on, I on foot. It was now two o'clock in the morning. The somber arch of the sky was beginning to pale; a faint dawn lighted the ground on which we trod, bringing with it a more glacial air than that we had hitherto breathed. In this pallid, lusterless light we presently saw before us something that looked like a house; we approached it, Jadin on his mule at a trot, and I running as best I could. The guide pushed open a door, and we entered the Casa Inglese, built at the foot of the cone for the comfort of travelers.

My first cry was for fire; it was one of those instinctive desires which are easier to form than to see accomplished; the upper limits of the forest are six long miles from the Casa, and in its neighborhood—all lava, ashes, and snow—not a blade of grass, not a plant can grow. The guide lighted a lamp that he found in a corner, closed the door as hermetically as possible, and told us to warm ourselves as best we could by wrapping our hooded coats about us and eating something, while he took the mules to the stable.

As, all things considered, the wisest thing to do was to get out of the state of torpor in which we were, we began to tramp up and down as well as we could. Within the house the thermometer was 6 degrees below zero (Réaumur), a difference of 41 degrees from the temperature of Catania.

Our guide returned, bringing a handful of straw and a few dry branches, which we owed no doubt to the munificence of some Englishman who had preceded us. It sometimes happens that those worthy insularies, always perfectly well-informed as to the precautions they ought to take, hire an extra mule, and in crossing the forest load it with wood. Little of an Anglomaniac as I am, this is a piece of advice that I give to whosoever intends to make the ascent of Etna. A mule costs one piaster, and I know I would gladly have given ten louis for a faggot.

The sight of the fire, however short its duration, restored our courage. We gathered to it as if to devour it, stretching our feet into the flame; and then, a little thawed, we proceeded to think of breakfast.

Everything was frozen—bread, chickens, wine, fruits; nothing but our rum remained intact. We devoured two of the chickens as if they were larks; we gave the third to our guide and kept the fourth for hunger to come. As for the fruit, it was like biting into ice; we therefore drank a cup of rum in place of dessert and felt ourselves a little revived.

It was half past three o'clock in the morning. Our guide reminded us that we had still before us an ascent of three-quarters of an hour at the very least, and that if we wished to reach the summit of the cone before sunrise there was no time to lose.

We left the Casa Inglese. Objects were now beginning to be distinguishable; all around us extended a vast plain of snow, from the middle of which, sloping at an angle of 45 degrees or about that, rose the cone of Etna. Below us all was darkness; in the east alone, the faintest tint of opal colored the sky, on which were vigorously defined the mountains of Calabria.

At a hundred steps beyond the Casa we found the first billows of a plain of lava, its jet-black tones contrasting with the snow in the midst of which it lay like a somber island. We were forced to mount its solid waves, clambering from one to another as I had already done at Chamonix upon the Mer de Glace—with this difference, that the sharp spines of the lava cut the leather of our boots and wounded our feet. This crossing which lasted a quarter of an hour, was one of the most painful incidents of the trip.

At last we reached the foot of the cone, which, though it rises thirteen hundred feet from the plateau on which we stood, was entirely free of snow, either because its slope is too rapid for the snow to remain, or because its inward fires will not allow a flake upon its surface. This is the cone, eternally in motion, that changes its shape with every new eruption, burying that shape in the old crater, and reforming itself with another.

We began to climb this new mountain, wholly composed of friable earth, mingled with stones which loosened beneath our feet and rolled away behind us. At certain places the pitch was so steep that we could touch with our hands the slope above us without stooping; and as we rose, the air rarefied and became at every moment less and less breathable. I remembered all that Balmat had told me of his first ascension of Mont Blanc, and I began to feel precisely the same effects.

Though we were already nearly a thousand feet above the line of eternal snows and had still eight hundred feet to climb, the hooded coat I had upon my shoulders became unbearable, and I felt it was impossible to carry it a moment longer; it weighed upon me like one of those leaden copes that Dante saw in hell's sixth circle crushing the shoulders of hypocrites. I therefore left it on the path, not having the courage to carry it farther, and told the guide to pick it up as we repassed. Soon it was the same with the stick I held in my hand and the hat I wore on my head. I abandoned the two articles successively, and they rolled to the foot of the cone, where they were stopped by the sea of lava, so steep was the descent. I saw Jadin in his turn getting rid of all the superfluities of his equipment, and stopping at every hundred feet to recover his breath.

We were only a third of the way up; we had taken nearly half an hour to climb four hundred feet; the eastern sky grew lighter and lighter; the fear of not arriving at the summit of the cone in time for the sunrise spurred our courage, and we started with fresh vigor, not pausing to look about us at the vast horizon that enlarged at every step around our feet. But the farther we advanced, the more the difficulties increased; the slope became more rapid, the ground more friable, the air more rarefied. Soon we began to hear, on our right, subterranean roars that forced themselves on our attention; our guide walked in advance, and led us to a fissure from which a great noise issued, and also—as if driven out by some current of air —a thick, sulphurous smoke. Approaching the edge of this cleft we saw, at a depth we could not measure, an incandescent red and liquid bottom. Fortunately, the wind did not send the smoke in our direction, or we should have been asphyxiated, so horrible an odor of sulphur came with it.

After a halt of some minutes on the edge of this furnace, we started again, going up diagonally for greater ease. My head began to beat and ring, as though the blood were coming out of my ears, and the air, that grew less and less breathable, made me pant as if my breath would fail me altogether. I wished to lie down and rest a moment, but the earth exhaled such an odor of sulphur that I could not do so. I then bethought me of binding my cravat across my mouth and breathing through its texture; that relieved me.

At last, little by little, we arrived at three-quarters of the ascent, and we saw at a few hundred steps above us the summit of the mountain. Then we made a final effort and, half upright and partly on all fours, we clambered that short distance, not daring to look below us for fear our heads should turn giddy, so steep was the fall of the ground. At last Jadin, who was a few steps in advance of me, uttered a cry of triumph; he was there! he stood in front of the crater, and a few seconds later I was beside him. We found ourselves literally between two abysses.

Once there, and needing no longer to make violent motions, we began to breathe with more facility; besides which, the spectacle before our eyes was so striking that our discomforts disappeared, great as they were.

We stood in front of the crater—that is to say, of an immense pit, eight miles in circumference and nine hundred feet deep, the walls of this vast excavation being covered from top to bottom with scarified substances of sulphur and alum. At the bottom, insofar as we could see from the distance at which we stood, there was some substance then in ebullition, and from the monstrous abyss rose a slender, tortuous smoke like a gigantic snake standing erect on its tail. The edges of the crater were scooped out irregularly and more or less elevated. We stood on one of its highest points.

Our guide left us for a moment to contemplate that spectacle in silence, merely catching us from time to time by our jackets when we went too near the edge; for the stone is so friable that it might easily give way beneath our feet and renew the old story of Empedocles. Then he asked us to stand at some twenty feet distance from the crater to avoid all risk of accident, and to look about us.

The east, which had passed from the opal tints we had seen at the Casa Inglese to a tender rose, was now suffused with the flames of the sun, whose disk was beginning to rise beyond the mountains of Calabria. On the flanks of those mountains, of a dark and uniform blue, the villages and town detached themselves like small white spots. The Straits of Messina seemed a little river, while to right and left the seas stretched away like mirrors. To the left the mirror was dotted with black specks; these specks were the islands of the Liparian archipelago. From time to time one of them shone out like an intermittent lighthouse; it was Stromboli, casting its flame. To the west, all was still dark. The shadow of Etna was thrown across the whole of western Sicily.

During three-quarters of an hour the sight grew more and more magnificent. I have seen the sunrise from the Righi and the Faulhorn, those titans of Switzerland; but nothing is comparable to what is seen from Etna. Before us, all Calabria from the Pizzo to Cape dell'Armi, the Straits from Scylla to Reggio, the Tyrrhenian Sea, and the Ionian Sea; to the left, the isles of Eolus, seemingly within reach of one's hand; to the right, Malta, floating on the horizon like a semitransparent mist; around us, all Sicily, seen as the bird sees it, with its shores dentelated by capes, promontories, ports, bays, roadsteads; its fifteen cities, its three hundred villages; its mountains that look like hillocks, its valleys like the furrow of a plowshare; its rivers, threads of silver through the meads; and last, the crater, immense, bellowing, filled with flames and smoke; above its head the heavens, and hell beneath its feet. Such a sight made us forget everything—fatigue, danger, suffering. I admired wholly, without restriction, in perfect faith, with the eyes of the body and the eyes of the soul. Never had I seen God so near and, consequently, so great.

We stayed an hour thus, surveying the entire old world of Homer, Virgil, Ovid, and Theocritus, without the idea occurring to either Jadin or myself to touch a pencil, so much did we feel that the scene entered deeply into our hearts and would remain engraved there without the help of sketch or writing. Then we cast a last long look on that horizon of fifteen hundred miles, which is seen but once in a lifetime, and began the descent.

Except for the danger of rolling from the top to the bottom of the cone, the difficulty of descending is not comparable to that of the ascent. In ten minutes we were in the lava island, and a quarter of an hour later at the Casa Inglese. The cold, though stinging, had ceased to be painful; we entered the house to arrange ourselves a little, for our toilet, as I have said, had undergone a variety of modifications during the ascent.

This English house, which the ingratitude of travelers will end by reducing to the condition of the Casa della Neve, is still a precious gift, although an indirect one, of the scientific philanthropy of our excellent host, Signore Gemellaro. He was scarcely twenty years of age before he saw of what incalculable benefit to persons ascending for meteorological experiments would be a house where they could rest during the fatigue of ascension, and get relief from the excessive cold that renders the region uninhabitable. As a result, he addressed his cocitizens, by voice and in writing, several times, trying to obtain from them a voluntary subscription; but his efforts had no success.

About this time a little inheritance came to him; he then resolved to have recourse to no one; and he built with his own money a little house, which he left open gratuitously for travelers. This house was situated, by his calculation and that of his brother, at a height of 9219 feet above sea level. A grateful traveler wrote upon its door these words: *Casa haec quantula Etnam perlustrantibus gratissima.* The house was thenceforth called La Gratissima.

But in building La Gratissima, Signore Gemellaro had done only as much as his individual means enabled him to do; that is, he had given a shelter for scientific men. That was not enough, he thought; he wished to supply means of study to such men by furnishing all the instruments necessary for those meteorological observations that they came from all parts of the world to make. This was at the period when the English occupied Sicily. Signore Gemellaro applied to Lord Forbes, the general of the British army.

Lord Forbes not only adopted Gemellaro's plan, but he resolved to give it an even broader development. He opened a subscription, at the head of which he put his own name for 71,000 francs. The subscription thus headed soon amounted to the desired sum, and Lord Forbes built, close beside the little house of Gemellaro, called for the last seven years La Gratissima, a building of three rooms, two studies, and a stable for sixteen horses. This was the house, a palace compared to its puny neighbour, which was called, after its founders, the Casa Inglese. At the present time La Gratissima is in ruins and the English house, dilapidated more and more by passing travelers, threatens soon to offer them nothing better than the shelter of four walls.[1]

---

[1] (Note in 1902 edition) It was repaired on the occasion of a visit from King Umberto, and is now kept up by the Italian Alpine Club. An observatory has been built beside it.

After a short halt of a quarter of an hour to dispose of our last chicken and the rest of our bread, we left the Casa Inglese and came out upon the plateau called, in derision no doubt, the plain del Frumento (wheat). It was entirely covered with snow, although this was the hottest time of the year. We turned aside to the left to see the valley *del Bove*; at every step we made in the virgin snow we sank six inches at the least.

The valley *del Bove* would make a magnificent decoration for hell in the "Diable Amoureux" or "La Tentation." I have never seen anything more gloomy, more desolate, than this gigantic precipice, with its Cascades of jet-black lava, congealed in their course down the incandescent earth. Not a tree, not an herb, not a moss, not a living thing; a total absence of noise, movement, and life itself. To the three regions dividing Etna there should certainly be added a fourth more terrible than the rest—that of fire. In the depths of the valley *del Bove*, we saw, three or four thousand feet below us, two extinct volcanoes opening their twin jaws. They looked to us like molehills, but they were really mountains 1500 feet high.

It needed all the insistence of our guide to tear us from this spectacle; the assurance that we had thirty miles to go before reaching Catania had little or no effect upon us. There was Catania beneath our feet; we could almost touch it; how could there be those thirty miles the guide talked of?

We mounted our mules, however, and started. Four hours later we were again with Signore Gemellaro; we had quitted him with a feeling of friendship, we returned to him with feelings of gratitude. And yet he is one of the men whom governments forget; no recollection of his merit seeks him out, no favors reward him. Signore Gemellaro is not even a correspondent of the Institute! It is true that this good and dear Gemellaro is neither the better nor the worse for that.

Chapter XIV

ADVENTURE TO THE END

Astonishing career, astonishing genius, astonishing personality, astonishing life. But the end had to come. What was admirable in a young man, and surprising in a middle-aged man, seemed somehow overdone in an old man. Dumas became a little ridiculous when, past sixty, he still turned out novels, plays, verse, articles for his newspapers and magazines, books of travel.

And when he still changed his mistresses as fast as ever.

People took his side in the Gaillardet authorship case, when Dumas's first great melodramatic success on the stage, the *Tower of Nesle*, became the subject of a hot dispute that ended in a lawsuit and finally in a duel between Gaillardet and Dumas. (No damage.) People still took his side when Granier de Cassagnac opened a big campaign against Dumas's plays, accusing him of having stolen all his best scenes by ransacking the plays of the world, those of Shakespeare, Goethe, Caleron, Schiller, etc. A blast that Cassagnac ended up with the following line:

"These I mention only because their names are known to all, but how can I be sure that Dumas did not borrow from lesser-known plays, from God knows what author writing in Turkish, in Chinese, or in the Finno-Ugric language of the Samoyedes."

And still Dumas's star rose. But ten years later came Eugène de Mirecourt's attack, an attack so violent that Dumas was able to have his opponent arrested for libel and put in prison for two weeks. This time it was not just a question of one author, Gaillardet, from whom Dumas was supposed to have taken a story, nor just a question of having copied famous scenes from dead playwrights, this time it was a full-scale attack, mounted with enormous evidence, and involving living writers, people like A. de Leuven, Paul Meurice, Paul Bocage,

Gerard de Nerval, Paul Lacroix, Auguste Maquet, Anicet-Bourgeois, Fiorentino, etc., etc. And of course especially Maquet.

It made no difference that all these people were Dumas's friends, or had been. And that all arrangements between them had been amicable. It made no difference that Dumas could ask: "Show me the *Monte-Cristos* that they have written alone. Show me *The Three Musketeers* that they have written without me!"

It made no difference that Maquet by himself could only write *La Belle Gabrielle,* where one would look (says Henri Clouard in his recent study *Alexandre Dumas,* in which he examines very closely this question) in vain for that which makes a good Dumas novel, the lively dialogues, the gripping plot, the solidity of the argument. Whereas Dumas alone, was still Dumas. For example in his *Memoirs,* in his *Travel Impressions,* in his *Chats* and in some of the novels he is known to have written all by himself.

It made no difference that Dumas could say with genuine honesty: "I have collaborators in the same way that Napoleon had generals." Just as the conquests and the victories were Napoleon's no matter what general commanded what troops, so Dumas's novels and plays were his own, no matter what collaborator was involved. True, Maquet was one of his best and most reliable coworkers. That's why theirs was the longest and most successful collaboration. But there were others.

Mademoiselle de Belle-Isle, for example, was one of Dumas's most successful plays. The original was by Brunswick. But it was only one act long. One of the main characters wasn't in it. The best part of the plot, the wager, wasn't there. And finally: the play was turned down by the theater for which Brunswick had written it.

But it made no difference. Dumas had become something rather unsavory. Popular, yes. Still popular, but in the better literary circles someone who was considered infra dig. Interesting yes, even exciting, but not really acceptable. Forever involved in some new literary scandal.

For example, this scandal, also cited by Henri Clouard. From the period when Dumas was editing his own paper, the *Mousquetaire.* One day one of his assistants, Urbain Fages, who under the name of Savigny was a Hellenist of some note, talked to Dumas about the *Iliad.* Dumas had never read it, and he listened goggle-eyed to Fages's recital of some passages, and his discussion of them both as poetry and as history.

Urbain Fages thought Dumas ought to read the Iliad for himself, but since Dumas didn't know any Greek, Fages set to work to translate the best parts of it for him. Dumas, excited, had these passages set in type and printed in his magazine.

And signed them: Alexandre Dumas! With "continued in our next number!"

The whole literary coterie of Paris buzzed with this new and ridiculous affair. But Dumas remained calm as ever. After all, hadn't he said that if his name would get people to read the Bible, he'd print it over his signature?

All the same it was an exciting paper, Dumas's *Musketeer*. It was modern, varied, full of this and that, whatever might interest people, and never boring. But of course Dumas was still the same spendthrift as ever, and he wrecked it financially, so that a journalistic idea that would eventually conquer the periodical field, and from which anyone else would have made himself into a millionaire, lasted only a short time and then went bankrupt.

His son took to avoiding him. "I see him only at funerals," the old man said. "The next time I see him, it will be mine."

The son didn't mind that his father should have a mistress—though he really couldn't ever forgive him for having let him be born illegitimate, nor could he ever forgive him for the millions he had earned and then spent leaving never a penny that would come to his son—no, he didn't mind that his father should have a mistress—but why should he cheat on her? That was really going too far.

And then the ridiculous aspect of it! His father nearing sixty and announcing to him that he had just had a baby. A girl baby! "I haven't had one for so long, I'm delighted to have a little girl!" She was Micaella Cordier.

So the son, now achieving his own fame as a playwright, avoided his father, and the father felt that his son disapproved of him. Especially after one particular incident.

Dumas had as mistress then a certain Adah Isaacs Menken. She was something of a Dumas herself. An adventuress. Her father was a Spanish Jew named Fuertos, and she was born in New Orleans as Dolores Adios. Her first husband had been a Jewish musician. But she was bursting with spirit and with ambition. She went from the arms of the musician to the arms of a professional boxer, Heenan. And from him to a journalist named Robert Newell.

She wrote poetry not without distinction. She became an actress and made a sensation in *Mazeppa*, a play based on Byron's poem, in which she did a daring appearance bound to a wild horse, apparently naked, but actually in pink skintights. She toured America and Europe in this sensational play, and fascinated such people as Mark Twain, Bret Harte, Joaquin Miller in the New World and Dickens, Charles Reade, Rosetti, and Swinburne in the Old.

And of course Dumas in France.

Adah had always admired Dumas, and Dumas was always ready for a new affair. The two were undoubtedly and genuinely fond of each other, but they committed the innocent indiscretion of having themselves photographed together in poses that were certainly not indecent, but perhaps too coy and too cloyingly sweet for a stout old man with frizzy gray hair, and a luscious young female who made a rich living out of exhibiting herself nearly nude.

The rascal of a photographer had no right to make hundreds of copies and broadcast them over Paris, but he did nevertheless, and the town laughed itself sick over this May–December romance.

Dumas, furious, sued the photographer, and also got himself involved in a duel, from which his son had to rescue him. But the romance was ruined, and it was obvious that the world had had just about enough of Dumas and his noise. From every direction came the cry, expressed in one form or another: you're old! you're old . . .

And thus to Dumas came that terrible moment in life when one realizes that, like everyone else, one is only descended from a long line of dead people, and that such heredity will tell. And that very secret and private little dream of immortality—that generally unconfessed belief that so many of us have that somehow we—just we alone—may somehow elude that heredity—all this "special miracle" which we manage to have faith in so long as we are young and full of energy, all this founders, disintegrates, dissolves, and leaves us face to face with the old syllogism: All men are mortal. Socrates is a man. Therefore Socrates is mortal.

Not that Dumas stopped work. Not that he couldn't be as gay and as energetic as ever. But only at times now, instead of all the time. The great days were over. Still when Prince Metternich asked him if he would autograph his album, Dumas said: "Delighted!" and immediately wrote: "Received from Prince Metternich 25 bottles of his oldest Johannesberg. Signed Alex. Dumas."

The prince laughed and paid up.

No, Dumas went on. Indeed he was to outlive his pretty little Jewish mistress. She suffered a fall from her horse, consumption set in, she lingered for a while, and then died—penniless, in spite of all her huge earnings. Friends erected for her the stone that now stands over her grave at Père Lachaise in Paris. A stone with the short inscription she had desired: "Thou knowest."

There was still life in Dumas. As much as he may have lived in the past with his historical romances, he was never blind to the present. He became excited by the Prussian war against Austria, the so-called Seven Weeks War, when Prussia, determined to exclude Austrian supremacy in some of the little German principalities, attacked Austria, overran the German lands that were allied to her, annexed Schleswig-Holstein, forced Austria to disgorge her Italian possessions, and thus prepared the way for the formation of the German Empire, the Italian kingdom, and the Austro-Hungarian monarchy.

And World War I. And then World War II.

The French people cried out against Napoleon III. Why hadn't he rushed to the relief of Austria and prevented the formation of this powerful German empire, ruled by the militaristic Prussian officer caste?

Dumas immediately accepted an offer from a Parisian anti-Prussian paper to investigate. He traveled to Frankfort, recently occupied by the Prussians, he went to Gotha, Berlin, Hanover. He visited the battlefields of Langesalza and Sadowa, where Austria had been crushed. And he wrote out of the material he gathered a novel that was largely history and to which he gave a prophetic title: *The Prussian Terror*.

From which we quote a passage taking place after the Prussian occupation of Frankfort. Frankfort, one of the free cities of Germany, had irritated Bismarck by condemning his attack on Denmark and opposing his policies toward Austria. Bismarck therefore ordered Frankfort occupied. This was done without any battle and Frankfort did not expect to be treated as a conquered city.

Although Frankfort welcomed the Prussian troops with a military band, General Manteuffel (Americans will recognize this and other names of Prussians in Dumas's book on the Prussian terror) immediately demanded a "war indemnity" of 25 million florins.

Why?

Dumas explains it in these few paragraphs:

The Prussians took no notice whatsoever of any friendly disposition on the part of the citizens.

Two cannon were immediately drawn up by galloping horses. One was aimed at the Zeil, the other at the Horsemarket.

The main Prussian column took up positions on Schiller Square and along the Zeil, remained mounted for perhaps fifteen minutes, and then lined up on foot, at attention, as if expecting orders any moment. The town was almost afraid to draw its breath. It could not know what orders might be given. For hours, until eleven o'clock at night, this terrible wait continued. Then suddenly, just as eleven was sounding from the belfry, the men broke up into groups of ten, fifteen, or twenty, and began to knock on doors, here, there, and took possession of whatever house they chose.

Naturally it was the most comfortable houses of town that they selected. Frankfort was obviously considered a conquered town. Although all this time the town band continued to play music for their "invaders." One battalion of the city had even presented arms for a quarter of an hour. But as the Prussian officers continued to ignore every amicable overture, the local commander could not do anything else but order his men to retire to their barracks, trailing their arms, and with the snares of their drums loosened as if for a military funeral.

And indeed it was a military funeral: the freedom of Frankfort was being laid to rest forever.

The ensuing night was passed in a state of terror as if the town had been taken by assault. Wherever Prussians found a door that didn't open fast, that door was smashed. Cries of terror were heard on all sides, but no one dared to investigate. Since the house of Hermann Mumm appeared to be the largest and most imposing in town, he was ordered to lodge and to feed two hundred soldiers and fifteen officers.

Another home, that of Madame Lutteroth, received orders to shelter fifty soldiers, who found it amusing to shatter the windows and reduce the furniture to firewood. This was justified on the grounds that Madame Lutteroth had supposedly given parties and balls to which she had invited not a single Prussian officer from the nearby garrison.

Accusations of this kind, accusations that served as pretext for any kind of violence, were preferred against all classes of society, from the lowest to the highest. The hotelkeepers were charged with having put their rooms only at the disposal of Austrian officers and declared themselves full when Prussians applied for shelter. And the Prussians retaliated by declaring that since these Frankfort rascals had lent Austria twenty-five million at no interest, anything that one could get from them was no more than they richly deserved.

It was useless to argue back that the town had never in all her history had twenty-five million in her coffers. And furthermore that such a loan would have had to be ratified by a decree of the Senate and the Legislature, and that any examination of the facts would have failed to disclose the slightest trace of such a loan.

It was in this atmosphere of Prussian terror that General Manteuffel, Commander-in-Chief of the Army of the Main, made his demand for a "war indemnity" of twenty-five million. The result of which was that the burgomaster of Frankfort committed suicide. Which didn't stay the hand of the Prussians. They determined to take it out of the citizens.

Dumas now introduces us to the Prussian commander:

General Sturm was a man of some fifty or fifty-two years, built close and solid to the ground, with a small, thick head that looked as if squashed. His round face was splotched with red, giving him a florid complexion that in moments of anger (which were not infrequent) would flame into dark crimson. His skin was hard and about his ears it was actually the color of brick. His graying hair, which he wore short, was thick and frizzy. One could still guess that originally its color had been red.

Because his eyes were sparkling and bold, and his pupils of a reddish gray, and because he never relaxed his stare when he talked, it was as if one was gripped and held fast by them. Moreover even the whites of his eyes seemed as if injected with blood.

His mouth was a slash, wide, with tightly compressed lips, while his teeth were stocky and yellow, festooned with indentations like the cutting-edge of a saw, and stuck into thick red gums. His eyebrows hung low over his eyes, twin dashes that worked his forehead into quick dark frowns. While his nose, high and sharp, was like a beak.

His chin jutted, projecting a short, hard little beard, while his ears were small and close to the skull, as if they too respected the cannon ball appearance of the head, and did not wish to spoil it.

And the cheekbones only added to the appearance of military solidity.

His neck was short, powerfully muscled, with blue-red veins tangling under the skin. Below were the brawny shoulders. Altogether he was compact, with a solid backbone, heavily fleshed, with big hips and bulging thighs and calves.

And with a voice to match: loud, commanding, sonorous. And gestures to go with such a voice: abrupt and brooking no argument. He strode rather than walked, despised danger, but never courted it unless convinced that it could serve for the advancement of his career.

He had a passion for plumes, in particular red ones, or of any showy color. The smell of powder intoxicated him. His words flew from his mouth like bullets, and beware then the man who dared contradict him! For the general's face would turn purple, his gray-red irises would seem to flash lightning, and he would forget everything but his rage. He would swear, insult, strike. And if his anger happened to collide against an equal, he would not hesitate for a moment in giving satisfaction in a duel.

He was not unaware of his spleen and bile, and knew that his life depended on his ability to shoot and handle the sword. And for that reason he spent his every spare moment with the provost and master-at-arms of his regiment, exercising himself in the art of killing.

As a result he was known as a master of steel and powder, and as an opponent with "an unfortunate hand," meaning that where another would have merely wounded, he damaged, and where another would have damaged, he killed.

In fact he had killed opponents ten or twelve times so far, with the result that it became impossible to call him by his real name which was *Ruhig*, for *ruhig* means quiet, peaceful, a name so inappropriate that he was given the nickname of *Sturm*, that is to say storm or tempest, and was now known by none other. Especially after the ferocity he displayed in the war against the Bavarians.

Encountering now the stubborn refusal of the magistrates of Frankfort to pay the twenty-five million demanded by General Manteuffel, General Sturm summoned his chief of staff, Frederick von Bülow.

Frederick, when he first presented himself, found his superior in a relatively calm state. In fact the general was seated, which rarely happened, and he was almost smiling.

"Ah, there you are," he said. "I was asking for you. General Roeder was just here. Where have you been?"

"Excuse me, General," Frederick explained. "I had gone to my mother-in-law for news of one of my friends, who was seriously wounded in the battle."

"Ah, indeed," said the general, "that Austrian. Heard about him. Well, too good of you really to worry about these imperial vermin. I would like nothing better than to see twenty-five thousand of them lying on the battlefield, where I would let them rot from the first man to the last."

"But, Your Excellency, he was a friend . . ."

"Let's say no more—that's not what I wanted to see you about. Besides I'm quite pleased with your work, Baron." General Sturm said this in a voice which another man would have used to say: "I loathe you!" But he went on: "As a matter of fact I would like to do something for you."

As Frederick bowed, the general continued: "I have a slight service that I wish to ask of you. About General Manteuffel's subsidy of twenty-five million. You've heard about it, haven't you?"

"Yes," said Frederick. "A heavy impost laid upon a poor city of only forty thousand inhabitants."

"You mean seventy-two thousand," said Sturm.

"No, there are only about forty thousand actual Frankfortians. There are some thirty thousand others who are not citizens."

"What's the difference?" said Sturm impatiently. "The count is still seventy-two thousand, and General Manteuffel has made his calculations on the statistics."

"But if he has made an error, it seems to me that those who are charged with the execution of his order must point it out to him."

"Ours is not to criticize, but to execute. We are told seventy-two thousand, and that's where it stands. We are told twenty-five million, and that's what we'll collect. Imagine those senators here telling us that they can't collect it, and that we may as well burn the town as to ask them to produce this sum!"

"I was myself present at that meeting," said Frederick quietly, "and it was not in a spirit of resistance that this inability to pay was declared, but in calm and dignified sorrow."

"Twiddle twaddle," said Sturm. "We have our orders. General Manteuffel transmitted them to General Roeder, and General Roeder handed them to the city. If their senate had decided to discuss the matter and show reluctance, that's their own lookout. General Roeder asked me about that, but I told him it was nothing to worry about. I told them that I had in you a chap who had married in this town and knew the place as well as I know the palm of my hand. I said you would indicate to me twenty-five millionaires living here, and that would take care of the matter. . . . There are twenty-five millionaires here, aren't there?"

"More than that," said Frederick.

"Good. We'll start with them. And if we can't collect the whole sum from them, you'll supply us with other names for the balance."

"And you're figuring on me to give you such a list of names?"

"Exactly. Here, sit down, my good fellow, and write me out twenty-five names, and twenty-five addresses."

Frederick sat down, took the pen, and started to write. What he wrote, however, was this:

"My honor forbids me to denounce twenty-five of my fellow citizens. I therefore beg Generals Roeder and Sturm to obtain this desired information elsewhere."

He signed it:

"Frankfort, July 22nd, 1866.
Frederick, Baron von Bülow."

Then, rising, and bowing low, he put the paper in the general's hands.

"So quick?" said the surprised general.

"Read it, General," said Frederick.

The general read it with his face turning purple. "Ah! So that is how I am answered when I ask for a small favor. Well, in that case, let me see how I am answered when I command. I order you to sit down and write . . ."

"Order me to charge a battery, and I will do it, but do not order me to become a tax collector."

"I gave my promise to General Roeder to give him these names and addresses. And I told him that you would supply them. Any moment now he will send for that list. What shall I tell him?"

"You will tell him that I have refused."

General Sturm folded his arms and advanced toward Frederick. "And you think that I will permit a man within my command to refuse me anything."

"I think that upon reflection you will see that you gave me not only an unjust but a dishonoring order, and you will appreciate my inability to obey. Please permit me to leave, and call an officer of the police. He will give you your list, since that falls in the line of his work."

"Baron," said Sturm, "I cannot reward an insubordinate officer." The general's face, already purple, was now splotched with livid marks. His eyes were as if gorged with blood. "The king shall hear of this!" he cried with fury. "The king shall learn how one of his officers refused to serve him!"

"Write your account, sir," said Frederick. "And I too shall write mine. So that the king may know how one of his generals seeks to dishonor an officer!"

Sturm reached out and grabbed up his riding crop. "Dishonored?" he raged. "Did you say dishonored? You will not repeat that word, will you?"

"Dishonored," said Frederick coldly.

Sturm gave vent to a choked cry and raised his whip to strike his young officer, but observing Frederick's utter calm he let his arm fall.

"Who threatens strikes, sir," said Frederick. "I must consider myself as if struck by you."

He turned back to the table and wrote a few lines. Then he opened the door to the antechamber, and calling the officers who were there, he said:

"Gentlemen, I confide this paper to your loyalty. Please read aloud what it says."

The surprised officers read: "I hereby tender my resignations as chief of staff for General Sturm and officer in the Prussian army. Dated at noon July 22, 1866, Frederick von Bülow."

"And what does that mean?" Sturm asked.

"It means that I am no longer in His Majesty's service, nor in yours. And it means that you have insulted me. Gentlemen, this man raised his riding crop against me. And as such owes me reparation. Gentlemen, you have my resignation, and can bear witness that as a man free from all military obligations, I have the right to tell this fellow, who is no longer my chief, and consequently not my superior, that he has given me a mortal insult, and that I must either kill him, or he must kill me."

Sturm burst out laughing.

"You gave me your resignation," he said, "but I did not give you my acceptance of it." He stamped his foot angrily. "Place yourself under arrest! Two weeks prison!"

Frederick snatched off the epaulets from his shoulders. "You have no right to give me an order!" he cried.

This time Sturm foamed at the mouth. Livid with rage he once more raised his whip against his officer and this time brought it down full force, slashing his cheek and striking hard against his shoulder. Frederick uttered a wild cry and leaped back for space to draw his sword.

"Idiot!" cried Sturm. And he burst into laughter. "You will be court-martialed and shot!"

At this Frederick lost his head and threw himself against the general, but found four officers in his path. One of them whispered to him quickly: "Save yourself. We'll calm him."

Frederick, choked up, muttered: "But I—I, who have been whipped—who will calm me?"

The officers clustered about him? "We give you our word of honor that we have seen no blow struck."

"You have not seen it—no. But I have felt it. And inasmuch as I have given my word of honor that one of us must die, I must act accordingly. Good-by, gentlemen."

Two of the officers tried to restrain Frederick, to argue with him. But Sturm's voice stopped them.

"No one is to leave this room!" he thundered. "The provost marshal is to arrest that madman at once!"

Unable to follow Frederick, the officers hung their heads, while Frederick burst from the room. The first person he met on the stairs was the Baroness.

"Good Heavens! What are you doing with a drawn sword?" she asked, frightened.

He quickly put his sword in his scabbard, and ran to his wife to kiss her and the baby.

But ten minutes later a loud explosion was heard coming from Frederick's room. A guard was the first to reach the room and open it.

Frederick lay dead on the floor, his forehead shattered by a bullet. He had left this note on the table:

"Struck in the face by General Sturm, who has refused to give me satisfaction, I could not continue to live in dishonor. My last wish is that my wife, in her widow's dress, should leave this evening for Berlin, and there beg from Her Majesty the Queen the remission of the subsidy of twenty-five million florins, which I testify the town is unable to pay.

Frederick, Baron von Bülow."

Dumas's *The Prussian Terror* was no great success, even though many recognized with him that the new danger to Europe was not in a revival of Napoleonism in France, but in the upsurge of the new Prussian militarism, from that land of docility in peace and ferocity in war: Germany—whose double aspect Dumas was one of the first to see, and whose activity would harass the world for the next eighty years.

"He who has not traveled in Germany," Dumas wrote, "can have no conception of the hatred the Prussians have for us. It is a kind of monomania that has attacked even the most clear-sighted among them. One cannot rise politically in Berlin except by hints, more or less veiled, that someday there will be war against France."

But as André Maurois points out in his book on *The Three Dumases*, who could take seriously a man who was still behaving like a sultan in a harem?

Though Arsène Houssaye, editor of a popular magazine, had reported that Dumas was not afraid of death: "Death will be kind to me," he is supposed to have said, "for I'll tell her a story," the truth is that as he neared his allotted years, he turned gloomy. He was more harassed than ever by financial problems. Sometimes he despaired.

Though five years before his death, Michel Lévy, the publishers, paid him forty thousand gold francs, easily worth $150,000, he was broke. And this wasn't all. For the next year he signed a new con-

tract for an illustrated edition of his works, for another substantial
sum. Dumas would sigh over this financial irresponsibility of his: "I
should have a fortune," he would say. "I've earned millions. Any
other man would have by this time 200,000 francs a year from in-
vestments alone, whereas I have 200,000 francs of debts."

He was by no means through. But the fashion—and the passion
—for Dumas, had gone. He was passé. No doubt of it. Even though
his old plays would still get an occasional production, and even
though his books would go on being printed. And he himself could
travel around France and give lectures, and find everywhere a full
house.

But in his last residence in Paris, on the Boulevard Malesherbes,
his landlord would have to dun him for his rent. His rooms were
bare. The walls showed nails and dark oblongs where paintings had
once hung. His servants complained that they weren't paid, and left
him, taking along some piece of art work in order to pay themselves.

A daughter of his, or some friend, would drop in and clean up a
bit. For this great hulk that had once never known what it was to
be tired, was now almost unwilling to leave his bed. And he would
sometimes sit for hours at his writing table, the place he loved so
much, but he wouldn't write a word.

His clothes were unwashed, unpressed. His furniture dusty. In the
kitchen dirty dishes accumulated, and the stove remained cold, the
fire unlit.

He had written the following, years before, in his travel book *On
Board the Emma:*

The need to work, which on land, unceasingly goads me, which
pursues me at my mealtimes, and even when I am with a beloved
friend or a pretty woman, not only disappears totally when I am at
sea, but becomes even distasteful.

I, who, whether in Paris or in the country, reproach myself for
spending an hour away from my precious writing paper, from my
friendly table, from my ink that slips so sweetly from the nib of
my pen, I, this insatiable monster for work, suddenly discover myself a completely different human being the moment my foot touches
a deck. I remain idle on-board ship, not just for an hour, but for
days on end.

Just as soon as my sight is lost in the immensity of space, my
thoughts lose their sequence, and I become wrapped in a dream.

What do I dream? God only knows. Of the infinite, I dare say, of the universes that roll around me, of the measureless sea sparkling below me.

Then there falls on my senses a delightful twilight, not exactly like the rise of the sun or its setting, but just as sweet. Something that smokers of opium or eaters of hashish would no doubt recognize—a certain kind of voluptuous absence of will power.

If anything should happen to distract me while I am in this floating state, I take it with a smile, for I know that in a moment I can recapture it. And let me say that the *Emma* is as if expressly made for such dreams. This swan from Liverpool carries me aloft as if she were a dream bird. Even when sailing close to the wind, which next to a calm is the most trying thing that can be asked of a ship, her pitching can scarcely be felt. She cuts the waves like a fish, without any effort, without fatigue or suffering. And not a creak is to be heard in her frame. In heavy weather one has no sense of danger. There are none of the shocks that are so trying on steamboats. Here I could work, yes, and how I would work—if the sea did not give me a horror of work.

It was being alone with the sea that did it. In that same chapter he wrote:

To be alone! It is perhaps the only ambition that I have never quite realized. Certain situations in life make solitude impossible. I have gone 60,000 miles to find it and have not found it. Everywhere there is always someone who knows me, or who thinks he knows me, or who wants to know me. And this someone is almost always an important person who cannot be denied, a curiosity-monger who will not be denied, or both.

But to be alone is to gather up all the mental threads that are always being scattered, disordered, broken up by the distractions of society. It is to enter into possession of one's mind which has been endlessly at the mercy of the first newcomer's indiscretions. It is the opportunity to think again of our dear departed, of loved friends. And to put together again the separate pieces of one's heart that one has scattered along the road of life, starting the moment one felt one's heart, and the moment one put one's foot on that road.

Oh think of me, all of you, of whom I would think if I had the happiness of being alone!

He was to have that dubious happiness now in his old age. More and more he felt himself abandoned. He would stir himself up now and then, and work on the one great volume which he had refused to have included in the general sale of his works to the firm of Calmann-Lévy, that is to say his great cookbook.

"There have been many who have read my books and declared afterward that I had no talent as a writer, but there has never been anyone who has tasted my dishes who has contested my ability as a cook."

Perhaps he had never followed his right bent. He should have been a cook, instead of a writer. It was writing novels and plays that had brought him to his present ruin. His cookbook would restore his fortune.

Too bad that he could not look into the future and see how right he was, in some respects. For though there was to be a period during which Dumas would be in eclipse as a literary figure, his cookbook, printed after his death, would become the most valuable of all his first editions, almost unprocurable. Perhaps, as F. W. Reed suggests in his *Bibliography*, because that eleven hundred page book was used in kitchens, and suffered from having its pages turned by fingers smeared with grease, or wet with water, or sticky with sugar.

He had used to be a firm believer in God. "Even in my darkest hour," he wrote in his *Memoirs*, "I have never been tempted to deny our Creator." But old age, when he needed his faith most, somehow deprived him of it. He not only doubted immortality, he doubted the existence of a soul. As for metempsychosis, of what value was it, even if true, since memory disappeared? And there was thus no link between one life and another.

He had doubts about his generation too, a generation that had seemed for him at one time as if breaking the darkness with a torch that would never be extinguished.

With that came a doubt as to whether he himself had written anything that would survive. His son would later tell of a time when he found his old papa absorbed in a book.

"What are you reading?"

"*The Three Musketeers*. I often promised myself that when I was old I would find out whether it was really good."

"Well? Where are you in it?"

"About finished."

"And what's your opinion?"

"It's good."

But when he came to read *Monte-Cristo*, he had this to say: "It's not up to *The Three Musketeers*."

Dumas was in Marseilles in 1870, when he heard of the declaration of war. About the same time he suffered a stroke that half paralyzed him. Nevertheless he recovered enough to seek out his son who was living at Puys.

"I've come to die in your house," he said. His son greeted him warmly and set aside the best room for him. The old man went to bed at once and fell asleep.

He didn't like being old. He didn't like dying. He pitied himself. And now and then he would weep and complain bitterly. But after a while a kind of somnolence set in. He talked little, slept much.

On nice days, even late in the year, he would be wrapped up warmly and rolled out in a wheel chair to the beach, where he would look for hours silently at the ocean. That ocean that he had once said transported him into a kind of voluptuous absence of will power.

His ten-year-old daughter Micaella would write to him from Marseilles, but the son didn't give her letters to her father because she wrote about his illness, and the family wanted to avoid this subject. About once a day Dumas would recover his spirits for a few moments. He would smile and say something cheerful or clever.

Two gold louis taken from his pocket were on the table beside his bed. He showed them one day to his son. "Look at that," he said, "everyone thinks of me as a wastrel. You yourself wrote a play about that and called it *The Prodigal Father*. You see how mistaken people can be? When I came to Paris as a young man, I had two gold louis in my pocket. And I still have them . . ."

The son wanted his own children to keep out of grandfather's room. But Dumas begged that they might come in. "I scarcely know them," he admitted, "but young girls are pure light."

He died peacefully—exhausted, one might say, from so much living, so much fun and so much work—while the German army was just moving toward nearby Dieppe.

He was buried at Neuville cemetery, and after the war, his son had the body taken back to Villers-Cotterêts, to be placed beside that of his father the general, and his mother who had been the daughter of an innkeeper.

Alexandre Dumas *fils*, who had so often been at odds with his father, wrote the following lines about him, which I quote here from the somewhat condensed version that I made of it for my novel.

You came into this world in the age of the great appetite, the age of man the devourer. A poem or two, the *Iliad*, the *Odyssey*, were enough to satisfy the Greeks for centuries. But today a new epic must be forthcoming every day.

Such an age requires heroic workers. And nature has provided such workers. African sunshine, American grandeur, were needed to make your ancestors. Your father was a soldier who could strangle a horse between his knees and crush a helmet between his teeth. Rome would have made a consul of him. But our age produces too many heroes. Just as it produces too many Homers.

Son of a soldier, you flung yourself into literature as your father had flung himself into battle. For nearly fifty years you fought, casting plays, comedies, tragedies, novels, books of travel and of history into the insatiable maw of the public.

France, Europe, America, fed on your work. Secretaries raced to keep up with you. Producers, publishers, translators, plagiarists, like looters after a battle, battened on the field of your energy. Like Vulcan at his forge, you labored. And in the heat you sometimes tossed bad metal into the fire. But you did not linger over your errors. You went on. Around your hearth gathered a multitude of writers whose genius could only flower where your heat was.

The envious, passing by, spoke of plagiarism, they spoke of literary industrialism, but you never stopped your work. I used to see you sometimes in your workshop, Papa. There were moments when you felt tired, and when you would let your hammer lie for a moment on the anvil, and, with your chest bared, your sleeves rolled back, you would come to the door for a minute or two to breathe the freshness of the night, to look for a moment at the stars, and wipe the sweat from your forehead. But only for a moment, and then you were back to work.

And when, avid for something new, you would rush off to Africa or to the Caucasus, it was your whole workshop that you loaded on your shoulders, and, as you climbed Mount Etna, as you camped among the Tartars, you never for a moment interrupted your gigantic labors. And the mob, loving energy, loved you for your feats of labor and of courage.

But just when you were at your best, another mood seized the crowd. What once had seemed magnificent suddenly seemed clownish. People whispered evil stories about you. But you didn't mind. You laughed. And even when people began saying: 'It's the son who really has the talent,' you didn't mind that either. On the contrary, you took me around the shoulders and said, 'Yes, you're my best work. Someday I shall be known only as your father.'

It was however at the unveiling of the impressive Dumas monument in Paris that the most beautiful tribute was paid to the great storyteller: "If all who have ever had their lives lightened for a moment by the reading of one of your books, would have contributed a penny toward your memory, we would have been able to cast your monument in gold."

D7